The Fourth Grade Wizards

The Fourth Grade Wizards

BY BARTHE DeCLEMENTS

SCHOLASTIC INC.
New York Toronto London Auckland Sydney

*This book is dedicated to my two delightful
grandsons, Scott and Kevin. And to their
lovely mother, Nicole.*

ISBN 0-590-42377-0

12 11 10 9 8 7 6 5 4 3 2 1   0 1 2 3 4 5/9

Printed in the U.S.A.   40

First Scholastic printing, September 1990

Contents

Your Name's on the Board   3

A Natural-Born Troublemaker   11

The Unwanted Guest   19

Jack Strikes Again   26

Greedy Eyes   35

The Fight   42

You Gotta Do the Work   49

Half a Wolf   57

Curved Fangs and Claws   65

Slower Than a Slug   74

It Won't Help to Cry   84

You're All I've Got   93

The Thief   103

How Stupid Can You Get?   111

Master Wizards   117

ACKNOWLEDGMENT

I would like to thank the staff and students of Frank Wagner Intermediate School in Monroe, Washington, for sharing their school experiences with me. I am especially grateful to Dr. Jim Lattyak, Diane Shalander and her fourth grade class, and Carolyn Davisson and her fifth grade class. It was Jim Lattyak and his staff who originated the Master Wizard concept.

Christopher Greimes, Mari Greimes, and Nicole Southard gave me invaluable help with the manuscript in progress. And my editor, Deborah Brodie, with her wonderful sense of humor and endless patience, deserved, at last, a gentle story.

B.D.

The Fourth Grade Wizards

Your Name's on the Board

1

Every student in our fourth grade class was supposed to be sitting up straight. Our eyes were to be on the blackboard where Miss Jewell was dividing rectangles into little boxes. "Now," she said, "this rectangle has three equal parts. If I shade this part, what part of the rectangle is shaded?"

As Miss Jewell scribbled in one of the boxes with her chalk, my eyes turned toward the windows. The white house across the street reminded me of the house where I used to live. I put my head down on my desk and thought about my mom.

First, I imagined her in the living room of our old

house. Then I changed my mind and put her in the kitchen. She was bent over the oven door, checking the oatmeal-raisin cookies. When they were done, we ate them at the table which was covered with the blue flowered cloth.

I reached for my third cookie while Mom explained that she hadn't really died. People only thought she had. She really had been thrown from the airplane into some bushes. When the police went through the burned wreck of the jetliner, they didn't see her behind the bushes . . .

"Marianne!" Jack whispered. "Sit up."

Slowly I raised my head.

"Sit up straight." He had turned around in his seat. "Your name's on the board."

I looked at the left side of the blackboard. Below the word *Recess* were L.T. and S.H. Lindsey Todd and Sharon Hinkler had probably been talking. Below their initials was M.R. for Marianne Rawlins. My face burned with embarrassment. Jack turned back around, but it was too late.

"Someone else hasn't been paying attention." Miss Jewell leaned away from her rectangles and wrote J.H. below the M.R. My face burned hotter. Now I'd gotten Jack into trouble.

I paid strict attention while Miss Jewell asked for a

definition of a numerator and a denominator. Jack raised his hand. So did most of the other kids. I didn't.

Miss Jewell called on Diane who said a denominator meant how many equal parts something is cut into. A numerator meant how many parts we were talking about. That was a big help. I wanted to put my head down again, but I didn't dare.

When recess time came, Miss Jewell called on the rows with the good kids first. Sharon's row was next to last. Our row was last.

In front of me, Jack slunk down in his seat while the kids lined up. I whispered, "I'm sorry, Jack."

He shrugged and whispered back, "No big deal."

When all the kids had filed out of the room, Miss Jewell suggested that Sharon, Lindsey, and Jack study their spelling words. She had me come up to the blackboard. She drew a circle with her chalk, made a line through the middle, and whitened in the lower part.

"What part is shaded?" she asked me.

"Half," I said.

"How do I write a half?"

I thought a minute. "One on the top and two on the bottom."

"Good girl."

I nodded, relieved that she hadn't asked me which was the numerator.

"Would you mind staying in a little longer?"

I shook my head. "No."

"Jack, Lindsey, and Sharon," Miss Jewel said. "You can go out to recess now."

Jack zoomed out of the room. Sharon and Lindsey followed him to the door. I could see Jo Mae go down the hall. Sharon saw her, too.

"There goes that scummy Jo Mae," Sharon said to Lindsey.

Miss Jewell put down her chalk and marched across the room. "Sharon!" she said in a loud voice.

Sharon was halfway out the door, but she turned and came back in. A worried look was on her face.

Miss Jewell stared down at her. "Weren't you the girl who was in here crying last week because the boys called you a nark?"

"Yes, but . . . "

"And now I hear you calling another girl a name?"

"I know, but . . ."

"No buts!" Miss Jewell said firmly. "I don't like to be called names. You don't like to be called names. And I don't think Jo Mae likes to be called names either."

Sharon was wiggling all over trying to get her excuses in. "Yes, but Jo Mae is . . ."

"Yes, but Jo Mae has feelings just like you do. It's

time for you to begin treating everyone the way you'd like to be treated. Today!"

Sharon opened her mouth, looked at Miss Jewell's unsmiling face, closed her mouth, and went meekly out the door. As I watched her go down the hall, I gradually stopped shivering. I hate trouble.

Miss Jewell sighed, stopped by the coffee maker on the counter, and poured herself a cup of coffee. When she joined me at the blackboard, she put her free hand on my head. "Marianne, I know that sometimes you feel sad. I feel sad for you sometimes."

I knew she was talking about my mother. To keep from crying, I opened my eyes wide and sucked in my upper lip and bit it hard.

Miss Jewell's fingers combed through my long hair. "Even if you feel sad, the schoolwork has to be done. Right?"

I couldn't answer her.

"Right?"

"Right," I mumbled.

She gave me a bright smile and my head a little push. "Go on out to recess now."

The girls from my room were on the tetherball court. I got in line behind Diane. Sharon and Jenny were up. There's a long, white mark drawn on the cement to separate the players. Sharon kept stepping over the mark, which you're not supposed to do.

Diane poked me. "Come on, Marianne. You're third in line and that makes you the referee."

That was true. I watched Sharon and Jenny's feet closely. "Sharon, you're out," I called.

"What do you mean I'm out?" Sharon put her hands on her hips and glared at me. "I am not out." Jenny had stopped batting the ball and it swung slowly around the post, hitting Sharon in the back of the head. She whirled around. "Jenny, you did that on purpose."

"Well, you're supposed to . . ."

"Don't be a jerk, Sharon. You went over the mark about ten times." Diane shoved Tara forward. "Go on and play."

Instead of getting behind me to take another turn, Sharon stomped off the tetherball court. "I can't stand her," Diane said, as she watched her go.

Tara is the tallest girl in the room and she creamed Jenny and then she creamed Diane. When it was my turn up, I batted the ball as hard as I could so it swung over Tara's head. I stood way out and kept batting the ball hard until it wound around the top of the pole.

"Hey, way to go!" Diane yelled.

I held the ball still until Jenny took Tara's place. Jenny batted it once. I leaped high in the air, caught the ball a good one, and kept it going my way.

The bell rang before I got it wrapped around the pole. "You would have won, anyway," Jenny said. "I can't figure out how you do it. You're the smallest kid in the room."

We were almost to the school door. As Jack went past us, he tapped me on the shoulder. "You left your jacket out again."

I ran back to get my jacket, which I'd dropped on the ground before I was up. I'm always forgetting my jacket. About halfway home after school, I was glad I had one.

The sky had been clear in the morning. I thought I didn't even need a jacket, but my dad handed it to me at the door. "Take it," he told me. "It could be raining later."

And it was, too. Big drops. I ran down my street and up the steps to the apartment house, mumbling the rhyme my mom used to say: "April showers bring May flowers."

There weren't any spring flowers inside our apartment. Just brown walls and a fat, dark red chair and lumpy davenport. I went in the kitchen and took a carton of milk out of the musty-smelling refrigerator. No cookies. No brownies. That heavy, sick feeling was beginning to crawl over me.

I set my glass of milk on the coffee table in the living

room and sat on the lumpy davenport. I could turn on the TV. I didn't really want to watch TV. I slid down sideways and laid my head on my arms to start a daydream.

I tried to picture the white house. I tried to put my mom in the sunny dining room arranging yellow daffodils in her green vase. It didn't work. All I saw was the ugly, brown walls in front of me.

My mom wasn't ever going to come back. She was dead.

A Natural-Born Troublemaker

I was moping along to school the next morning when I saw Jo Mae. She was sitting on the sidewalk with her legs crossed and her head bent over the sole of a silver boot. She was going, "Oh, oh, ohhh."

I ran the half-block between us and crouched down beside her. "Are you hurt?"

She looked up at me, her face scrunched into lumps of misery. "No, I'm not hurt. It's this here ol' boot. I stepped on a rock and it went right through the worn part and made a hole."

She held her foot out for me to see. Sure enough, there was a hole with her yellow stocking peeking through it.

"I guess you'll have to get new shoes. Or get those fixed," I said. I thought it might be better if she wore running shoes, anyway. Those silver boots with their fancy decorations of colored stones were one of the things that Sharon Hinkler made fun of.

I stood up and dusted off my jeans. Jo Mae stayed on the ground, poking at the hole and moaning. "What am I going to do? What am I going to do? Now my sock will wear out."

"Well," I said, "walk over on the grass until we're on the school grounds. Then we can go in my room and get some cardboard from Miss Jewell. If you put that in your boot, it will last until you get home this afternoon."

She stood up, too, and brushed off the yellow skirt that matched her socks. The skirt was spotless, like everything else that Jo Mae wore. I could see, though, that it was mended in several places.

I walked quietly down the rest of the block with Jo Mae hopping beside me. I was thinking that maybe she wouldn't get another pair of shoes. Maybe she was poor and that was why she was also worrying about her stocking.

When we got into my classroom, Miss Jewell was there making coffee. I explained to her about the rock and the hole. She got out a piece of cardboard and helped us make a pattern for a new inside sole.

Jo Mae and I sat together at my desk while she cut out the pattern. "How does it fit?" I asked her when she tried the cardboard in her boot.

She stamped up and down. "Fine. I can't even feel it."

Miss Jewell was standing beside us, sipping her fresh coffee. "Um, Jo Mae, the PTA has a collection of used clothes. They keep them over at the administration building. I could take you there after school and we could see if they have some shoes in your size."

Jo Mae immediately became solemn. "Oh, no, ma'am. Our family don't take handouts."

Miss Jewell smiled down at her. "It isn't charity. When their children grow out of clothes, the mothers in the school district just gather them up for the PTA. The PTA keeps them for other children to use."

Jo Mae had turned her head to the side and was concentrating on the rules that were written on a poster hanging on the wall.

"Maybe the PTA would have some running shoes," I suggested to get her attention.

She kept looking at the poster. "I don't know if my daddy would like that."

"I tell you what," Miss Jewell said. "I'll give your mother a call and find out."

Jo Mae shot her one quick glance. "We live with my daddy's folks."

Miss Jewell nodded. "That's OK. I'm sure I can get the phone number from the office."

The first bell rang and Jo Mae turned to leave. "I thank y'all for your help."

When she said "help," it sounded more like "hep." After she was out the door, I asked Miss Jewell, "Is Jo Mae from the South?"

Miss Jewell laughed. "I think so."

The kids were piling into the room by then and I noticed something funny about Jack. At first I thought he had two lunch sacks. He put one on the shelf in the coat rack. The other one he kept sort of hidden by his side as he slithered up our aisle.

I was sitting in my seat when he went by me. "You swiped somebody's lunch," I said.

"No way." He had a wicked grin on his face as he took a wooden contraption out of the brown sack and carefully eased it into his desk.

I leaned clear over my desk to get a better look. "What's that?"

He slipped the thing forward a bit. "It's a spitball projector."

"You're kidding."

"No. See, you pull back this wire and put it into the

top of the clothespin. You put the spit wad against the rubber band that's hooked to the wire. And then you open the clothes pin and wham! Sharon gets it in the ear."

I slid down into my seat. "You're going to get in trouble."

"No. No way."

I pointed to the poster. " 'You will not throw anything in the classroom.' "

"I'm not breaking the rule. I'm not throwing anything. I'm just working my projector."

The second bell rang and Miss Jewell walked up to the front of the room to take roll. Jack leaned forward, hiding the opening to his desk. All I could see now was the back of his red head, but I knew he'd have a sweet, innocent look on his face.

We were doing reading when Jack first used his projector. I was back at the SRA kit, putting one orange card in and taking out another. I had just turned around to go to my seat when Sharon let out a yelp. I saw her put her hand on her neck and look wildly around the room.

Miss Jewell was bent over Tara's desk checking her scores. At the yelp, Miss Jewell glanced up at Sharon. "What's the problem?"

"Something just hit me." Sharon had her mouth drawn

into a tight knot as she glared first at Jack, who was busy reading and then at Lester, who held out his hands, showing he had nothing in them.

"Let's keep our attention on our work," Miss Jewell said and went back to checking Tara's answers.

I took my reading card to my seat. I had finished the story on it and was going over the second paragraph for the meaning of a word. As I was about to circle the answer "b," I saw Jack's shoulders hunch forward.

I moved to the side and stretched up so I could see into his desk. The spit wad projector was slowly being pulled out. One of Jack's hands disappeared toward his face and came back down to place a wet, gray blob of chewed paper on the rubber band.

The wire was slipped into the clothespin. The projector was pointed toward Sharon's head. I held my breath. Nothing moved.

I turned quickly to look for Miss Jewell. She was bent over Jenny's paper. I looked back at the projector. Jack's fingers were on the bottom of the clothespin. They squeezed. The rubber band zinged free and the gray blob flew through the air, landing on Sharon's pink barrette and dribbling into her hair.

I clamped my hand over my mouth to muffle my giggle as Sharon clamped her hand over the gray mess on her head. She took her fingers down and stared at them. "Oh, ick. Miss Jewell," she cried, "Miss Jewell!"

"OK," Miss Jewell said, standing up straight. "That will be all of that. Who is throwing the spit wads?"

Silence. I kept my eyes on Miss Jewell. I didn't dare look at Jack.

"Lester," she said, "have you thrown any spit wads today?"

"Me?" Lester pointed to his chest. "Not me. No way."

"Jack?" Miss Jewell was raising her eyebrows at him.

I scrinched down in my seat, afraid of what was to come.

"Do you mean did I *throw* a spit wad today?" Jack asked. "No, I did not *throw* a spit wad today."

Miss Jewell eyed him suspiciously.

Just at that moment, the door opened and Mr. Douglas, the principal, walked in. He's a huge man and my heart started to beat fast. But he didn't seem to pay attention to what was going on in the room. He just smiled at Miss Jewell and said, "The eagle flies."

She smiled back as she went over to him. He gave her an envelope from the pack he had in his hand. "Don't spend it all in one place," he told her.

She nodded happily. I guess principals think kids don't know that when the eagle flies it's paycheck time. You'd have to be real dense not to know, because the eagle flies at the end of every month.

Miss Jewell peeked inside her envelope before she put it in her purse. She seemed to have forgotten all about spit wads. When she got back to the front of the room, she told us to put our reading away and to take out our science books.

Sharon didn't forget about the spit wads, though. At recess she announced to us girls, "Just wait until I tell my mother that Miss Jewell didn't do anything about my getting hit in the head twice."

At the end of the day, I watched to see if Jack would take his projector home. He saw me watching him shake open his bag and stuff the contraption in. "Don't worry," he said. "I'll bring it back tomorrow."

The Unwanted Guest

3

I didn't see Jo Mae on the way home. Maybe she'd gone with Miss Jewell, I thought. Maybe she'd get some jeans and look like the other kids.

I slowed down as I came near the apartment house where I lived. I hated the old brick building and its smelly halls. When we'd moved in, my dad had said it was only temporary. He said we'd get a new place soon, but he never seemed to do anything about it. After dinner, he mostly sat and stared at his newspaper.

Brittany was waiting for me at my door. She goes to a religious school that gets out earlier than mine does. I really didn't want to let Brittany in my apartment, but I didn't want to hurt her feelings, either.

She followed me right into my bedroom. I tried to watch her while I hung my jacket in the closet. The hanger slipped off the pole, though, and I had to turn my head to put it on right.

Before I could get to her, Brittany had opened the jewelry box that was sitting on my dresser. "This looks so neat," she said, slipping on the garnet ring. "It just fits my finger."

I picked up the box and held it out. "Please put the ring back," I told her. "It's my mom's."

Brittany whirled away from me. "That doesn't matter. She's dead. Why don't you give me this for a present? Red matches me better than it does you. A blue stone would go better with your gray eyes. Is there a blue stone in there?"

I clapped the top shut on the box. "No, there isn't. And this jewelry is the only thing I have of my mom's. So please give me the ring back."

Brittany held her hand up to the light coming from the bedroom window. "Is this real? It looks pretty big to be real. Do you know if it is?"

"I think so. It used to be my grandmother's."

"Well, then, it wasn't your mother's in the first place. So you could give it to me. You've got more junk in there, anyway. You don't need it."

My stomach began to feel sick. I didn't know how to get the ring back from Brittany. I couldn't yank it off her finger. She's a fifth grader, and she's about twice as big as I am.

Brittany started for the door. "Let's go see if you have anything decent to eat."

I stayed where I was with my hand out. "Please give me the ring first, Brittany."

She turned on me. "Why do you need it?"

"Because it was my mom's."

"You've got a whole bunch of her junk. Don't be such a pig."

My breath was catching in my chest and I knew I was going to cry and I hated to. "Give it to me. Please give it to me." I reached up my arm to wipe my tears away.

Brittany's mouth curled down with disgust. She ripped the ring off and threw it at me. "Here, take it, baby!"

I crawled on the floor to get the ring from under the dresser while she laughed at me. "You're such a baby you can't even catch."

I put the ring in the box and put the box back on the dresser.

"Well," she said, "have you got anything to eat?"

"Just milk."

"Haven't you got anything decent like Oreos or popcorn?"

"No," I said quietly. "Maybe you should go back to your apartment if you're hungry."

"Oh, I'll drink the milk."

We sat together at the card table Dad had propped up in the kitchen. While Brittany drank her milk, she eyed my earrings. "You even get to wear earrings to school."

I touched one of the small gold loops in my ears. "My mother bought these for me."

"My mother spends all her money on the apartment or herself. She never buys me any pretty things." Brittany's mouth turned down and for a minute I thought she might cry. Instead, she plopped her glass hard on the table and the milk spilled over. I got up to get another napkin.

She seemed a little embarrassed as she watched me wipe up the spill. "This table sure is wobbly."

I threw the wet napkin in the garbage can under the sink before I sat back down. "I know. We're going to buy our own furniture when we get another house."

"What happened to your old house?"

"My dad didn't want to live in it after . . ."

"After your mother died? Did he think her ghost would come there or something?"

"No, I just think it made him feel bad." And me, too, I thought.

"You know what my mom says?" Brittany was leaning across the table and looking into my eyes. "My mom says it's about time your dad started to live a little. She's thinking of asking him over for a decent meal. Wouldn't it be neat if they got together since my mom's single and your dad's single? Maybe they'll buy a house together. They should get one with three bedrooms, though. Since you're younger than I am, we should have our own rooms. Don't you think so?"

I didn't answer that. The whole idea was so depressing I couldn't drink the rest of my milk. "I think I'd better do my homework now," I said.

After dinner, I curled up on the davenport beside my dad. "What do you do," I asked him, "when you can't get rid of someone you don't want in the house?"

He closed his newspaper and put his arm around me. "Did you have a fight with someone?"

"Well, kind of."

He thoughtfully pinched the bridge of his nose. "Hmm. If the person's a guest, I suppose you have to do the best you can with how they are. And make sure you're not doing anything to make it worse." He tilted his head at me. "That's not much help, huh."

"Not much," I agreed.

"I guess the important thing is to make sure you're

being nice. And then try to find something you both would like to play."

"Sometimes that's a little hard."

He was still thinking, I could tell. Before he could say any more, there was a knock at the door. I jumped up to answer it.

Mrs. James, Brittany's mother, was standing in the hall with a big smile on her face. Some of her bright, red lipstick was smeared on the bottom of her front teeth. "Is your daddy home, dear?" she asked me.

I said yes and opened the door wide for her to come in.

She went right up to my dad with her hand outstretched. "I'm Josephine James. I think I've seen you in the laundry room."

Dad popped off the davenport and shook her hand. "Yes, yes, I think so. Won't you sit down?"

Mrs. James sat in the old chair. The broken springs let her sink down farther than she expected. She gave a little laugh and arranged her skirt before she told my dad, "Since Brittany and Marianne have become friends, I thought we should get to know each other."

My dad nodded and smiled and put the folded newspaper onto the coffee table.

"It's good they have each other to play with after school while you and I both work."

He nodded some more.

Mrs. James looked down, pressed her skirt over her knees, and then looked up at him through her long eyelashes. "Well, what I came to ask you is, would you and Marianne like to come to dinner next Saturday evening?"

That seemed to startle him. "Umm, I think we could. It would be a relief from my cooking."

I got up quick from my perch on the footstool so Dad couldn't see my face. I didn't want to spoil anything for him. "I think I'll get ready for bed," I said.

While I put my pajamas on, I could hear her high voice and his low voice as they said good-bye. I hopped into bed before the front door closed.

He came into my dark room. "You're not asleep already?"

"No."

"Do you mind going over there for dinner?"

"No, she's real pretty. And I guess you should live a little."

A laugh burst out from my dad. It was the first time I'd heard him laugh in months. He leaned down and kissed me good night. "It was Brittany you didn't get along with, huh?"

"Yes," I said.

"Well, we don't have to stay long after dinner. Just long enough to be polite."

I sure hoped so.

Jack Strikes Again

4

When I got to school the next day, I met Jo Mae in the hall. She was wearing jeans and running shoes, just like I'd hoped. "Hey, you're looking fine!" I told her.

She moved over close to me and whispered in my ear, "Don't tell anyone where I got the clothes."

I grabbed her by the neck and whispered back, "Don't worry, I won't."

There was a thump on my back. I turned around to see Jack behind me with his two lunch sacks. "Out of the way. Out of the way," he said. "You're blocking the halls."

I laughed and Jo Mae laughed as he marched on

into our room. "He must like you," she said.

Sharon stopped smack in front of us. "Who likes you?" she demanded.

I didn't say anything. Jo Mae didn't say anything. Sharon moved nearer the wall to get away from the pile of kids who were going to their classes. "Who likes you, Marianne?"

"Nobody. Jo Mae just thought someone in our room did."

"I bet it was Jack. He better not throw any spit wads at me today. If he does, my mother's going to talk to the principal." She eyed Jo Mae's new clothes. "I thought you only wore skirts to school."

"Not today." Jo Mae turned at the sound of the bell and went down the hall to her class.

Sharon watched her go. "That green T-shirt looks just like the one I had. It had a rip in the seam so my mother gave it to the PTA."

"I didn't see any rip in Jo Mae's shirt." I figured if there had been one, it would be mended now. Lucky for Jo Mae.

Miss Jewell started off our class with a bunch of stuff about the Heart Association contest. It was called a Jump-a-thon and we were supposed to get a permission slip signed by our parents and then get some sponsors for each minute we jumped and then jump rope at recess. I wasn't very interested because I'm not big on asking people for money.

When Miss Jewell said there'd be five kids on each team, Jack went into action. He made pointing motions at Lester. Lester nodded and pointed back. Tom pointed wildly at his chest and looked pleadingly at Jack. Jack nodded. Diane stared at Jack with her mouth dropped open. He nodded at her. Then he turned around to me and said, "You're on my team, too."

"I don't know any sponsors," I whispered.

"Don't worry. I'll get the sponsors." His voice sounded loud in the heavy silence. He whipped around in his seat. Miss Jewell was standing quietly with her eyebrows raised. "I'm sorry," Jack told her.

"Jack," she said with a big sigh, "you're never going to make Master Wizard."

You get to be a Master Wizard in our school if you're responsible, get all your work done, and have perfect behavior. My behavior was all right, but I didn't get my work done. Jack got all his work done, but his behavior needed improving. Diane was a Master Wizard until she mouthed off to the playground teacher and had to give her pin back.

Sharon's mother came to school to find out why Sharon wasn't given a pin. I don't know what the principal told Mrs. Hinkler, but Sharon still isn't a Master Wizard.

Jenny and Tara are. That means they can go in the hall, go to the bathroom, and go to the library without asking for a pass. They can leave the playground at recess and come into the building as long as they're wearing their pins.

All the stage crew and the office helpers are Master Wizards. You don't get to do much around the school unless you are one. All the kids want to be one, even though Sharon said her mother said it wasn't important. You get to hear a lot about Sharon's mother when Sharon's in your class.

After Miss Jewell passed out the Jump-a-thon permission slips for our parents to sign, we had reading. I started out doing the questions under "How Well Did You Read?" Pretty soon, though, I put my head down and began thinking about what it would be like if my mom lived in our apartment.

When I got home from school, Brittany would be waiting. Mom would open our door and tell Brittany she was sorry, but I couldn't play now. Then Mom and I would go inside and eat cake with German chocolate icing and Mom would tell me she had been in the hospital since she got rescued and she couldn't remember who she was, but when she got well, she remembered . . .

Miss Jewell tapped me on the shoulder. I sat up straight.

"Marianne," she said, "you simply have to pay attention to your reading. Most of the students are at least on the brown cards and you're way back on the orange cards. You're the only one in my class still on an orange card."

I looked down at my desk, totally ashamed.

She shook my shoulder a little. "Now, come on. Let's get to work."

I picked up the card and tried to focus on the third question. Miss Jewell went on to check Jack's scores. He was on a rose card, which is almost at the end of the reading kit.

Before she left him, Miss Jewell asked, "Jack, are you chewing gum?"

"No," he said, "I'm not."

Jack never lied. He wouldn't be chewing gum, I knew. He'd be chewing paper.

I finished "How Well Did You Read?" and was on "Learn About Words" when I noticed Jack's shoulders hunch forward. I looked around to see where Miss Jewell was. She was near the back wall, supposedly straightening books on the shelf. But she wasn't watching what her hands were doing. She was watching our corner of the room.

I didn't dare poke Jack. I faced the front and hissed at him. His hand went up to his mouth and down to the side of his seat. I scrunched under my desk a little and tried to kick him. My legs weren't long enough to reach his.

I wanted to peek around to see if Miss Jewell was still watching. I didn't dare do that, either. I hissed again. Jack didn't seem to hear me.

I sat helplessly while Jack turned to the side and squinted at Sharon, shifted his position back a little, checked Sharon's head again, and shifted a little more. Zingo! The gray blob landed on Sharon's chin.

She let out a yell. I heard Miss Jewell's high heels hit hard on the floor as she marched toward Jack. Before I could swallow, she had him by the arm and out of his seat. "You know the rules in this room."

"Yes, but I haven't broken any rules."

She turned him toward the poster on the wall. "Read rule six."

" 'You will not throw anything in the classroom.' "

"Well?" she prompted him.

He looked up into her frowning face. "I didn't break the rule. I didn't throw anything."

"That wasn't your spit wad that hit Sharon?" Miss Jewell sounded so fierce I could hardly breathe.

"Yes, it was my spit wad, but I didn't throw it."

"Oh, then who did?"

"Nobody did."

Miss Jewell's eyes were glittering dangerously and I guess Jack thought he'd better tell her everything. He pointed to the contraption on his seat. "I really didn't throw it. The projector propelled the spit wad through the air."

Miss Jewell seemed confused. She dropped Jack's arm and stared at the contraption.

He picked it up, put it on his desk, and pulled at the thick rubber band. "See, you hitch this to the clothespin wire and put the spit wad in here."

The frown broke away from Miss Jewell's face. For a minute, I thought she was going to laugh. But instead, she took in a long breath and sucked in her cheeks. "I guess we'll have to make an addition to our rules."

She went up to her desk for her Magic Marker, went over to the poster, and wrote below rule six, "Or cause anything to fly through the air."

Sharon was watching all this with her chin stuck out and her lips pursed together. Miss Jewell turned and looked at her and then at Jack. "Jack," she said, "you may have technically circumvented the rule this time, but I think there are some other issues we need to deal with. You hurt Sharon . . ."

"Wet spit wads don't hurt," Jack said.

"Maybe they don't actually hurt, but I imagine they

sting. And it certainly bothers Sharon to be picked on. Why are you picking on her?"

We all looked first at Jack and then at Miss Jewell. Our whole class knew why he hated Sharon. She narked on him all the time. The last time she got him in trouble was when she told the playground teacher, Mrs. Wilson, that he'd said the F-word at recess.

Jack didn't answer Miss Jewell. He didn't tell on anybody. Not even Sharon.

"Well," Miss Jewell went on, "I think you need to make more than an apology to Sharon. I think you need to do something very nice for her. Nobody likes to be used for target practice. This is Friday. So by Monday morning I expect you to have thought up something nice that you can do to make Sharon feel better."

Sharon's chin relaxed. A pleased smirk spread over her face. Jack slunk down in his seat.

"Now let's get back to our reading," Miss Jewell said.

At recess, the boys all crowded around Jack, asking him what he was going to do for Sharon. He shoved his friends away and went up on the bars and hung down by his knees.

Sharon was watching all this from the tetherball court. When there was no more action around Jack, she turned her attention to Jo Mae. Jo Mae wasn't waiting in any line for a turn. She was just standing uncertainly in the middle of the court.

Sharon bent forward to take a good look at the left side of Jo Mae's shirt. I walked in front of Sharon's face. "See, I told you it didn't have a tear in it."

Before Sharon could figure out if the shirt had been mended, I pushed Jo Mae toward an empty pole. "Come on and play a game with me. Nobody's on this one."

Maybe they don't play tetherball in the South where Jo Mae used to live. She caught on fast, though. By the time recess was over, she could wham the ball hard and keep it going above my head. She leaped up in the air a couple of times on the way back to the building. "You can sure jump higher in Nikes than you can in boots," she said.

Lester and Jack were behind me when I went into our room. "My sister made sugar cookies once," Lester was telling Jack. "Only she made a mistake and used salt instead of sugar. That'd make a nice gift for Sharon."

Greedy Eyes

5

On Saturday evening, I put on my best blouse and joined Dad in the living room. "You look handsome," I told him. He looked *too* handsome, I thought. Brittany's mother was sure to be impressed.

He bent down and kissed me. "Thank you very much."

"And you smell good, too." It was the clean smell of his fresh, shaved face that I liked.

As we walked down the hall to Brittany's apartment, I tried to be happy. This was better than having my dad spend the evening staring sadly at his newspaper.

"Come in. Come in," Mrs. James said at her apartment door. She had her big smile on and a purple and blue cotton dress that came down to the floor.

"I like your dress," I said politely.

"This old caftan. I always wear it when I cook for company because it doesn't show any splatters."

Brittany came in the living room with a tray of drinks. She passed the tray to Dad, her mother, and then to me. She took the last glass and sat beside me on the davenport. Our parents sat on fuzzy, peach-colored chairs.

Mrs. James saw me looking at the walls that matched the chairs. "Do you like the paint job?" she asked.

"Sure beats our brown walls," I said.

"I hated those depressing, gloomy rooms. Before we even moved our furniture in, I was up on a ladder painting and had Brittany doing the trim."

Brittany made a face at me. "It took a whole week."

"I bet it did," Dad said. "The place looks great."

Mrs. James seemed pleased with herself.

"Do you like the drink?" Brittany asked me.

"It's very good."

"All you do is put orange juice in the blender with some frozen strawberries. It comes out pink and frosty."

It was good, all right. The dinner was, too. Fried chicken and mashed potatoes and green beans with toasted almonds sprinkled on top. When we came to the blackberry pie, I was almost enjoying myself. Then Brittany brought up my mom's jewelry.

"You know," she said, looking at her mother, "Marianne has a whole box of stuff. Earrings and beads and rings."

"That must be fun when you play dress-up." Mrs. James didn't need to smile at me so sweetly. Nobody plays dress-up in the fourth grade.

"She has the neatest ring. I'd sure like a ring with a red stone." Brittany's dark eyes were squinted into greedy slits.

"Well," Mrs. James said, "maybe if you share something with Marianne, she'll share some of what she has with you."

I looked at my father for help. He was quietly forking up the last bite of his pie.

"Let me get you another piece," Mrs. James suggested to him.

Dad held up his hand. "No, no. That was just right. It was the best meal I've had in months."

"Anytime," she said with raised eyebrows.

He smiled back at her and the whole thing made me so sick I couldn't even think of being happy for him.

I got even sicker after dinner when Brittany took me into her room. She went straight to her dresser and began pawing through her top drawer. She pulled out a black beaded purse. "Isn't this neat?" she asked me.

I shrugged. "What's it for?"

"My grandma gave it to me. She took it with her

when she went dancing. Do you like it?"

"I guess so," I said.

"You can have it."

"No thanks. You keep it, if it's from your grand-mother."

"No, I want to give it to you." She shoved the purse at me.

I backed away. She wanted to give it to me, I knew, so she could have my mom's ring.

"Go on. Take it," she insisted.

"No. My dad said you aren't supposed to give away presents."

"Well. Well, that's stupid. Everything we have was a present once."

I stood there with my hands at my sides, trying to be sure I didn't make things worse. "Do you have a game we can play?"

"Sure, I've got some games. Do you want a game?" She threw the purse down on her bed and dived into the bottom of her closet.

"I . . . I didn't mean to keep. I meant to play."

She didn't pay attention to what I was saying. She was too busy throwing out dirty clothes and old shoes. The crushed box of a Monopoly game was in her hand when she crawled out of the mess. "Hey, how about this?"

Mrs. James opened the bedroom door. "Oh, were you two just starting to play?"

"No. No! We were just talking. Is my dad ready to go?" I hurried past her and out to the living room.

I stayed close to my dad while I thanked Mrs. James for the delicious dinner and thanked Brittany, too, for having us over.

On the way back to our apartment, Dad said, "I think you'd better put your mother's jewel box away. It's too much of a temptation for your friends."

"Don't worry," I told him. "I'll hide it good."

Miss Jewell zeroed in on Jack right after she took roll on Monday morning. "Did you think of something nice that you could do for Sharon?"

"Yes," he said, "I brought something. I'll give it to her at lunch."

When she heard that, a smile turned up Sharon's lips. She exchanged secret glances with Lindsey. I hoped what Jack had for her wasn't salted cookies or he'd be in trouble again.

During reading, I started up a daydream about my mom. Mrs. James's face kept jumping into my head, though. I didn't want to picture her. I didn't even want to live near her. What if I got Brittany for a stepsister?

Miss Jewell's hand was on my shoulder, giving it a

sharp shake. "Marianne! Sit up and get to work."

The look she gave me was stern. No more gentle words about being sad for me. Miss Jewell meant business. I picked up my card and tried to concentrate on question six.

At lunchtime, Jack took two sacks to his seat. He peeked in the smaller one, pulled out a cupcake, walked across the room, and plunked it down on Sharon's desk. "I'm sorry I hit you with spit wads."

Before Sharon could say a word, he beetled back to his desk. Miss Jewell nodded towards him. "That was very nice, Jack."

Sharon looked down at her cupcake. The chocolate frosting was smashed over the sides. She frowned as she pushed it back over the top. I watched her until she licked the frosting off her finger. She didn't screech so I guessed it was OK.

After I'd eaten my sandwich, Jack turned around. He was munching on a cupcake. He held another one out to me. "I brought three," he said. "I made them myself."

The frosting on my cupcake was a bit messy, but it hadn't gotten smashed down in the sack. I took a big bite of it quick, before Sharon could spot the difference between hers and mine.

At recess, Sharon must have told some of the kids

in the other fourth grade room that Jack gave her a cupcake. Leon kept darting up to him on the playground. "Jack's got a new girl. Jack likes Sharon."

Jack swatted at him and Leon danced away. "Jack likes Sharon."

Sharon was watching from the tetherball court, trying to hide a smile behind her hand. Leon sang out again, "Jack likes Sharon."

This time Jack grabbed Leon by the shirt and yanked him around in a circle. "Shut up or I'll shut you up!"

Mrs. Wilson swooped down on them. "Jack, you go sit on the bench."

Jack dropped Leon's shirt and moved away towards the bench, mumbling, "Well, tell him to shut his face."

"Hey," Leon called after him, "I can't help it if you . . ."

"Leon," Mrs. Wilson ordered, "keep quiet and go stand by the wall."

"I only said . . ."

"Go stand by the wall!"

Leon did.

For the rest of lunch recess, I swung on the bars with Jenny and Diane. Sharon and Lindsey walked around the playground, whispering. Jack sat slumped on the bench.

The Fight

I walked partway home with Jo Mae after school. She was hoping and hoping her dad would find a job pretty soon. "It's really packed at my grandma's," she said.

"I bet," I agreed.

"Where do you live?" she asked me.

"About four blocks down in an old apartment building. We just moved there so I could stay in the same school until Dad finds us a new house. I wouldn't hate the place so much, but there's a girl there who bothers me."

Jo Mae slowed her steps and looked closely into my face. She has pretty, light-blue eyes, but I think she must be nearsighted. "Can't you just keep away from that girl?"

"No." I shook my head. "She gets home before I do and waits for me at my door."

"You only have one door?"

I came to a full stop on the sidewalk. "Wow, you're right. I can go in the back way!" I wanted to hug Jo Mae, I was so relieved. Instead I tapped her on the shoulder. "Thanks. I don't know why I didn't think of that."

She kicked at a small rock, smiling shyly. "I know how you feel. I don't like that ol' Sharon much."

"She can be real nosey."

"Well," Jo Mae said. "This is my grandma's street."

I said good-bye to her, then ran three blocks, turned, and slipped down the alley. I passed the garbage cans, went through the metal service door, and climbed the concrete stairs. Up in our kitchen, I took in a few big breaths to get my wind back.

I wasn't as depressed as I usually am when I get home. Dad had bought some gingersnaps. I took the box of them in the living room, pushed the footstool close to the TV, and turned it on real low. There was an after-school special on. It was about a couple of kids who were trying to save their grandpa from being put in a nursing home.

Most of the time, I switched the sound off at the

commercial. When I did, I could hear Brittany shuffling against the front door. Once I didn't turn the sound off. I was thinking, Why don't the kids just take turns caring for their grandpa so their mother wouldn't feel he was too big of a burden for her?

While I was wondering this, a man in a used-car commercial blasted out, "Come in and see Uncle Denny! He'll give you the best deal in town!"

There was loud knocking at my door. Oh, oh! I switched the sound off and huddled down on the foot-stool. The knocking turned to banging.

I put the remote control back on top of the TV. The kids in the movie were stupid anyway. I crept out of the living room and into my bedroom and stayed there until Brittany finally gave up.

The next day after school, I came in the back way again. This time, though, I read my library book and left the TV off. That night Dad took me to McDonald's for Chicken McDLT's.

We had barely gotton home when there were more knocks at the door. My stomach told me it would be Brittany and her mother. It was.

Dad let them in. Mrs. James was carrying another blackberry pie oozing with dark red juice. "I just took this pie out of the oven," she said gaily. "And I thought it might be fun to share it with you people."

We ate the pie on the rickety table in the kitchen. Dad apologized for our lack of furniture. "We sold ours with the house," he told Mrs. James.

A bitter look crossed Mrs. James's face. "My ex-husband kept all of ours. And the house, too."

"But he gave us money for new furniture," Brittany said.

"He didn't have much of a choice." Mrs. James pushed her black hair back from her face and then focused on me. "Have you been sick, Marianne?"

"No," I said.

She raised her eyebrows. "Just playing hookey?"

"No," I said.

"Well, Brittany tells me she doesn't see you come home from school. But she hears the TV playing inside the apartment."

Dad put down his fork and looked at me, too.

I stared from face to face, trying to get my courage up. "Sometimes I come in the back way."

"Why do you do that?" Mrs. James's voice was sharp.

At first I wasn't going to answer her. But, finally, when the silence got heavy, I murmured, "Sometimes I don't feel like playing with anybody."

"Why didn't you just tell Brittany that? Don't you think it's unkind to let her wait and wait and wait for you?"

I kept my eyes focused on my half-eaten pie as I nodded my head.

To my relief, Dad took over then. "We've had some troubles adjusting . . . "

"Oh, yes, of course. Of course," Mrs. James's voice had turned sugary again.

"Perhaps," Dad went on, "when Marianne feels like having company, she could go down to your apartment to ask Brittany if she wants to play."

"Oh. Oh. I guess that would be fine." Mrs. James seemed taken aback for a minute. "But, the only thing is . . . I did think it was comforting to know the girls were together when we couldn't be with them."

"I call Marianne every afternoon," Dad explained, "to be sure she's home and to be sure she's all right."

"Yes, but that isn't quite the same . . . Well, I do understand that you won't be yourselves for a while. I just wonder if isolating yourselves is the answer." She turned her wide smile on Brittany. "Well, dear, it's about time for you to be getting at your homework."

Dad saw them to the door. I sat at the table wondering if he liked Mrs. James and if I was messing up his chances of having fun with her. My dad never says mean things about people so it's hard to tell what he feels about them.

"Do you like Mrs. James?" I asked him when he came back in the kitchen.

"She makes good pies," he said.

She did that all right.

At school the other fourth grade class was still teasing Jack about giving Sharon a cupcake. They didn't know Miss Jewell made him or that I had one, too. Leon was the worst heckler. He wouldn't let up on Jack.

Most kids like Jack. Miss Jewell reminds him that he's a natural leader when she's trying to get him to behave. She tells him other kids follow him and he should try to set an example. It is kind of hard to set an example when someone rushes up to you and pokes you and says you like Sharon Hinkler.

Leon did that for three days, until Jack had really had it. It was at noon recess that he grabbed Leon by the shirt again. This time he didn't just yank him around. He threw Leon on the ground and jumped on top of him.

All the kids gathered around in a circle to watch. I kept one eye on the fight and one eye on Mrs. Wilson who was busy scolding a fifth grader over by the wall. She wasn't noticing the crowd cheering the fight on. That was good, too, because Jack was pounding three days of being mad into Leon's face.

"You can just shut up about me and Hinkler," Jack snarled, smashing Leon in the mouth again.

"OK. OK." Leon was panting and squirming and trying to get out from under Jack.

"You sure you're going to remember?" Jack held his fist over Leon's head.

"Ya, I'm sure." Leon had his arm over his bloody nose to ward off any more blows.

"Jack, Jack!" I edged inside the circle and pulled at his sweater. "Jack, Mrs. Wilson's coming."

He got up quick. Leon got up, too. Not soon enough, though. Mrs. Wilson took them both by their necks and marched them off to the principal's office.

Jack didn't come back to the room after recess was over. He didn't come back all afternoon. Every time our classroom door opened, I looked around to see if it was Jack. It never was.

After school, I went into the office to see if he was there. He and Leon were sitting in chairs outside the principal's door. "What's going on?" I wanted to know.

Jack tilted his head toward the closed door. "Our moms are in there."

"Will she be real mad?" I asked.

"Naw, she's used to it."

"Mine will kill me," Leon said.

You Gotta Do the Work

7

The next morning, Jack was in his seat before I was. "What happened?" I asked him as I settled down.

"Not much," he said.

"But what?"

"Well, my mom told me not to be so sensitive about being teased. She knows Mrs. Hinkler and Mrs. Hinkler's a pain just like Sharon, and you can't get upset by people like that."

"Didn't Mr. Douglas do anything?"

"He gave me a big lecture about setting goals and talked to me about all the things I could do in the school if I became a Master Wizard."

"That's all?"

"No. He said if I get in another fight, he'll send me home for three days." Jack's eyes shifted to the side for a few seconds, before he slowly looked back at me. "I heard something else. I'll tell you about it at lunchtime."

"OK," I agreed. "But do you want to be a Master Wizard?"

"Hmmm. Maybe. It'd be neat to be on the stage crew."

I guessed it would be neat. I figured I'd never make it. I daydreamed too much. When I put my head down that day, though, Jack turned around and ordered, "Sit up!"

I did. And every time I forgot, he turned around again. I don't know how he knew when my head went down. He had never talked mean to me before, and about the third time, I asked, "Why?"

"I said I'd tell you at lunch," he whispered.

At lunchtime, he scooted his chair around to my desk. Between bites of his egg-salad sandwiches, he told me that when Mrs. Wilson had left Leon and him outside the principal's door, he heard Mr. Douglas and Miss Jewell talking inside the principal's office. Miss Jewell was saying that she didn't know what to do with me. She said I was a nice girl and she understood that I might be lost without my mother, but that I wasn't doing any work.

"You gotta do the work," Jack told me.

"I know," I said.

"What do you do when you get home from school?"

"There's nothing to do. Nothing I like, anyway."

"You need a dog," Jack decided. Then he bit his upper lip in thought. "A wolf hybrid."

"A wolf?"

"Half a wolf. They're half wolf and half dog. They're real smart. My uncle has one. I want one, but my brother already has a spaniel and my mom says that's as much as she can put up with."

A wolf. I thought I'd love a wolf. Even half of a wolf. "Oh," I said, imagining putting my arms around a big, furry ruff, "I'd like to have a wolf."

"They're real cool," Jack said. "Ask your dad tonight. Wolves have puppies in the spring. So you should be able to get one now."

"Where do you get one?" I wanted to know.

"Look in the ads in the newspaper. That's what my uncle did."

Lester came up to us then and bumped Jack's leg with his knee. "Check out the clock."

"Oops, recess time." Jack wadded up his sandwich wrappings and stuffed them inside his lunch sack. "Come on," he said to me. "The contest starts today. We have to go to the gym and jump. I wanna win a camera."

The Heart Association got the money the sponsors donated for each minute we jumped, but there were prizes for the students who brought in the most money. Like, if you brought in $25, you got a kite. If you brought in $50, you got a T-shirt with a red heart on it. If you brought in $100, you got a jacket and a glow rope. And if you brought in $400, you got a camera. There were other prizes, too, but Jack was zeroed in on the camera. His big brother, Kevin, had one, but Kevin wouldn't let Jack touch it.

The only sponsor I had was my dad, so I couldn't win anything. I just went along with Jack. I was following dreamily after him and Lester, when Jenny caught up with me at the gym door. "What were you talking about at lunch?"

"Jack was telling me about wolf-dogs," I said. "He thinks one would keep me company."

"Or eat you up," she suggested.

"No, wolves are real nice," I said.

I explained that again to my dad when he got home from work. "They're intelligent, too," I told him.

"I'm sure they are," he said, "but we can't have one in an apartment."

"I thought we were going to move pretty soon." I

was sitting next to him on the davenport and I pushed down the lumpy springs in one of the cushions. "And leave this old thing behind."

He nodded. "I guess it's past time all right. I'll tell you what. I'll call a real-estate office tomorrow. After we get a house, we'll talk about a dog."

"Half a dog," I corrected him.

"Hmmm. We'll see." He gave me a teasing grin. "But are you sure you wouldn't rather have a tiger?"

"Very funny," I said.

Later in bed, I didn't think it was so funny. I really *would* like to have a tiger. Next best was a wolf hybrid.

It took two Saturdays and Sundays of looking before the real-estate man started to get impatient. "This house is near your school and it's got a good-size yard." He glanced at Dad and then at me. "The couple who owns it are getting a divorce. Otherwise you'd never get a rec room and three bedrooms in your price range."

The last thing I wanted was three bedrooms. Brittany hadn't been bothering me lately, but I didn't want to take any chances of having a house big enough for her and her mother.

"Well, kitten?" Dad said. "It seems fine to me."

We were standing on the front lawn, looking out at the sidewalk. The three bedrooms weren't all that worried me. The yard really wasn't large enough. Jack said a wolf hybrid has to have lots of room to run and hunt mice.

I could feel the real-estate man frowning while he waited for my answer. "The place is neat," I mumbled, "but the yard's too little."

"Too little?" His voice boomed in my ears. "It's seventy-five feet by a hundred feet. That's almost twice as big as an average lot."

"I know." I kept my head down so he couldn't see my face. "But it's still too little."

He sighed. "Well, let's go back to the office and check on any new listings that might have come in."

Dad and I stood beside the man's desk while he clicked at his computer and then thumbed through a big notebook. About halfway into the notebook, he held a page out to us. "There is this little cottage on one and a third acres that's also in Brier. It's only four rooms and a bath. The living room is extra large, though, and it has a stone fireplace."

A stone fireplace. An acre and a third. Joy bubbled up inside me as Dad and I peered at the picture of a one-story house with a wide porch all around it. Flowers were climbing over one side of the porch.

"Does it have two bedrooms?"Dad asked.

"Yes," the man said.

"Is that enough?" I was watching Dad's face closely.

He smiled down at me. "I don't think we need any more, do we?"

I hoped not.

When the real-estate man pulled up in front of the house, we stayed in the car a minute looking at it. The flowers growing over the porch were roses. Mom had a rose garden.

The sad, heavy feeling came down over me again. My dad sat quietly in the front seat. The real-estate man must have thought we didn't like the house. "Do you want to see the inside?"

"Sure," my dad said and we got out of the car.

Before we went up the porch steps, the man pointed at the roses. "They're Climbing Royal Sunsets. They're fine plants. Hardy and everblooming."

"My mom had a red rose growing over the fence by our old house. She said it was called Blaze."

"Climbing Blaze is attractive." The man broke off a flower and handed it to me. "But smell this."

The flower had the colors of a sunset, pink and peach and yellow. It smelled delicious.

In the living room, I ran my hand over the big, rough stones of the fireplace. "This room smells good, too," I said.

The man nodded. "That's the cedar boards on the

walls. They'll smell good forever." The wood walls were a soft golden color. Not a bit like the ugly, brown plaster in the smelly apartment.

I went outside to check out the yard while the real-estate man and Dad checked out the plumbing and the house's foundation. There were fruit trees way in the back and a little building.

I pushed open the door made out of wooden slats. The floor was made of cement. The place looked like a small barn. Perfect for a wolf-dog, I thought. And as I imagined him there, my sadness slipped away.

When I returned to the house, the man explained that the building had been used for goats. It'd seemed a bit goaty, all right. "I'll have to scrub it out for Ki-pluck," I told my dad.

"Oh?" He raised his eyebrows. "So you've already named your wolf and moved him in."

The real-estate man looked startled for a minute. "A wolf?" Then he put his beaming-salesman face back on and asked Dad, "Well, do we have a deal?"

"I think so," my dad said.

Half a Wolf

Usually we jumped for the Jump-a-thon only at recess. But because this Monday was the last day of the contest, we were allowed in the gym before school. Tom, Lester, and I were at the gym doors before Mr. Douglas even had them opened. I was surprised Jack wasn't there.

As soon as the kids were inside, everyone grabbed for a single rope. Mr. Douglas started the music and we all started jumping. When two minutes were up, he turned off the music and recorded the names of the jumpers. Then he started the music again. I was getting pretty pooped by the time Jack and Jenny showed up.

Jack looked like he was trying not to cry. Especially

when he saw there were no more single ropes. I dropped mine and picked up one of the long ones. "Here, Jenny," I said, "take the other end."

We got the rope swinging and Jack hopped in just as the music began again. Jenny and I kept swinging and Jack kept jumping until the first bell rang and Mr. Douglas hollered out, "That does it!"

After Jack had his name checked off, he and Jenny and I walked to our room together. He still looked miserable. "So much for a camera."

"You'll win something, though," Jenny told him.

"Yeah, a stupid glow rope or jogging shorts."

"I'd like a glow rope," I said.

"If I get one, you can have it." He let out a long sigh. "I asked my mom to give me the alarm clock. But she said no, Dad needed it and she'd be sure to wake me up."

"She forgot?" Jenny asked.

"She forgot," Jack said.

I was dying to tell him about the new house, but he felt so bad I thought I'd better wait. By lunchtime he'd feel better, I figured.

He started eating all by himself. Most days he moved over to sit with Lester. Sometimes he ate with me. Especially if Jenny and the other Master Wizards were invited to eat with the principal.

I chewed on my peanut butter sandwich until I couldn't wait any longer. "Jack, Jack!" I poked him on the shoulder.

"What, what?" he said and turned around.

"We bought a house. With an acre and a third. And it's empty so we get to move in and rent until the bank papers are signed."

"Awright!" Jack said. "I'll call my uncle tonight and find out where he got his wolf-dog."

I told Jo Mae, too, when I caught up with her after school. She was already smiling because her dad had found work. "It's just a little ol' night watchman's job," she explained. "We can't buy a house yet, but Mama's trying to find something to rent near our school."

"Don't let her get a place in my smelly building," I warned her.

When I got to the apartment, Brittany was hanging around the alley. She followed me in the back door. I was feeling so good I didn't even get upset when she went on following me right into my bedroom. As I hung up my jacket, I could see her looking over my dresser.

"Where's that jewel box?" she asked.

"My dad told me to put it away."

"Why? What's the matter with playing with it?"

"Dad would rather we didn't. Let's go in the living room to watch TV."

She didn't have much choice but to come in the living room, too. When she sat down on the davenport, she picked up the *Consumer Reports Buying Guide Issue* that Dad had left there. "What's this for?" she wanted to know.

"We're getting a new refrigerator and stove."

"You could sure use some new stuff . . ." She stopped talking mean suddenly, as if she were remembering something. "We've got enough furniture for two families."

I didn't answer her. I just kept switching the TV programs, trying to find something better than cartoons for four-year-olds.

"Oh, I almost forgot," Brittany said loudly. "Mom and I are going to the science center Saturday afternoon and she thought you and your dad would like to come along."

I turned the TV off. "We can't."

"Why not?"

"Because we're moving Saturday." I watched her eyes get big.

"Moving? You're moving? Where?"

"In a house."

"Where? Around here?"

"Oh, about a mile away, I guess. On an acre and a third. The real-estate man said the lady next door has a horse. I'm going to get a wolf hybrid."

"You mean one of those half-wolf, half-dog animals? I heard someone on TV say those are dangerous because they can turn wild on you."

"I hope so," I told her. "I like wild wolves."

At school the next morning, Jack handed me a slip of paper with a phone number and the name "Mrs. Thompson" written on it. "Call that lady," Jack said. "My uncle thinks she should have some puppies now. He got his last May."

"What color are they?"

"White," he said.

"*White?*"

"Sure," he said. "They're half artic wolf and half Samoyed."

The last bell rang and Miss Jewell stood in front of the room waiting for our attention. Jack had to turn around. While Miss Jewell took roll. I sat there feeling itchy with disappointment. I had expected a gray and black wolf like the girl had in the movie *The Journey of Natty Gann*. Not a white one. My wolf-dog could have white legs and a white belly, but not be all white.

That night Dad brought home fish and chips. He wanted lots of time after dinner to pack kitchen stuff like canned food, flour, baking powder, and cinnamon and syrup. While we ate, I read through the pet ads in the paper. There were three inches of ads for free kittens, but none for wolf hybrids.

"I had a border collie when I was a kid," my dad said. "They're good dogs."

"I want a wolf-dog," I said.

There were still none advertised on Tuesday or Wednesday or Thursday. "Wait till Sunday," Dad advised me. "There are a lot more ads then."

But I didn't have to wait until Sunday. Friday night there were two ads. The first one said, "WOLF HYBRIDS 8 wks old. Remarkably intelligent, healthy, make loving companions." The number to call was Mrs. Thompson's.

The second ad said, "Wolf-mix. 6 wks old. 5 females, 2 males."

"That's it," I told Dad. "I'll call right now."

"Hold on. You haven't filled up those cartons I put in your room. The appliance men will be at the house at eleven tomorrow morning with the stove and refrigerator. So we have to have the U-Haul trailer packed and over there by then. So get crackin'."

"I will. I will," I promised him. "I'll just call and see what the puppies are like."

I was dialing the phone before he could say no. But when the man at the other end said, "Hello," I couldn't think of what to ask.

"Um . . . um, you have puppies?"

"Yes," the man said.

"Well, um, what are they like?"

"Oh, they're brownish-gray and pretty lively."

That sounded good. "What's the mother and father like?"

"She's a German shepherd. My wife knows a little more about the father. She was visiting her sister when a neighbor's animal got to our dog. My wife said he looked like a gray wolf."

"Thank you." I put the phone down slowly and went to find my dad. He'd gone into his bedroom to finish emptying his drawers.

"The man said the puppies' father 'looked like a gray wolf.' "

"Well, you can *look* at the puppies after we're moved and after we're settled in the new house."

"Sunday," I said and dashed for my bedroom before he could tell me to get crackin' again.

My dad is slow to get started. But once he gets going, he wants to "do it right." Doing it "right" meant that hauling our stuff into the new house from the trailer was only the beginning.

Sunday morning, I·had to wash the insides of all the kitchen and bathroom cupboards while he cut the paper to line them. Only then could we unpack the boxes and put things away.

When he'd burned the last of the packing material

in the fireplace and I'd finished sweeping, I begged, "Please, can we go look at puppies now?"

"Aren't you hungry?" he asked. "I am."

"Let's get a hamburger on the way," I pleaded.

Even though we'd gone shopping Saturday night and the new refrigerator was full of food, he tilted his head down, rolled his eyes up, and said, "We-ell, I guess we could do that."

Finally! I grabbed the phone to call the man with the wolf-mix puppies for his address. After I'd gotten it, Dad said, "You'd better call that Mrs. Thompson for her address, too. Just in case."

So I did.

Curved Fangs and Claws

9

The wolf-mix puppies lived in a neighborhood of shabby houses and tiny yards. I looked down at the broken boards on the porch as Dad rang the bell. This didn't seem to be a very good home for animals.

The man I had talked to on the phone let us in. He took us through the messy house and into the backyard. Out there was a skinny police dog with a bunch of grayish-brown puppies running after her. They were all trying to get at her belly for a drink of milk. She kept pulling away from them, but the fenced-in area was so small she couldn't get very far.

I felt sorry for the mother dog. She looked worn-out.

"Do you have a picture of the father?" I asked the man.

"No, I don't. My sister-in-law said her neighbor told her he was part gray wolf."

Only a part, I thought. That would make the puppies less than half. The front doorbell rang and the man left us to let some more people in. I whispered to Dad that I didn't think the puppies looked very wolfish. He whispered back that he didn't think the mother dog looked very healthy.

When the man brought a lady and a boy out to the dirt yard, my dad thanked him for showing us his dogs. We went back to the car and found Mrs. Thompson's address on our map. On the ride there, I tried to picture a white wolf in my mind.

Mrs. Thompson lived way out in the country. When we turned off the Machias road, we passed an old-fashioned church. "Look at that." I pointed out the window. "It has a steeple with a bell."

Mrs. Thompson's place wasn't far from the church. Dad parked the car outside the fence. A huge, white wolf-dog with slanted eyes jumped at the gate as my dad tried to push it open. A gray-haired woman hurried down the long path from the house. "Come on in," she called. "He's friendly."

He might be too friendly, I thought. He could easily knock you flat on your back. As we went through the gate, I sort of edged away from him.

"Stay down, Aluke!" she ordered the dog. He minded her, but I could see he still wanted to jump on someone. Instead he loped around Mrs. Thompson while she took us over to another slant-eyed wolf-dog who was stretched out in the shade of a cedar tree. Some furry, fat puppies were sleeping in a pile beside her. One was tugging at the end of her fluffy tail. Two others were wrestling in the grass.

The mother dog didn't get mad at the puppy pulling her tail. She just reached around and pushed him away with her nose. It was then Aluke crouched down on his two front legs and the puppy dashed to attack him. Aluke whirled away with the fat puppy scrambling after him.

I sat on the grass and petted one of the sleeping puppies. It stirred awake and crawled towards a nipple. The mother wolf-dog gave a low growl. The puppy decided to chew on my sandals instead.

"She makes them mind," I said.

"Oh, yes," Mrs. Thompson agreed. "When she decides it's time for them to be weaned, they're weaned."

"Ow!" I yelled. "Cut that out." I tried to pry the puppy's jaw open to save my toe. Its teeth were caught in my sock.

Mrs. Thompson sat down beside me, unhooked the

puppy's tooth, turned up its lip, and showed me its needle-sharp fangs. "See, the fangs are curved," she explained. She pressed on the puppy's paw with her fingers, making its toes spread out. "See, he has claws instead of toenails. He'll naturally want to put up his paws when he plays with you. He doesn't know the claws can rip your skin. You have to teach a wolf hybrid to keep his paws down."

My dad kneeled on the grass in front of me. "Are you sure this is what you want?"

"I'm sure." I looked at Dad and then at Mrs. Thompson. "I could train one, couldn't I?"

"Of course, but you don't make pets of them quite the way you do dogs. They are more your friends. They try to understand what you want and you try to understand what they want. If they make a mistake and wet on the rug, you pick them up immediately, say 'No' in a loud voice, and put them out on the ground. You never hit them. They wouldn't hurt you. If you hurt them, they can decide they don't want you for a friend."

I stared at Mrs. Thompson in horror. "Oh, I would never, never hurt one."

She leaned over and stroked the mother wolf-dog's head. "What kind of a puppy were you looking for? A playful one, a bossy one, a male, a female?"

While I thought that over, I watched Aluke who was

far out in the yard. He was crouched down again, waiting for the panting puppy to catch up to him. "Well," I told Mrs. Thompson, "at first I imagined one like the girl had in a movie I saw . . ."

"One more like a malamute? Whitehawk's mother was part malamute." Whitehawk raised her front leg so Mrs. Thompson could scratch under her chest.

"We understood they were half arctic wolf and half Samoyed," my dad said.

"Aluke is. Whitehawk is arctic and malamute."

"How come she's so light?" I asked.

"I wanted a female to match Aluke, so I picked out the lightest one in the litter." Mrs. Thompson stopped scratching Whitehawk and pulled a puppy out of the bottom of the sleeping pile. "This one is the darkest in this litter." She handed me a puppy with gray shading down his back and around his face. "He has a pretty mask."

I took the puppy in my arms. He opened his almond eyes, stretched up, and licked my chin with his little pink tongue. "Ohhh, Kipluck," I crooned.

Mrs. Thompson and Dad both laughed. I didn't care. I just hugged my puppy tighter.

The ride home scared Kipluck. He spent most of it with his head burrowed under my arm. Just as Dad parked in front of our house, I saw a lady with blonde hair flying behind her come down the road on a galloping horse.

After we climbed out of the car, she pulled up the horse beside us. "What have you got there?" she asked me. "Look at those slanted eyes. It's part wolf, isn't it?"

"Yes," I told her proudly, "he's a wolf hybrid."

She leaned over the side of her horse and peered into Kipluck's face. "What color are his eyes going to be?"

I shifted Kipluck around in my arms. He was heavy and my arms were getting tired. "His mother's eyes were yellow and his father's eyes were brown. The woman we bought him from said puppies' eyes are blue when they're born."

"They look muddy-green about now," Dad said.

"Bring your puppy over to see me one of these days," the lady invited. "I'm Lacy."

"I'm Marianne."

"And I'm Jim," Dad said.

We were all smiling at each other when a car drove up behind the horse. Lacy clacked her tongue twice. The horse broke into a trot, turned at the house next door, and went around to the barn in back.

"What a neat neighbor," I said to my dad. The way he was still smiling made me think he thought so, too.

There was a honk from the car, which hadn't moved.

I turned to look at it. Rats! Brittany and Mrs. James were inside.

They got out of the car and took a picnic basket from the trunk. "I thought maybe you two would enjoy a home-cooked meal in the midst of your moving," Mrs. James said. She and Brittany lugged the basket into our yard.

I put Kipluck down. He sniffed around the grass and then squatted to pee. "Oh, it's cute." Brittany reached out to Kipluck. He backed up to me and let out a growl.

"He doesn't know you," I explained. "And you have to be careful how you play with him because he has claws and fangs."

Mrs. James's big smile dropped from her face. "What kind of dog is he?"

"He's a wolf hybrid," I told her.

She looked at my dad with alarm. "Is that safe for a little girl?"

"I guess we'll see," he said.

I rolled Kipluck over and rubbed his fat, pink tummy. Brittany stood uncertainly beside me. "Well? Well? How do you play with him?"

"Easy," I said. I got a dead branch from under one of our apple trees and dragged the tip along the ground. Kipluck pounced on it. I pulled from my end. Kipluck sank his teeth in the wood and pulled from his end.

When the branch broke, Kipluck dashed away with his piece. I chased after him, grabbed at the stick, and tugged it free. I sat on the ground whirling the branch around me while he ran after it. After a while he crouched down and just watched the stick going around and around.

I had to shift hands behind me to make the full circle each time. As I slowed to shift, Kipluck zipped in back of me and caught the branch. "See how smart he is?" I said to my dad. "He figured out how to get it."

My dad nodded. Mrs. James seemed a little bored. "I understand you have a new refrigerator and stove. Shall we put the casserole in the oven?"

"Sure." Dad picked up the basket and headed for the house. "But that's about all we have inside."

"Well, that's about all you need. For a while." She was looking up into his face as she walked beside him. Yuck, I thought to myself.

Brittany isn't the kind of girl who can stay out of the action for long. "Here. Let me play with the puppy now." She undid the belt from around her waist and dangled it above Kipluck.

Kipluck dropped the branch and went after the belt.

"Be careful," I warned. "He might put scratches on it."

"Oh, it's old." She was bending from her waist with

her head pointed towards Kipluck while she held her arm up in the air.

"Be careful of his claws," I warned again, but Brittany isn't the kind of girl who listens to you.

She jerked the belt up and down. Kipluck jumped for it. "Watch out . . ." I started to say just as Kipluck's paw hit Brittany's mouth. His sharp claw raked her lower lip as he bounced back to the ground.

Blood poured down Brittany's chin. She let go of the belt and clapped her hand over her mouth. When she took her hand away and saw the blood, she screamed, "Mama!"

Slower Than a Slug

An hour and a half went by before Brittany and her mother returned from the hospital emergency room. I expected Brittany to have stitches on her lip. She didn't have to have any, but she did have to have a tetanus shot. That was so she wouldn't get an infection from the wolf claws, Brittany explained. "And I don't think much of your dog," she added.

"How much was the bill?" my dad asked quietly.

"Eighty dollars," Mrs. James said, handing him her receipt.

Dad sat down at our card table and wrote out a check.

When he handed it to her, Mrs. James took it slowly. "I don't know if you should be paying all of this. After all, Brittany was playing with the dog."

"The pup is our responsibility," he said firmly.

I stood in the middle of the kitchen feeling awful. My dad had told me not to worry. Accidents like this could happen with any puppy. I still felt awful, though. Especially about the money. After he made the house down payment, Dad had said we had just enough savings left for our furniture.

Kipluck had cost a hundred and fifty dollars. The hospital cost eighty dollars. And there were still puppy shots and wire fencing to buy.

I looked at Kipluck sleeping in the corner of the kitchen. He was curled into a furry ball with his closed eyes making slanted lines toward his nose. I knew I could feel better if I held him in my lap and loved him. But puppies need their naps.

"Well, shall we put the casserole back in the oven?" Mrs. James suggested with a bright smile. "I'm hungry. Aren't the rest of you hungry, too?"

I didn't feel much like eating. I sort of picked at my food. Brittany ate plenty—between big fusses about how bad it made her lip hurt.

I was relieved when they left. Before Dad and I got the dishes done, Kipluck woke up. I hurried him out to the yard. When he squatted in the grass, I told him, "Good Kipluck! That's a good boy!"

He wasn't such a good boy in the middle of the night. But that was my fault. He tried.

Dad said the pup could stay in the house just for the first night. After that, he would have to sleep out on the porch. Wolf hybrids need to be in the cold to grow their heavy coats of fur.

I put an old blanket in the corner of the kitchen and sat on it. Kipluck immediately climbed on my lap. I played tug-of-war with him and rubbed his tummy until he was sleepy. But when I got up to sneak off to bed, his eyes popped open.

Every time he trotted after me, I put him on his blanket and told him to stay. He whimpered a bit, but he finally gave up, lay down with his head on his paws, and watched me sadly as I went to my room without him.

It seemed like I was barely asleep when Kipluck's whines woke me up. I took him outside and shivered in the night air while he sniffed around for a place to pee. It must have been past midnight when he cried again. I shoved my feet into my slippers, hurried to the kitchen, opened the door, carried him down the steps, and set him on the grass. Just in time.

Back in the house, he scampered around, ready to play. I was groggy, but I petted him awhile, anyway, and then told him to stay on his blanket. I wasn't even asleep before he whined some more. I decided he was lonesome and would have to get used to sleeping without his brothers and sisters. He howled, but I still didn't get up. I was sure he didn't have to go again so soon.

In the morning, Kipluck greeted me with hops and jumps at my legs. His sharp claws pricked through my jeans. "No, no," I told him, "that hurts."

Before I picked him up to take him outside, I sniffed. And sniffed again. There was a bad smell in the house.

After I brought Kipluck inside, I went into the living room. A brown pile was in the middle of the rug. How dense can you get, I told myself. I had forgotten all about his having to do that, too.

It wasn't so easy to clean up the mess. Kipluck kept attacking me while I was trying to hold my breath and scrape the rug clean with wet paper towels. When I shrugged him off my back, he went for my shoes. When I kicked him away from my feet, he dived for a towel. When I snatched that from him, he tugged on my shirt.

I gathered up the stinky towels, tried to stand up, and heard my shirt rip. I had to get down and unhook his little curved fangs before I could get to the kitchen garbage can. Dad was cooking breakfast. "Doesn't smell too good in here," he said.

I hated putting Kipluck in the goat shed before I left

for the school bus. I had to do it, though. Until Dad attached wire screening to the wooden fence around our property, Kipluck would be able to crawl out of the yard. If he got killed running in the road, that would be worse than locking him in the goat shed.

Jo Mae got on the bus two stops beyond mine. She looked around nervously for a seat while she came down the aisle. "Jo Mae. Jo Mae. Here!" After she saw my waving arms, her face relaxed into a smile.

"I didn't think you'd be taking a bus, too," she said as she settled down beside me.

We compared our new addresses and decided we must live about a half mile apart. If we cut through fields, it might be less. She said her new place was just "a little ol' shack." I said mine couldn't be much bigger, but it had a huge yard and I had a puppy!

I spent the rest of the ride telling Jo Mae all the things that Kipluck did and how cute he was and how it was too bad his claw caught in Brittany's lip, but maybe now she wouldn't come back. Jo Mae shook her head doubtfully. "I don't know. If her mama wants your daddy . . ."

Jack was hanging around the schoolyard when our bus pulled in. I hopped down the bus steps, rushed up, and grabbed his shoulder. "I got my wolf puppy. I got him from Mrs. Thompson. He's mostly white, but his back is grayish and he's got a gray mask."

"Awright!" Jack said. "Do you have a strong fence?"

"Not yet," I told him. "We're going to put one up. Mrs. Thompson said to bury the wire in a four-inch trench and then pour in concrete mix. When it rains, she said, the mix will harden and Kipluck won't be able to dig out."

"That's what my uncle did. But you better build it in a hurry. Wolves are used to traveling in a large territory."

The first bell rang. As we all headed for the school building, I worried a bit about how fast my dad would build the fence. He doesn't do much hurrying. My mom used to say she'd never enter him in a slug race because the slugs would beat him.

When Miss Jewell finished taking roll, Mr. Douglas came in the room with a big box. He stood quietly in front of the room for our attention. We gave it to him, of course. We knew if we didn't, Miss Jewell wouldn't let us go out for lunch recess.

I guess Mr. Douglas didn't know that because he complimented her on what a fine class she had. Miss Jewell smiled sweetly.

"I've got the prizes here for the students who have turned in their sponsors' money." He looked down in the box. "Quite a few prizes for this class."

Some of the kids leaned forward in their seats, trying to look in the box, too. I didn't. And Jack didn't.

"Jenifer Sawyer," Mr. Douglas called out.

Jenny came up to him and he gave her a jacket with a heart on the pocket.

"Sharon Hinkler?"

Sharon came up and was given a glow rope.

"Jack Hanson?"

Jack got up slowly. First Mr. Douglas handed him a jacket. Then he gave him a glow rope. Jack tossed that to me. Last, Mr. Douglas gave him a pair of red jogging shorts.

Jack held the shorts in front of him. The legs came down to his knees. He bunched up the top to fit his skinny waist with one hand, waved his other hand in the air, and swiveled his hips like a hula dancer. We all laughed.

Mr. Douglas took the shorts away from him. "How about settling for a T- shirt and another jump rope?"

Jack took the T-shirt and tossed me the second glow rope. I noticed Sharon Hinkler didn't look happy about that. I thought the ropes were neat. One was orange and one was red. They both had wooden handles. The ropes in the gym just had knots tied at the ends.

After Mr. Douglas handed out all the prizes, Miss Jewell started us on our reading. I put my glow ropes in my desk and got down to work. The ache for my mom wasn't hurting so bad these days.

At lunch, Jack turned his chair around to my desk. He reminded me again that I'd have to get a fence up fast. Wolves live in packs. And mine might look for other animals to play with. Jenny brought her chair over. While I was telling both of them about Brittany and the claw, Miss Jewell stopped by my desk.

"You have a wolf hybrid?" she said after she listened to my story awhile. "There's a book in the library called *Kavic the Wolf Dog*. As soon as we're finished with *How to Eat Fried Worms*, I'll get it and read it to the class." She ran her fingers through the ends of my long hair. "And Marianne, I like the way you've been working today."

When Miss Jewell moved on to another group of kids, Jenny told me, "If you keep on working, you can be a Master Wizard before the end of school. Mr. Douglas lets the new group of kids have any job they want for the last two weeks. You could be an office girl with me." She tilted her head towards Jack. "And he could be on the stage crew for the awards assembly during the last week of school, if he ever stopped getting into trouble."

"I'd like to be an office girl," I said.

"I wouldn't mind being on the stage crew," Jack put in.

It suddenly dawned on both Jenny and me that Jack

hadn't been in trouble since his fight with Leon. To avoid our stares, he ducked his head to take a bite of his sandwich. I don't think he wanted us to see the pink that was spreading under the freckles on his face.

I thought the bus ride home would never end. Jo Mae said good-bye to me at her stop. I kept my arm on the seat in front of me, ready to dash off at my stop.

Kipluck started scratching on the door of the goat shed as soon as I hit the backyard. When I let him out, he leaped for me. I put my books on the grass and kneeled down to hug him and he covered my face with his little puppy kisses.

He hopped up the porch steps after me. I got a glass of milk for me and puppy chow for him. After we ate, I took the broom out to the shed to sweep it clean. Straw was stuck all over Kipluck's fur and he smelled like a goat.

The job wouldn't have taken very long if I hadn't had to pry Kipluck's teeth off the broom after every sweep. I finally gave up and went back to the house for the dust mop. The first time I swished it over the floor, he dropped the broom and dashed for the strings on the mop.

The shed was clean, but I was sweating by the time Dad got home. At dinner, I tried to talk to him about getting the fence up fast. He seemed to think Kipluck would be all right in the shed until the weekend. "I'll work on the fence then," he promised.

The next morning, Kipluck struggled to get away from me when I tried to drag him through the shed door. It took me about ten minutes to get him stuffed inside and I was almost late for the bus.

It Won't Help to Cry

The first few days I had Kipluck, he stayed near the house. But gradually he investigated more and more of the yard. He especially liked the dead branches he found under the apple trees. Sometimes I brought my homework outdoors and worked on it while he chewed the wood into splinters.

Reading didn't seem so boring when I had Kipluck beside me. After I moved up to the gold cards in the SRA kit, Miss Jewell was pleased. She said I might even get to be a Master Wizard if I made it to the brown cards in the next two weeks.

On Thursday afternoon, I left Kipluck while I ran

into the house to answer the phone. It was Dad making his afternoon call to see if I was all right. When I came back outside, I couldn't find Kipluck. I searched all around the yard. I couldn't figure out how he disappeared so fast. I finally found him three houses down, playing with a black dog on the side of the road.

As soon as I got up to him, he turned from the dog with a big smile on his face. "No, no!" I scolded. "You have to stay in your yard. It's dangerous out here."

From the way his tail drooped, I was sure he understood that he'd done something bad. I wasn't sure he understood what, though. That night when I put him to bed on the porch I felt uneasy. Jack's warnings made me nervous. My dad said not to worry. Dogs know where their meals come from. I didn't argue back that Kipluck wasn't all dog.

I opened the kitchen door in the morning, expecting to find him all waggy-tailed and eager for loves and breakfast. He wasn't there. I called him. He didn't come.

I went around to the front of the house and called some more. There he came down the road with his tongue hanging out of his mouth. When he jumped up on me in a happy greeting, I decided it was useless to scold him again. I wished and I wished I could do something about getting the fence up faster, though.

After school that day, Kipluck crawled all over me

when I opened the door of the shed. But when I went inside to get his empty water bowl, he backed away into the yard. "No, no," I told him, "I'm not going to put you in again now."

He hated that shed. And I hated worrying about him running away. I thought maybe if I started the trench, my dad might help me in the evening. When he promised he'd "work on the fence" during the weekend, that didn't mean he'd finish it. I dragged the shovel out of the garage.

Fortunately, Kipluck couldn't bite into metal. He chewed on his nylon bone while I dug into the dirt. I hadn't gotten very far when Lacy drove up next door.

She walked over to pet Kipluck and tell me my shovel looked pretty big. "I know," I said. "It's my dad's."

"I think I've got one with a shorter handle. After I get out of my work clothes, I'll bring it over."

Her "work clothes" were a blue suit with a lavender blouse. Her long hair was braided around her head and she carried a black leather briefcase. I wondered if she was a lawyer or an insurance saleswoman. When she came back, she was wearing jeans. One long pigtail flopped down her back. I got up the nerve to ask her what she did.

"I'm a social worker," she said. "I find foster homes for children who are neglected or hurt."

I put down the big shovel and took the one she gave me. "That must be a sad job."

She nodded. "It is, sometimes. But some other times, when the foster parents are kind and I know the children are safe, it can be a happy job."

I guessed so. But it was bad enough losing my mom. I'd hate to be taken away from my dad. Even if he were ever mean to me.

Lacy went off to ride her horse. I hacked away at the ground until Dad came home. He gave me a hug and let Kipluck tug at his newspaper instead of his pants leg. "Where'd you get the shovel?" he asked.

"Lacy lent it to me."

He raised his shoulders and stared up at the sky. "I guess I'll just be forced to return it to her after dinner."

I was too worried about getting the fence done to think that was funny. "Couldn't we work on the trench a little while first?"

"We-ell, maybe until the ball game comes on."

I let out a big sigh. Of all the things to keep from our old house, it had to be the rickety card table and the stupid TV. Dad ruffled my hair. "After I change my clothes, I'll get something nice out of the back of the station wagon."

I hoped it would be the wire fencing. It wasn't. It was two recliner chairs. I had to admit they were neat.

You can stretch way back in them with your feet on a footrest or you can sit up straight. We sat up straight to eat our TV dinners.

Afterwards, Dad worked on the trench with me. I didn't say so, but I was glad to quit when he did. He carried the shovel back to Lacy and I went in the house to put Band-Aids on my blisters.

Much to my relief, Kipluck came hopping up the steps as soon as I called him in the morning. He thought Saturday and Sunday were great. He wasn't put in the shed and he got to tag after Dad and me all day.

By Sunday evening, the trench was dug. Dad said he'd buy the wire fencing during the week and we'd get it up the next Saturday. I was disappointed, but I couldn't think of any way to make him go faster.

Before I went to bed, I took Kipluck to his blanket on the porch. "You stay there now," I told him. He put his head on his paws and looked up at me with his almond eyes. I gave him an extra love before I went in the house.

He wasn't on the porch in the morning. He didn't come when I called. I walked around to the front of the house and called some more. I was feeling impatient because he might make me miss the bus.

I called and called. He still didn't come. My impatience was turning into panic. I ran down the road a ways, calling and calling. But no Kipluck came clippety-clip into sight.

I went back to the house and looked under the porch where I thought he might be sleeping. He liked to crawl under things and into small places. I searched around the shed and in the garage.

Instead of telling Dad where I was going, I raced into the street again, ran up and around the houses. Lacy had already left for work, but I looked in her barn and under her porch. I couldn't find Kipluck anywhere. I went to the fields behind the houses, calling and calling, my heart pounding with fear.

When I got back to the road, some kids were walking down to the bus stop. "Have any of you seen a white and gray puppy?" I asked them.

They hadn't.

I asked a man who was climbing in his car. "No," he said, "I'm sorry. I haven't."

I raced to my house. Dad was just coming out the front door. "Where've you been?" He was scowling with annoyance. He was probably late for work.

"Kipluck's gone," I told him. "I can't find him anywhere."

"Well, it won't help to cry. He can't have gone far. Go get your jacket and we'll hunt for him on the way to school."

"But what if we don't see him?" I wiped my tears away with my arm.

"He'll come back. Even puppies can find their way home. Now, go get your jacket or we won't have time to search."

I ran in the house for my jacket. Dad already had the car started up when I climbed in. I'd forgotten my arithmetic book, but I didn't care.

"Which way have you gone?" he asked.

I pointed down the road past Lacy's house. "That way."

"All right." He turned the steering wheel. "We'll go the other way."

Dad drove slowly along the streets. I had my head out the window, calling and calling and calling. But there was no white and gray puppy. There was no puppy anywhere. As Dad circled the car around to the grade school, I was crying again. "I don't want to go to school. I'll wait for him at home."

"No, you won't. You go on in to class. Kipluck will probably be there when you get back to the house. Don't worry about it."

"That isn't any help," I said.

"I haven't got more help right now. I've got to get to work." He leaned over to kiss me good-bye. "I'll phone Animal Control when I get to the office."

I shrank back from him. "The dog pound! They'll kill him."

"No, they wait three days before they put an animal to sleep. We won't leave him there one day."

I stumbled out of the car. I could barely see through my tears. Jo Mae was the first kid I bumped into. "How come you weren't on the bus . . ." she started out. "Ohhh, what's the matter?"

"My puppy ran away," I told her.

"Ohhh, no." She put her arm around me and walked me to my room.

Before Jack slid into his seat, he stared at me. "What happened to you?"

"Kipluck's gone."

"When?"

"This morning before I could lock him in the goat shed."

Jack shook his head. "You should have got your fence up."

Jenny came over to my desk and I had to tell her, too.

"What's going on?" Miss Jewell asked when she saw us all crowded together.

"Marianne lost her wolf-dog," Jack told her.

Miss Jewell closed her eyes a second, muttered, "Oh, my—" She stopped herself, and said, "I'm sorry, Marianne."

Instead of starting us on our reading after she took roll, Miss Jewel read some more of *How to Eat Fried Worms*. The rest of the kids laughed at the funny places. I just stared at the blackboard, hating my whole life. If my mom were alive, she would have made my dad finish the fence.

At recess, Jack tried to make me feel better by telling me that sometimes wolf hybrids go out to hunt. I thought Kipluck was too little to hunt, but I hoped anyway. I hoped and hoped on the bus riding home and Jo Mae hoped with me.

I raced from the bus stop to my house, praying I'd see my white and gray puppy on the porch waiting for me. He wasn't there. He wasn't in the front yard or in the backyard. He wasn't anywhere.

You're All I've Got

After tramping up and down the road, asking at every
door if someone had seen a puppy, I came back to sit
on my porch. I was so tired and sad I just sat there
seeing pictures of Kipluck in my mind. Kipluck with his
head on his paws watching me leave to go to bed. Kipluck rolling over to have his fat tummy scratched. And
the one that made me saddest of all, little Kipluck back-
ing away from the shed he hated.

Lacy drove up to her house. I caught up with her on
the way to her front door. "Did you happen to see
Kipluck anywhere?"

"No, why? Is he gone?"

"He ran away this morning." After I said this, I felt my face scrunch up and tears run down my cheeks.

"Oh, honey, that's too bad." She put her arm around me. "Come on in. I'll put on my boots and we'll ride Zimba out to look for him."

"I've looked and looked and my dad's looked with the car," I told her.

"Yes, but Zimba can go where cars can't go."

Zimba is a great big cream-colored horse with a black mane and black tail. He flicked his ears and arched his neck around to peek at me. I didn't know how I'd ever get on him.

Lacy did. She brought a box out of the barn and placed it next to him on the grass. "Now stand up on that," she told me. "Put your left foot in the stirrup. Swing your right leg over his back. I'll give you a push up and you take your foot out of the stirrup and grab onto his mane."

It worked. I sat way up there while Lacy took the box away, put her foot in the stirrup, and swung up to sit behind me. She reached around to take the reins from Zimba's neck, clacked her tongue, and we were off.

First, we rode all through the fields behind our houses. Then we went up the hill and into some woods. I called and called. Once I saw something white behind some bushes, but it was only a sack with empty pop bottles in it.

The afternoon sun was hot on our backs when we came down out of the woods. Lacy trotted Zimba up and down side roads. I called and called Kipluck until my voice was just a scratchy whisper.

"He must have followed a dog home and is playing in someone's backyard," Lacy said. "You probably should get him a female to keep him company while you're in school."

I probably should, but I didn't think my dad would go for it. I thought he'd want a davenport first. And all I really wanted was Kipluck.

Lacy turned Zimba towards her house. It was the end of searching for that afternoon. I tried hard not to start crying again as Zimba cantered up to the barn like a big rocking horse.

After Lacy helped me down, she asked, "What happened to your mother?"

"She died. She was coming back from visiting my grandpa and the airplane crashed."

"Was that the jet that crashed outside of Denver?"

"Yes," I said.

She pulled the saddle off Zimba's back. "I remember seeing that on TV. It must have been very rough for you."

I nodded.

"Would you like to come in for some tea? I made a coconut cake yesterday."

"No thank you," I said. "Thanks for helping me look for Kipluck, though."

I went on back to my house while Lacy took the saddle into the barn. Most times coconut cake would have sounded good, but not this day. I sat by myself in one of the recliner chairs until the big, empty room got so depressing it drove me outside.

I wandered around the porch. My legs felt like roasted chicken legs from being spread out over Zimba's back. The fragrance of the roses made me sick. I picked one bud anyway, sat down on the steps, and leaned my head against the railing. I sat there until Dad got home, not even bothering to wipe away the tears dripping down my chin.

Dad was carrying a sack. He placed it between his legs as he sat down beside me. "Your mother used to like roses."

"I know." I began tearing each petal off the bud and dropping it on the steps.

He watched me for a minute. "I have a little good news. I went to the Animal Control center. Kipluck wasn't there, but they said they hadn't had any calls about a puppy being hit by a car."

I leaned my head over my lap and sobbed. The thought of Kipluck dead on the road hurt so bad I couldn't stand it.

Dad pulled me over to him. "I brought home some marking pens and cardboard so we could make lost-puppy signs. We'll put them on the telephone poles in the neighborhood. OK? We'll write our phone number on them and offer a ten-dollar reward. That should get kids looking out for him.

"Come on. Let's eat something and then go make the signs, OK?"

We made ten signs. Stuck them all up and down the road. I called and called some more, but my voice was almost gone.

In bed, the picture of Kipluck with his nose on his paws kept floating in my head. He was watching me with his slanted eyes. They had turned almost yellow before he ran away.

I tried to think of something else. Something besides my mom. Something to rock my mind to sleep. I couldn't think of anything.

"Do your work anyway," Jack told me at school the next morning. "So you can be a Master Wizard. My uncle said his wolf-dog was gone for two days before he fenced him in."

I did my work. I didn't care one way or the other. Miss Jewell gave my head a pat as she walked by.

On the bus ride home, Jo Mae kept trying to make me feel better. "That puppy's going to come home," she insisted. "Sometimes I just know things. Grandma says I'm like her. I can feel things in my bones."

Watching Jo Mae get off the bus, I thought she was a really neat person. Some kids, like Sharon, were mean to her and some kids didn't pay much attention to her because she was poor and different. But I liked her.

I didn't want to get my hopes up, though. After I got off the bus, I tried to walk slowly. But the nearer I came to my house, the faster my legs went. As I passed Lacy's, I thought I saw something white on my porch.

I raced to my gate and pushed it open. There he was, flashing down the steps. I crouched to the ground as he leaped on me and covered my chin with his wet puppy kisses.

"Where have you been, Kipluck? Where have you been?" I took his soft, furry head in my hands and looked into his eyes. "Where did you go?"

His only answer was more kisses. I hugged him to me and cried, "I haven't got a mother, Kipluck. My mom died. You can't do this to me again. You can't run away, Kipluck. You're all I've got. You and Dad are all I've got. If you aren't here when I come home, I'm all alone."

Kipluck pulled away from me and sat with his head held stiffly back. He didn't seem to understand my cries and tears. I tugged his head close to mine. "You can't run away ever again, Kipluck. You can't leave me, please."

I petted his fur over and over until I remembered. "Oh, are you hungry?" I asked him. I gathered my books up from the grass and he followed me into the house.

Mostly he wanted water. After that, he gulped down a can and a half of dog food. I was thinking to myself that I would keep him in the house at night until the fence was finished. He could sleep with me. So I'd know exactly where he was.

We were playing in the yard when Lacy drove up in front of her house. I called to her, "Kipluck's home! Kipluck came home."

She came right over. "It looks like you've been crying, honey," she said.

I ducked my head down. "Yes. I was so glad to see him. And I don't want him to run away again."

"I bet you don't." She tucked her skirt under her and sat down on the step beside me. "You got lonesome, huh?"

"Don't you get lonesome in your house alone?"

"Sometimes," she agreed. "Sometimes in the evening."

"You never got married?"

"Once I was. But it turned out that he wasn't a very kind man."

"And you didn't have any children?"

"No, I never had any children," she said. "And it was lucky I didn't, because my husband wouldn't have made a very nice father."

"My father's nice. Except he's slow."

Lacy smiled. "I noticed. But I think you have to look around at other kids' dads and see they have faults, too. There are worse things than being slow. You can love your dad even if he isn't perfect."

"Oh, I do. It's just that I lost Kipluck."

"And that was hard." She looked into my face. "Especially after you lost your mother."

I nodded. Talking to Lacy was like talking to a friend. I wasn't even embarrassed when I asked her questions. "Didn't you ever wish you could have children?" I wondered.

"Yes. I still wish it."

"Why don't you take home one of those kids who has bad parents?" This time I looked in her face to see what she would answer.

"Lots of times I've wanted to take one in," she said. "But it's against the rules of my job."

My dad drove up then. There were big rolls of wire

fencing sticking out of the back of his station wagon. "Good," I said. "I told him Kipluck was back when he called. He promised he'd bring the wire and concrete tonight."

After Dad gave me a kiss and greeted Lacy, I asked, "You got everything?"

"Not quite. The concrete was too heavy to carry in one load. I'll bring the rest on Friday." Kipluck was jumping on him, trying to say hello. Dad petted him and rolled him around the grass.

"How about going out to dinner to celebrate?" It seemed like he meant both Lacy and me.

"Oh, I don't want to put Kipluck in the shed now," I protested. "Couldn't we get some Chinese food to go and have a picnic?"

"Sure."

"And Lacy, too?"

"Sure." Dad smiled.

"Let's have it on the picnic table in my backyard," Lacy suggested. "And I'll make some iced tea."

Dad looked up from playing with Kipluck. "Sure," he said again, and his smile was even bigger.

I got tired right after we ate. I hadn't had much sleep the last two nights. "You look done in," Dad said.

"Why don't you take Kipluck to our house and I'll help Lacy clean up."

"All right." I got slowly up from the picnic bench. "And he'll have to stay inside tonight so he doesn't run away again."

Before Dad could object, Lacy put in quickly, "My dog always slept with me when I was a kid."

By the time I had had my bath and was settled in bed with Kipluck, Dad still wasn't home. That was OK with me. And the rule that Lacy couldn't take in kids from her job was OK with me, too.

The Thief

13

At school everybody was glad that Kipluck had come back. Jo Mae said, "I knew it. I could just feel him coming home." Jenny jumped up and down. Diane said, "Rad!" Miss Jewell said, "Thank goodness." And Jack said, "Awright! Now get your fence up."

We did. My dad started out early Saturday morning. He pushed the first big roll of wire against the wooden posts beside the gate. I followed after him with a wheelbarrow that held concrete mix and a shovel. After Dad nailed the wire to a post, he shoveled concrete along the trench.

We were at the corner next to Lacy's house, when

she came out her door. Her yellow hair was hanging down her back, the way I liked it best. She watched us a minute and then crawled through the boards of the old wooden fence into our yard. "Looks like you could use a little help."

She unwound the big roll of wire ahead of Dad so all he had to do was nail and shovel. It went faster this way. I was beat by eleven o'clock when Dad suggested we stop to make some sandwiches and coffee.

After he and Lacy went in the kitchen, I stretched out on the grass. I didn't get to relax very long, though, because Kipluck woke up from his nap and leaped on me. "You crazy dog," I told him and rolled on top of him. He squirmed out from under me, crouched down like his daddy did, and then made another leap for me.

"Soup's on!" Dad yelled from the kitchen. I raced Kipluck to the house. He ate puppy chow while I ate tuna-fish sandwiches at the card table with Dad and Lacy. Every so often I had to stop eating to scratch.

"Mosquito bites?" Lacy asked.

"No, flea bites," I told her. "Kipluck's been sleeping with me."

"Marianne!" Dad said.

"Well, he must have gotten the fleas when he ran away. If I'd told you," I explained, "you'd have made Kipluck stay on the porch and then he'd run away again."

"You're wrong," he corrected me. "I would have squirted you both with flea spray."

"Anyway, as soon as the fence is done, Kipluck can sleep outside."

"Wolves are social animals," Lacy said. "What you need is a female to keep him company. Then you could have puppies, too."

Puppies! I'd love a whole batch of puppies.

Dad carefully placed his cup on the wobbly table. "What we need first," he said, "is some dining room furniture."

"Maybe we could get a female in the fall," I suggested.

Lacy shook her head. "Wolves only have cubs in the spring. I should think wolf hybrids would be the same." She looked at me thoughtfully. "When's your birthday?"

"July ninth." I put down the crust of my sandwich and scratched my wrist where I had three flea bites in a row.

Dad leaned across the table. "How about another cup of coffee, Lacy?"

"Hmm, I think not," Lacy said, standing up. "I think Marianne needs that fence up more than I need coffee."

I loved that Lacy!

We were way in the backyard by the apple trees

when Jo Mae showed up. She had found the way through the fields to our house all by herself. "See?" She ducked her head shyly and held her hand out to me. "My Grandma gave me this ring. She wore it when she was a girl."

The stone was the same color as Jo Mae's eyes, a pretty light blue. Lacy admired the ring, too.

I explained to Jo Mae that I would have to work for a while. She offered to help, but there was really nothing for her to do. "Play with Kipluck," I said. That suited her fine because she just loved "that little ol' puppy." They ran around the trees after each other while I pushed the wheelbarrow along the trench. Kipluck had the big smile on his face that he gets whenever he's having a great time.

Dad gave a last big pound of the hammer on a corner post. There was one side of the yard left to go. It was only two o'clock, but I was afraid he was going to quit. "You through for the day?" I asked, really disappointed. Since he knew about the fleas, I was sure he wouldn't let Kipluck in my bed that night.

"Nope, have to do a store run. No more nails." He raised his eyebrows at me. "And while I'm out, I'll get some flea spray."

I shrank away from him, but Lacy put her arm around me. "Don't worry, honey," she said. "He'll spray Kipluck and you can take a shower."

After Dad and Lacy left for the store, Jo Mae and I threw a Frisbee back and forth. Once in a while, we'd miss a catch and Kipluck would pounce on the Frisbee. We were chasing Kipluck around the yard, trying to get it back from him, when Brittany and Mrs. James drove up.

I explained to them that Dad wasn't home.

Mrs. James's black hair was done up in stiff curls all over her head. She patted them with her hand. "Well, when will he return, dear?"

I hated it when she called me "dear." When Lacy called me "honey," it made me warm inside. "I'm not sure when he'll be back," I said.

Jo Mae had gotten the Frisbee away from Kipluck by then, so I introduced her to Mrs. James and Brittany. Kipluck kept jumping up on Jo Mae, trying to get at the Frisbee.

"You'd better be careful of that dog," Brittany warned her. "He'll hurt you."

"No he won't!" I usually try not to cause trouble, but that made me mad. "And I might be getting a female to keep him company."

Mrs. James's jaw pushed forward. "One of those animals is bad enough. You don't need two."

"He split my lip open," Brittany said. "I suppose you think that didn't hurt?"

Jo Mae was hanging back behind me. I pulled her

forward by her hand. "Look at Jo Mae's new ring. Her grandma gave it to her."

Brittany bent over Jo Mae's outstretched finger. "What kind of a stone is that?"

Mrs. James took a close look. "An aquamarine, isn't it?"

Jo Mae nodded. "My grandma wore it when she was a girl."

"I wish I had a ring." Brittany shot her mother a nasty glance. "Everybody else has one."

Mrs. James ignored Brittany and shifted her attention to me. "As long as we're here, why don't all you girls play Frisbee? I'll wait in the car for a while."

I knew I should take Mrs. James in the house and let her sit on one of the recliner chairs, but I was afraid she'd stay there until Lacy and Dad got back. Then Lacy might leave. I moved out in the grass. Jo Mae tossed me the Frisbee and I tossed it to Brittany.

Every time Brittany caught it, she threw it fast so Kipluck would gallop away from her. I thought Mrs. James would never get tired waiting, but she finally did. She honked the horn twice.

"Just a minute," Brittany called to her. "I have to go to the bathroom."

Brittany went into the house. Jo Mae and I flopped down on the ground. We let Kipluck have the Frisbee so he wouldn't attack us. After a while, he got tired of chewing on it and jumped on us anyway.

"That girl's been in there a long time," Jo Mae whispered to me. "Wonder what she's doing?"

I wondered, too. Just as I got to the porch, Brittany walked out the front door.

"Did you need something?" I asked.

"No," Brittany said, hurrying past me.

Almost as soon as she and Mrs. James left, Dad and Lacy came home. I mentioned casually that Brittany and her mother had been visiting. Dad gave me a quick look, but he didn't say anything.

Jo Mae had to leave at four o'clock. At five o'clock Dad stopped pounding, dangled the hammer from his hand, and rubbed his shoulder. "How about we knock this off and all go out to dinner?"

"Oh, come on," Lacy said impatiently. "There's only one section left. Let's finish it up."

He finished it up, much to my relief. But I worried a bit about Lacy. I didn't know whether she liked my dad or not.

They seemed to get along all right at dinner. We went to a Mexican restaurant that Lacy knew about. I wished we'd gone to the Chinese place so I could eat fried prawns.

When we got home, Kipluck bounced against the gate

as soon as he saw me get out of the car. He was a little disappointed, though, when he had to go to sleep on the porch.

Before climbing into bed, I pulled back the covers to search for fleas. I wondered if I should spray inside my sheets. But if I did, then wouldn't the fleas jump on me?

I was almost asleep, when the memory of Brittany walking out of our house came up in my mind. She had kept her left hand in her jeans pocket as she hurried past me. The ring! I hopped out of bed, opened my bottom dresser drawer, took out my mom's jewel box, and looked inside. I didn't see the garnet ring. I searched all through the earrings and beads. My mother's ring wasn't there.

How Stupid Can You Get?

14

At breakfast, I told my dad about Mom's ring being gone. I explained how Brittany had wanted a ring and how she'd stayed in the house by herself for a long time. Dad thoughtfully sipped his hot coffee. "We can't be sure she took it, but I guess we'd better go see."

The cooked-cabbage smell was still in the halls of the old apartment house. I stood behind Dad while he knocked on the James's door. Mrs. James answered his knock.

"What a nice surprise. Come in. Come in." She gave us her big, white smile.

Brittany was in the living room, reading the Sunday

funnies. When she saw us, she stuck her left hand in her jeans pocket, stood up, and took a step towards the hall door.

"We have something we'd like to talk to you about," Dad said as he and Mrs. James settled into the fuzzy peach chairs.

"You sound serious," Mrs. James said.

"I guess I am." He nodded at Brittany who was edging out of the room. "Won't you sit back down, Brittany. This concerns you, too."

"Well, I was just going to wash my hands. We had pig sausages for breakfast."

"Sit down," Mrs. James ordered.

Brittany sat on the corner of the davenport with me.

"If you don't mind," Dad told Mrs. James, "I'd like to make a request of Brittany."

"Fine with me," Mrs. James said.

He turned to Brittany. "Will you please take your hand out of your pocket?"

She slowly pulled her hand free. The garnet ring hung over the knuckle on her finger.

"May I have that?" Dad asked. "That was Marianne's mother's ring."

Mrs. James rose to her feet, went over to Brittany, and took the ring away from her. Before she handed it to Dad, she examined it closely. "Jim, is this real gold?"

"Yes, it is," he said.

"Oh, my, I thought it was costume jewelry. Marianne should never have given it to Brittany."

"I didn't," I said. "Brittany went into our house by herself when she told you she was going to the bathroom. And stayed a long time."

"You followed me in the house and gave me the ring." Brittany stared into my eyes with that mean look on her face.

"No I didn't." I stared straight back at her. "I met you on the porch and you went right by me."

Red color covered Mrs. James's forehead and poured down to her neck. She had to remember Brittany going into our house alone and coming out our door alone. She could see us from her car. "I can't believe this." Mrs. James clasped her hands to her chest. "I don't know what to say."

"Maybe Brittany has something to say," Dad suggested.

Brittany darted one frightened look at her mom and then concentrated on the toes of her slippers.

"Well," Dad said, standing up. "I'm sorry this happened, but I'm glad to have the ring back."

I almost tripped over my shoes going out the door. When Dad closed it, I bent down to tie the laces on my Keds. We could hear Mrs. James's voice coming through the wall. It didn't sound the same as when she'd apologized to us over and over.

"You idiot!" she raged. "Why did you do such a dumb thing? How stupid can you get? Now how are we ever going to see them again?"

Who cares, I thought to myself.

On the way to our car, Dad didn't say anything about what we'd heard. Instead, he suggested that we check out davenports on the way home.

We checked out about twenty of them. Most of them were fat with icky colors. There was a neat, navy-blue leather one, but it cost two thousand dollars.

"Lacy has lots of furniture," I told Dad as we left the last store. "She could move in with us and rent her house."

"Oh, what about her horse?"

"Well, she doesn't have to rent her barn," I explained. "Just her house."

Dad looked down at me with his eyebrows raised. "You'd like that, huh?"

Sure I would. Who wouldn't?

Lacy was working in her yard, when we got home. "I'm starved," I whispered to Dad. "Let's invite Lacy out to dinner."

Lacy is the kind of person who doesn't make a big fuss about being fancy. "I'd like to go," she told us, "if you don't mind my jeans."

"That's what we're wearing," Dad said.

"Nobody dresses up at the Chinese restaurant," I reminded them. They agreed, so I got my fried prawns.

After the waiter cleared the table, he left a fresh pot of tea and a plate with three fortune cookies. I chose the first one, broke it open, and took out the slip of paper.

"What does it say, honey?" Lacy asked.

"It says, 'You will get your wish.' "

"Don't tell what it is," she warned me, "or it won't come true."

While I watched her break open the next cookie, I tried to decide on a wish. I wanted another puppy so Kipluck wouldn't be lonesome while I was in school. I couldn't have my mom back, of course, but I thought Lacy might make a nice mother.

" 'Good news coming,' " Lacy announced. "I hope it's a raise."

Dad straightened out his paper. " 'You will get a lot done in this world.' "

"Slowly," I added, and they both laughed.

After we left the restaurant, Dad dropped me off at our house so he and Lacy could go for a ride in the warm, spring evening. I played with Kipluck awhile and then went to bed. I woke up a bit later to the sound of rain. Good, I thought, the cement in the trench will get hard.

Then I wondered if Kipluck was wet. He always dragged his blanket around the porch and it might be out beyond the edge of the roof. I got up to see.

He wasn't on the porch. I called, "Kipluck, Kipluck."

He slowly crawled out from under the steps to give me some sleepy licks on my chin. When I heard Dad's car, I stopped petting Kipluck's soft fur, stood up from my crouch, and listened for voices. They weren't coming nearer. They were fading away.

I went around to the side of our porch. Dad and Lacy were going up Lacy's steps. When they were right under her front door light, I saw Lacy turn to Dad, reach up her arms, and pull his head down to hers. Awright! Lacy did like my dad! I gave Kipluck a good-night hug and tiptoed back to bed.

Master Wizards

Monday morning, Jenny caught up with me on the way to our classroom. "Listen, I know something neat." She pulled me over against the wall. "But don't tell anyone, because I'm not supposed to tell you. You and Jack and Lester are going to be Master Wizards!"

"Really! How do you know?"

"Shh!" Jenny didn't say any more until Sharon had gone by. "I know because I worked in the office Friday morning. The secretary had me take the certificates to the bus drivers and the playground teachers to get them signed. We're going to have a Master Wizard meeting today and you guys are going to be invited."

"You mean Mrs. Wilson signed Jack's certificate?"

"Yes, she did, and she wrote a note to Mr. Douglas saying Jack had been a little gentleman on the playground for the last month." Jenny put her hand over her mouth to cover her giggles.

We giggled all the way to our room. Jack was leaning on the other side of my desk when I got to it.

"Hey, look at the red bird out there." He pointed to the windows.

"Where?" I couldn't see any red bird.

"I guess you missed it," he said.

I sat down in my chair.

Ppppuuttt!!!

I sprang up again.

"Marianne!" Jack shouted. "Shame on you!"

Everybody in the classroom was laughing. I yanked the whoopee cushion off my seat. "Jack, you jerk!"

I was going to throw the cushion in the waste basket, but he jumped over my seat and grabbed it. We were both tugging on it, when Diane said, "Cool it. Here comes Miss Jewell."

I let go of the cushion and Jack stuffed it in his desk before Miss Jewell got in the room.

During reading, I was trying to figure out how to warn Jack about the Master Wizard meeting. It wasn't a very big honor to get a certificate and pin so late in the year. Still, I didn't want him to miss being on the stage crew for the awards assembly.

I felt Miss Jewell watching me. I got down to work answering the questions on my brown card. I knew it was because I'd made it to the brown cards that she'd put me on the Master Wizard list.

We were finished with our reading and working on the Lewis and Clark expedition when Mr. Douglas came to our door. Miss Jewell went out in the hall to talk with him. As soon as she was out of sight, Jack pulled out his whoopee cushion. Before I could get him to listen to me, he was up at Miss Jewell's desk, slipping the cushion under the pad on her chair.

I glanced over at Sharon. She was watching Jack closely. She had that goody-good, tattletale look on her face. I got up and stood in the aisle. "Put that thing back in your desk."

"No way," he said. "And you'd better sit down or you'll get in trouble."

I didn't sit down. I marched up to Miss Jewell's chair, snatched the cushion from under the pad, and threw it in the wastebasket.

"Hey, cut that—"

"Cool it," Tara warned.

Jack slipped into his seat and I hurried toward mine, too late.

"Marianne, what are you doing?" Miss Jewell's smile had turned into a scowl.

"I just put something in the wastebasket."

"You aren't supposed to be away from your desk when I leave the room."

"I'm sorry," I mumbled.

"Well, you really know better." As she walked to the front of the room, she frowned at the piece of paper in her hand. I supposed she was thinking about whether I should be a Master Wizard or not. She tapped the paper several times on the edge of the front table before she made her announcement. "There will be a Master Wizard meeting in the library at ten-fifteen. Jack, Lester, and Marianne have been invited to attend."

Jack raised his hand. "I thought they held those meetings on Friday."

"Mr. Douglas usually does," Miss Jewell agreed. "But he was out of the building last week."

So that's why Jack had the whoopee cushion! After Friday was over, he must have given up on being a Master Wizard.

Miss Jewell nodded at me. "And you'd better get to work, young lady."

I dived into my notebook and wrote furiously on Captain Cook's sighting of majestic Mount Hood. At ten-fifteen, Miss Jewell said the Master Wizards could go to the library. I guessed she was calling Jack and Lester and me Master Wizards, too.

There were about fifty kids in the library. Jack, Lester, Tara, Jenny, and I sat at a table together. Mr. Douglas stood by the card catalog and gave us a talk about how he was always proud to welcome new Master Wizards into the group. He said it didn't matter how long it took to reach a goal. The important thing was to accomplish it.

There were seven new Master Wizards. He called us up to stand beside him. He shook our hands and gave each of us a certificate and pin. And then he started clapping and the rest of the kids clapped for us, too.

When Mr. Douglas asked us what we wanted to do for the school, Mrs. Leland, the librarian, wrote down our jobs. A couple of kids wanted to work in the library. I said I wanted to be an office girl. Jack and Lester said they'd be on the stage crew.

A bowl of punch and a tray of donuts were on the check-out counter. Mrs. Leland told us the new Master Wizards got to be first in line. After we'd carried our food to the table, I asked Jack if he was still mad at me for throwing away his whoopee cushion.

"Naw," he said. "I'll get it back at lunch."

"You'd better take it home then."

"Maybe." He gave me his wicked grin. "Or maybe

I'll put it in my desk until the awards assembly is over."

Jenny poked me. "How's your pup?"

"Great. Except he chewed the handles off one of my glow ropes. And you know what?" I put down my cup of punch and leaned closer to her. "My dad's going out with the lady next door."

Jenny finished the last bite of her donut and wiped her hands on her paper napkin. "So you might get a stepmother."

A fifth grade kid sitting in front of us turned around. "You poor thing," he said.

"What would you call her?" Jenny wondered.

"Lacy, I guess. That's what I call her now."

"What does she call you?" the fifth grade kid asked me.

I couldn't keep a smile from curling around my mouth. "She calls me 'honey,' " I said.

Fodor's 2000 Pocket Washington, D.C.

Excerpted from *Fodor's Washington, D.C. 2000*

Fodor's Travel Publications, Inc.
New York • Toronto • London • Sydney • Auckland
www.fodors.com

Fodor's Pocket Washington, D.C.

EDITORS: Ellen E. Browne, Deborah B. Kaufman

Editorial Contributors: Holly Bass, Thomas Head, John A. Kelly, Bruce Walker, CiCi Williamson

Editorial Production: Brian Vitunic

Maps: David Lindroth, *cartographer*; Rebecca Baer, Robert Blake, *map editors*

Design: Fabrizio La Rocca, *creative director*; Lyndell Brookhouse-Gil, *cover design*; Jolie Novak, *photo editor*; Melanie Marin, *photo researcher*

Production/Manufacturing: Mike Costa

Cover Photo: (The Capitol, Washington, D.C.): James Lemass

Copyright

Special Sales

Important Tip

Although all prices, opening times, and other details in this book are based on information supplied to us at press time, changes occur all the time in the travel world, and Fodor's cannot accept responsibility for facts that become outdated or for inadvertent errors or omissions. So **always confirm information when it matters,** especially if you're making a detour to visit a specific place.

CONTENTS

On the Road with Fodor's   *v*

Don't Forget to Write *v*

Smart Travel Tips   *x*

1   **Destination: Washington, D.C.**   *1*

"America's Hometown" 2
New and Noteworthy 4
Pleasures and Pastimes 4
Quick Tours 6

2   **Exploring Washington, D.C.**   *8*

The Mall 13
The Monuments 25
The White House Area 34
Capitol Hill 46
Old Downtown and Federal Triangle 58
Georgetown 72
Dupont Circle 81
Foggy Bottom 90
Adams-Morgan/Cleveland Park 94
Around Washington, D.C. 99

3   **Dining**   *108*

4   **Lodging**   *131*

5   **Nightlife and the Arts**   *145*

6   **Shopping**   *167*

Index   *186*

Maps

Washington, D.C., Area
   vi–vii
Washington, D.C., Metro
   System *viii–ix*
Exploring Washington,
   D.C. *10–11*
The Mall *16–17*
The Monuments *26*
The White House Area *35*
Capitol Hill *47*
Old Downtown and
   Federal Triangle *60–61*

Georgetown *75*
Dupont Circle and Foggy
   Bottom *82*
Adams-Morgan/Cleveland
   Park *96*
Adams-Morgan/Cleveland
   Park Dining *111*
Washington Dining
   116–117
Washington Lodging
   134–135

ON THE ROAD WITH FODOR'S

EVERY Y2K TRIP is a significant trip. So if there was ever a time you needed excellent travel information, it's now. Acutely aware of that fact, we've pulled out all stops in preparing *Fodor's Pocket Washington, D.C.* To direct you to the places that are truly worth your time and money in this important year, we've rallied the team of endearingly picky know-it-alls we're pleased to call our writers. Having seen all corners of Washington, they're real experts on the subjects they cover for us. If you knew them, you'd poll them for tips yourself.

Holly Bass, who updated the Shopping and Nightlife and the Arts chapters, contributes regularly to the *Washington CityPaper,* teaches creative writing at the Duke Ellington School of the Arts, and does spoken-word performances in D.C.'s nightclubs and coffeehouses.

Dining-chapter updater **Thomas Head** is the executive wine and food editor at *The Washingtonian* magazine. He's happy to report that, in the 15 years that he has lived in Washington, the city's restaurant scene has gotten better and better.

Bruce Walker, a D.C.–area resident for most of his life, has been with the *Washington Post* since 1981. He has perfect credentials for a Fodor's reviser: he's old enough to be a seasoned journalist with an eagle eye for detail yet hip enough to be up on the latest goings-on about town. Bruce updated the Exploring chapter.

CiCi Williamson has been a food and travel writer and syndicated newspaper columnist for almost two decades. In revising the Lodging chapter, CiCi drove 1,000 mi, visiting more than 100 hotels and sights. She met and married her husband and writing partner, **John A. Kelly,** in Annapolis and lives in McLean, Virginia.

Don't Forget to Write

Keeping a travel guide fresh and up-to-date is a big job. So we love your feedback—positive and negative—and follow up on all suggestions. Contact the Washington editor at editors@fodors.com or c/o Fodor's, 201 East 50th Street, New York, NY 10022. And have a wonderful trip!

Karen Cure
Editorial Director

Washington, D.C., Area

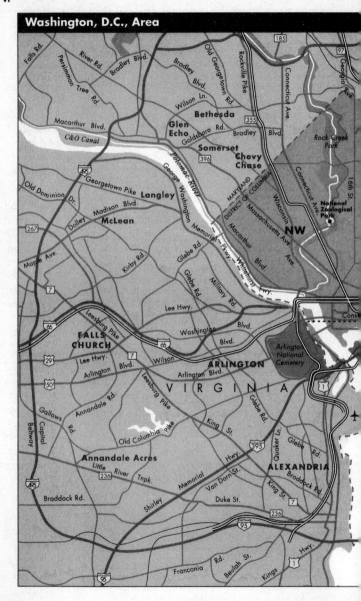

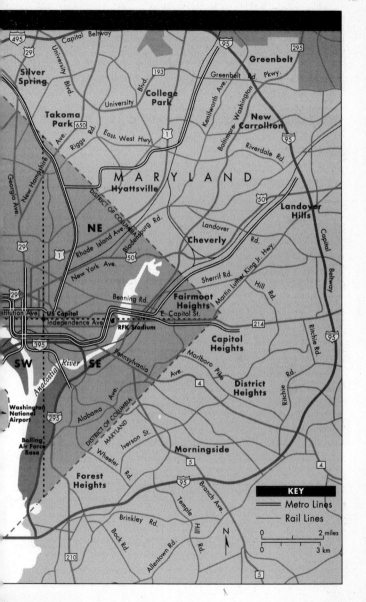

495 Capital Beltway **95** **295**

29 University Blvd.

Silver Spring **193** **Greenbelt** Greenbelt Rd. Pkwy.

College Park

Takoma Park **650** University **1** **New Carrollton** **95**

Riggs Rd. East-West Hwy.

Georgia Ave.

New Hampshire Ave.

M A R Y L A N D

Riverdale Rd.

Hyattsville **50**

DISTRICT OF COLUMBIA **Landover Hills**

NE Rhode Island Ave. Landover Rd. **Cheverly** Capital Beltway

29 **1** Bladensburg Rd. **50**

New York Ave. Sherrif Rd. Hill Rd.

Martin Luther King Jr. Hwy.

Benning Rd.

29 **Fairmont Heights** Ritchie Rd. **95**

titution Ave. **US Capitol** E. Capitol St.

Independence Ave. **RFK Stadium** **214**

SW **395** **SE** **Capitol Heights**

River Anacostia Pennsylvania Marlboro Pike

District Heights Ritchie Rd.

Ave.

Washington National Airport **295** **4**

Alabama Ave.

Bolling Air Force Base DISTRICT OF COLUMBIA MARYLAND Iverson St. **Morningside**

Wheeler Rd. **5**

Forest Heights **95** Branch Ave. **4**

Temple Hill Rd.

Brinkley Rd.

Boch Rd. **KEY**

Allentown Rd. ══ Metro Lines

210 **N** ── Rail Lines

5 0   2 miles

0   3 km

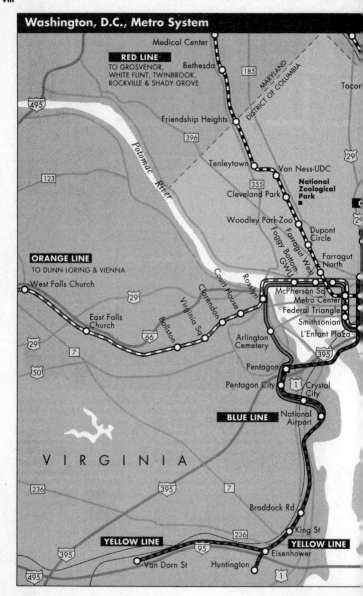

Washington, D.C., Metro System

Medical Center

RED LINE
TO GROSVENOR,
WHITE FLINT, TWINBROOK,
ROCKVILLE & SHADY GROVE

Bethesda

185

MARYLAND

DISTRICT OF COLUMBIA

Tacor

495

Friendship Heights

396

29

Potomac River

123

Tenleytown

Van Ness-UDC

355

Cleveland Park

National Zoological Park

Woodley Park-Zoo

29

Dupont Circle

Farragut West

Foggy Bottom

ORANGE LINE
TO DUNN LORING & VIENNA

Farragut North

West Falls Church

Court House

Rosslyn

GWU

McPherson Sq

Clarendon

Metro Center

East Falls Church

Virginia Sq

Ballston

66

Federal Triangle

Smithsonian

29

7

Arlington Cemetery

L'Enfant Plaza

50

395

Pentagon

Pentagon City

1

Crystal City

236

VIRGINIA

BLUE LINE

National Airport

395

7

Braddock Rd

236

King St

YELLOW LINE

395

95

YELLOW LINE

Eisenhower

495

Van Dorn St

Huntington

1

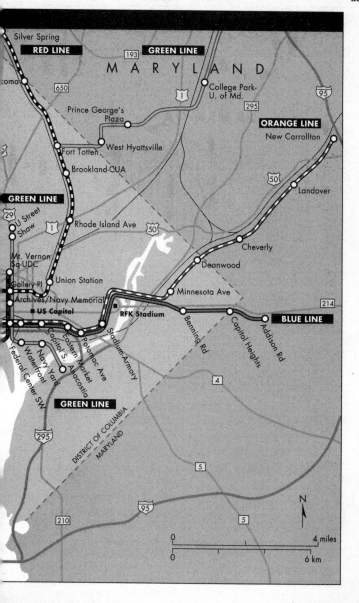

Silver Spring
RED LINE   **GREEN LINE**
193
M A R Y L A N D
coma
650
College Park-
U. of Md.
1
295
95
Prince George's
Plaza
ORANGE LINE
New Carrollton
Fort Totten   West Hyattsville
50
Landover
Brookland-CUA
GREEN LINE
29   U Street
Shaw
1   Rhode Island Ave
50
Cheverly
Mt. Vernon
Sq-UDC
Deanwood
Gallery Pl   Union Station
Archives/Navy Memorial
Minnesota Ave
■ US Capitol
RFK Stadium
BLUE LINE
214
Eastern Market
Capitol S.
Potomac Ave
Anacostia
Stadium-Armory
Benning Rd
Capitol Heights
Addison Rd
Federal Center SW
Waterfront
Navy Yard
4
GREEN LINE
DISTRICT OF COLUMBIA
MARYLAND
295
5
210
95
5

N

0   4 miles
0   6 km

SMART TRAVEL TIPS

Basic Information on Traveling in Washington, D.C., Savvy Tips to Make Your Trip a Breeze, and Companies and Organizations to Contact

AIR TRAVEL

CARRIERS

➤ MAJOR AIRLINES: **Air Canada** (☎ 800/776–3000). **America West** (☎ 800/235–9292). **American** (☎ 800/433–7300). **Continental** (☎ 800/525–0280). **Delta** (☎ 800/221–1212). **Northwest** (☎ 800/225–2525). **TWA** (☎ 800/221–2000). **United** (☎ 800/241–6522). **US Airways** (☎ 800/428–4322).

➤ SMALLER AIRLINES: **Air Tran** (☎ 800/825–8538) to Dulles. **Midway** (☎ 800/446–4392) to Ronald Reagan National and BWI. **Midwest Express** (☎ 800/452–2022) to Ronald Reagan National. **Southwest** (☎ 800/435–9792) to BWI.

AIRPORTS & TRANSFERS

The major gateways to D.C. include **Ronald Reagan National Airport,** in Virginia, 4 mi south of downtown Washington; **Dulles International Airport,** 26 mi west of Washington; and **Baltimore-Washington International (BWI) Airport,** in Maryland, about 25 mi northeast of Washington.

➤ AIRPORT INFORMATION: **Baltimore-Washington International (BWI) Airport** (☎ 410/859–7100). **Dulles International Airport** (☎ 703/572–2700). **Ronald Reagan National Airport** (☎ 703/417–8000).

TRANSFERS BY BUS

Dulles airport is served every half hour (hourly on weekends) by **Washington Flyer.** The ride from Dulles to downtown takes 45 minutes and costs $16 ($26 round-trip). The bus takes you to the Washington Plaza Hotel at 10 Thomas Circle NW, where you can board a free shuttle bus that serves downtown hotels. The bus will also transport you from your hotel to the Thomas Circle address to catch the main airport bus on your return journey. Fares may be paid in cash or with Visa or MasterCard; children under age six ride free.

Reagan National, Dulles, and BWI airports are served by **SuperShuttle.** Buses leave BWI every half hour for 1517 K Street NW; from Reagan National and Dulles, make reservations at the ground transportation desk. The 20-minute ride from Reagan National costs $8; the 45-minute ride from Dulles costs $20; the 65-minute ride from BWI costs $21 ($34 round-trip); drivers accept major credit cards in addition to cash.

➤ BUS INFORMATION: **SuperShuttle** (☎ 800/258–3826). **Washington Flyer** (☎ 703/685–1400).

TRANSFERS BY LIMOUSINE
Private Car has a counter at BWI Airport and charges $63–$69 from there to downtown; or call ahead to have a car waiting for you at Reagan National ($45–$55 plus 15% tip) or Dulles ($74–$82 plus 15% tip).

➤ LIMOUSINE INFORMATION: **Private Car** (☎ 800/685–0888).

TRANSFERS BY METRO
If you are coming into Ronald Reagan National Airport, have little to carry, and are staying at a hotel near a subway stop, it makes sense to take the Metro downtown. The station is within walking distance of the baggage claim area, but a free airport shuttle stops outside each terminal and brings you to the National Airport station. The Metro ride downtown takes about 20 minutes and costs either $1.10 or $1.40, depending on the time of day.

TRANSFERS BY TAXI
Expect to pay about $13 to get from Ronald Reagan National Airport to downtown, $45 from Dulles, and $50 from BWI. Unscrupulous cabbies prey on out-of-towners, so if the fare strikes you as astronomical, get the driver's name and cab number and

threaten to call the **D.C. Taxicab Commission.** A $1.25 airport surcharge is added to the total at Ronald Reagan National.

➤ TAXI INFORMATION: **D.C. Taxicab Commission** (☎ 202/645–6018).

TRANSFERS BY TRAIN
Free shuttle buses carry passengers between airline terminals and the train station at BWI Airport. **Amtrak** and **Maryland Rail Commuter Service** trains run between BWI and Washington's Union Station from around 6 AM to midnight. The cost of the 40-minute ride is $14–$24 on an Amtrak train, $5 on a MARC train (weekdays only).

➤ TRAIN INFORMATION: **Amtrak** (☎ 800/872–7245). **Maryland Rail Commuter Service** (MARC, ☎ 800/325–7245).

BUS TRAVEL

Washington is a major terminal for **Greyhound Bus Lines.** The company also has stations in nearby Silver Spring, Maryland, and in Arlington and Springfield, Virginia.

➤ BUS INFORMATION: **Greyhound Bus Lines** (✉ 1005 1st St. NE, ☎ 202/289–5160 or 800/231–2222).

BUS TRAVEL WITHIN D.C.

WMATA's red, white, and blue Metrobuses crisscross the city and nearby suburbs. Free transfers, good for 1½ to two hours, are available on buses and in Metro stations. Bus-to-bus transfers are accepted at designated Metrobus transfer points. Rail-to-bus transfers must be picked up before boarding the train. There may be a transfer charge when boarding the bus. There are no bus-to-rail transfers.

FARES & SCHEDULES

All bus rides within the District are $1.10, and some routes run 24 hours.

➤ BUS INFORMATION: **Washington Metropolitan Area Transit Authority** (WMATA, ☎ 202/637–7000 or 202/638–3780 TDD); open weekdays 6 AM–10:30 PM and weekends 8 AM–10:30 PM.

CAR RENTAL

Rates in Washington, D.C., begin at $38 a day and $139 a week for an economy car with air-conditioning, an automatic transmission, and unlimited mileage. This does not include tax on car rentals, which is 8%.

➤ MAJOR AGENCIES: **Alamo** (☎ 800/327–9633; 020/8759–6200 in the U.K.). **Avis** (☎ 800/331–1212; 800/879–2847 in Canada; 02/9353–9000 in Australia; 09/525–1982 in New Zealand). **Budget** (☎ 800/527–0700; 0144/227–6266 in the U.K.). **Dollar** (☎ 800/800–4000; 020/8897–0811 in the U.K., where it is known as Eurodollar; 02/9223–1444 in Aus-

tralia). **Hertz** (☎ 800/654–3131; 800/263–0600 in Canada; 020/8897–2072 in the U.K.; 02/9669–2444 in Australia; 03/358–6777 in New Zealand). **National Inter-Rent** (☎ 800/227–7368; 0345/222525 in the U.K., where it is known as Europcar InterRent).

INSURANCE

When driving a rented car you are generally responsible for any damage to or loss of the vehicle as well as for any property damage or personal injury that you may cause. Before you rent see what coverage your personal auto-insurance policy and credit cards already provide.

For about $15 to $20 per day, rental companies sell protection, known as a collision- or loss-damage waiver (CDW or LDW), that eliminates your liability for damage to the car.

In most states you don't need a CDW if you have personal auto insurance or other liability insurance. However, **make sure you have enough coverage to pay for the car.** If you do not have auto insurance or an umbrella policy that covers damage to third parties, purchasing liability insurance and a CDW or LDW is highly recommended.

REQUIREMENTS & RESTRICTIONS

In Washington you must be 21 to rent a car, and rates may be higher if you're under 25. You'll pay extra for child seats (about $3 per day), which are compulsory for children under five, and for additional drivers (about $2 per day). Non-U.S. residents will need a reservation voucher, a passport, a driver's license, and a travel policy that covers each driver, in order to pick up a car.

CAR TRAVEL

A car can be a drawback in Washington. Traffic is horrendous, especially at rush hours, and **driving is often confusing,** with many lanes and some entire streets changing direction suddenly at certain times of day. The traffic lights sometimes stymie visitors. Most don't hang down over the middle of the streets but stand at the sides of intersections. Radar detectors are illegal in Washington, D.C., and Virginia.

LAY OF THE LAND

Interstate 95 skirts D.C. as part of the Beltway, the six- to eight-lane highway that encircles the city. The eastern half of the Beltway is labeled both I–95 and I–495; the western half is just I–495. If you are coming from the south, take I–95 to I–395 and cross the 14th Street Bridge to 14th Street in the District. From the north, stay on I–95 south before heading west on Route 50, the John Hanson Highway, which turns into New York Avenue.

Interstate 66 approaches the city from the southwest. You can get downtown by taking I–66 across the Theodore Roosevelt Bridge to Constitution Avenue.

Interstate 270 approaches Washington from the northwest before hitting I–495. To get downtown, take I–495 east to Connecticut Avenue south, toward Chevy Chase.

CONSUMER PROTECTION

Whenever shopping or buying travel services in Washington, **pay with a major credit card** so you can cancel payment or get reimbursed if there's a problem. If you're doing business with a particular company for the first time, **contact your local Better Business Bureau and the attorney general's offices** in your state and the company's home state, as well. Have any complaints been filed? Finally, if you're buying a package or tour, always **consider travel insurance** that includes default coverage (☞ Insurance, *below*).

➤ LOCAL BBBs: **Council of Better Business Bureaus** (✉ 4200 Wilson Blvd., Suite 800, Arlington, VA 22203, ☎ 703/276–0100, FAX 703/525–8277).

CUSTOMS & DUTIES

When shopping, **keep receipts** for all purchases. Upon reentering the country, **be ready to show customs officials what you've bought.** If you feel a duty is incorrect or object to the way your clearance was handled, note the inspector's badge number and ask to see a supervisor. If the problem isn't resolved, write to the appropriate authorities, beginning with the port director at your point of entry.

IN AUSTRALIA

Australia residents who are 18 or older may bring home $A400 worth of souvenirs and gifts (including jewelry), 250 cigarettes or 250 grams of tobacco, and 1,125 ml of alcohol (including wine, beer, and spirits). Residents under 18 may bring back $A200 worth of goods. Prohibited items include meat products. Seeds, plants, and fruits need to be declared upon arrival.

➤ INFORMATION: **Australian Customs Service** (Regional Director, ✉ Box 8, Sydney, NSW 2001, ☎ 02/9213–2000, FAX 02/9213–4000).

IN CANADA

Canadian residents who have been out of Canada for at least 7 days may bring home C$500 worth of goods duty-free. If you've been away less than 7 days but more than 48 hours, the duty-free allowance drops to C$200; if your trip lasts 24–48 hours, the allowance is C$50. You may not pool allowances with family members. Goods claimed under the C$500 exemption may follow you by mail; those claimed under the lesser exemptions must accompany

you. Alcohol and tobacco products may be included in the 7-day and 48-hour exemptions but not in the 24-hour exemption. If you meet the age requirements of the province or territory through which you reenter Canada, you may bring in, duty-free, 1.14 liters (40 imperial ounces) of wine or liquor or 24 12-ounce cans or bottles of beer or ale. If you are 16 or older you may bring in, duty-free, 200 cigarettes and 50 cigars. Check ahead of time with Revenue Canada or the Department of Agriculture for policies regarding meat products, seeds, plants, and fruits.

You may send an unlimited number of gifts worth up to C$60 each duty-free to Canada. Label the package UNSOLICITED GIFT—VALUE UNDER $60. Alcohol and tobacco are excluded.

➤ INFORMATION: **Revenue Canada** (✉ 2265 St. Laurent Blvd. S, Ottawa, Ontario K1G 4K3, ☎ 613/993–0534; 800/461–9999 in Canada).

IN NEW ZEALAND

Homeward-bound residents 17 or older may bring back $700 worth of souvenirs and gifts. Your duty-free allowance also includes 4.5 liters of wine or beer; one 1,125-ml bottle of spirits; and either 200 cigarettes, 250 grams of tobacco, 50 cigars, or a combination of the three up to 250 grams. Prohibited items include meat products, seeds, plants, and fruits.

➤ INFORMATION: **New Zealand
Customs** (Custom House, ✉ 50
Anzac Ave., Box 29, Auckland,
New Zealand, ☎ 09/359–6655,
FAX 09/359–6732).

IN THE U.K.

➤ INFORMATION: **HM Customs
and Excise** (✉ Dorset House,
Stamford St., Bromley Kent BR1
1XX, ☎ 020/7202–4227).

IN THE U.S.

Non-U.S. residents ages 21 and
older may import into the United
States 200 cigarettes or 50 cigars
or 2 kilograms of tobacco, 1 liter
of alcohol, and gifts worth $100.
Meat products, seeds, plants, and
fruits are prohibited.

➤ INFORMATION: **U.S. Customs Service** (inquiries, ✉ 1300 Pennsylvania Ave. NW, Washington, DC
20229, ☎ 202/927–6724; complaints, ✉ Office of Regulations
and Rulings, 1300 Pennsylvania
Ave. NW, Washington, DC 20229;
registration of equipment, ✉ Resource Management, 1300 Pennsylvania Ave. NW, Washington,
DC 20229, ☎ 202/927–0540).

DINING

Price categories are as follows for
restaurants:

CATEGORY	COST*
$$$$	over $35
$$$	$26–$35
$$	$15–$25
$	under $15

*per person for a three-course
meal, excluding drinks, service,
and 10% sales tax*

DISABILITIES &
ACCESSIBILITY

The Metro has excellent facilities
for visitors with vision and hear-
ing impairments or mobility problems. Virtually all streets have
wide, level sidewalks with curb
cuts, though in Georgetown the
brick-paved terrain can be bumpy.
Most museums and monuments
are accessible to visitors using
wheelchairs.

➤ LOCAL RESOURCES: The **Washington Convention and Visitors
Association** (☎ 202/789–7000)
has a four-page publication full of
tips and contacts. The **Washington
MTA** (☎ 202/637–7000) publishes a metro and bus system
guide. The **Smithsonian** (☎ 202/
357–2700 or 202/357–1729
TDD) publishes an access guide to
all its museums.

EMERGENCIES

➤ DOCTORS & DENTISTS: **1–800–
DOCTORS** (☎ 800/362–8677) is
a referral service that locates doctors, dentists, and urgent-care clin-
ics in the greater Washington area.
The **D.C. Dental Society** (☎ 202/
547–7615) operates a referral line
weekdays 8–4.

➤ EMERGENCY SERVICES: Dial 911
for **police, fire,** or **ambulance** in an
emergency.

➤ HOSPITALS: **Children's National
Medical Center** (✉ 111 Michigan
Ave. NW, ☎ 202/884–5000).
**George Washington University
Hospital** (✉ 901 23rd St. NW,

☎ 202/994–3211 emergencies only). **Georgetown University Medical Center** (✉ 3800 Reservoir Rd. NW, ☎ 202/342–2400). **Washington Hospital Center** (✉ 110 Irving St. NW, ☎ 202/877–7000).

➤ 24-HOUR PHARMACIES: **CVS Pharmacy** operates 24-hour pharmacies at 14th Street and Thomas Circle NW (☎ 202/628–0720) and at 7 Dupont Circle NW (☎ 202/785–1466).

INSURANCE

The most useful travel insurance plan is a comprehensive policy that includes coverage for trip cancellation and interruption; default, in case your tour operator, airline, or cruise line goes out of business; trip delay; and medical expenses.

British and Australian citizens need extra medical coverage when traveling overseas.

Always **buy travel policies directly from the insurance company;** if you buy it from a cruise line, airline, or tour operator that goes out of business, you probably will not be covered for the agency or operator's default, a major risk. Before you make any purchase **review your existing health and home-owner's policies** to find what they cover away from home.

➤ TRAVEL INSURERS: In the U.S., **Access America** (✉ 6600

W. Broad St., Richmond, VA 23230, ☎ 804/285–3300 or 800/284–8300), **Travel Guard International** (✉ 1145 Clark St., Stevens Point, WI 54481, ☎ 715/345–0505 or 800/826–1300). In Canada, **Voyager Insurance** (✉ 44 Peel Center Dr., Brampton, Ontario L6T 4M8, ☎ 905/791–8700; 800/668–4342 in Canada).

➤ INSURANCE INFORMATION: In the U.K., the **Association of British Insurers** (✉ 51–55 Gresham St., London EC2V 7HQ, ☎ 020/7600–3333, ☎ 020/7696–8999). In Australia, the **Insurance Council of Australia** (☎ 03/9614–1077, ☎ 03/9614–7924).

LODGING

Price categories are as follows:

CATEGORY	COST*
$$$$	over $270
$$$	$205–$270
$$	$145–$205
$	under $145

All prices are for a standard double room, excluding 13% room tax and $1.50 per night occupancy tax in D.C.

Assume that hotels operate on the European Plan (EP, with no meals) unless we specify that they use the Continental Plan (CP, with a Continental breakfast daily).

METRO TRAVEL

The WMATA provides bus and subway service in the District and in the Maryland and Virginia suburbs. The Metro, opened in 1976, is one of the country's cleanest and safest subway systems.

FARES & SCHEDULES

Trains run weekdays 5:30 AM–midnight, weekends 8 AM–midnight. During the weekday rush hours (5:30–9:30 AM and 3–8 PM), trains come along every six minutes. At other times and on weekends and holidays, trains run about every 12–15 minutes. The base fare is $1.10; the actual price you pay depends on the time of day and the distance traveled. Children under age five ride free when accompanied by a paying passenger, and there is a maximum of two children per paying adult.

Buy your ticket at the Farecard machines; they accept coins and crisp $1, $5, $10, or $20 bills. If the machine spits your bill back out at you, try folding and unfolding it before asking a native for help. The Farecard should be inserted into the turnstile to enter the platform. Make sure you **hang onto the card**—you'll need it to exit at your destination.

Some Washingtonians report that the Farecard's magnetic strip interferes with the strips on ATM cards and credit cards, so **keep the cards separated in your pocket or wallet.**

➤ SUBWAY INFORMATION: **Washington Metropolitan Area Transit Authority** (WMATA; ☎ 202/637–7000 or 202/638–3780 TDD); open weekdays 6 AM–10:30 PM, weekends 8 AM–10:30 PM.

DISCOUNT PASSES

For $5 you can **buy a pass that allows unlimited trips for one day.** It's good all day on weekends, on holidays, and after 9:30 AM on weekdays. Passes are available at Metro Sales Outlets and at many hotels, banks, and Safeway and Giant grocery stores.

MONEY MATTERS

Washington is an expensive city, comparable to New York. A big bonus to visitors is that most attractions in this city are free. A cup of coffee in D.C. will cost $1 at a diner or $4 at an upscale café, a sandwich will set you back $4.50–$6. Taxi rides cost upwards of $4 depending on your destination. Prices throughout this guide are given for adults. Substantially reduced fees are almost always available for children, students, and senior citizens. Sites listed in Chapter 3 include admission prices for children.

ATMS

Most ATMs in the Washington, D.C., area are linked to national networks that let you withdraw money from your checking account or take a cash advance from your credit card account for an additional fee. ATMs can be found at most banks, in many grocery stores, and in some major tourist attractions. For more information on ATM locations that can be accessed with your particular account, call the phone number found on the back of your ATM or debit card.

CREDIT CARDS

Throughout this guide, the following abbreviations are used: **AE,** American Express; **D,** Discover; **DC,** Diner's Club; **MC,** Master-Card; and **V,** Visa.

➤ REPORTING LOST CARDS: To report a stolen or lost credit card contact: **American Express** (☎ 800/300–8765), **Diner's Club** (☎ 800/234–6377), **Discover** (☎ 800/347–2683), **MasterCard** (☎ 800/826–2181), and **Visa** (☎ 800/336–8472).

NATIONAL MONUMENTS

Look into discount passes to **save money on monument and battle-field entrance fees.** The Golden Eagle Pass ($50) gets you and your companions free admission to all parks for one year. (Camping and parking are extra.) Both the Golden Age Passport ($10), for those 62 and older, and the Golden Access Passport (free), for travelers with disabilities, entitle holders to free entry to all national parks, plus 50% off fees for the use of many park facilities and services. You must show proof of age and of U.S. citizenship or permanent residency (such as a U.S. passport, driver's license, or birth certificate) and, if requesting Golden Access, proof of disability. All three passes are available at all national park entrances where entrance fees are charged. Golden Eagle and Golden Access passes are also available by mail.

➤ PASSES BY MAIL: **National Park Service** (✉ National Capitol Area Office, 1100 Ohio Dr. SW, Washington, DC 20242).

PASSPORTS & VISAS

➤ U.K. CITIZENS: **U.S. Embassy Visa Information Line** (☎ 01891/200–290; calls cost 49p per minute, 39p per minute cheap rate) for U.S. visa information. **U.S. Embassy Visa Branch** (✉ 5 Upper Grosvenor Sq., London W1A 1AE) for U.S. visa information; send a self-addressed, stamped envelope. Write the **U.S. Consulate General** (✉ Queen's House, Queen St., Belfast BTI 6EO) if you live in Northern Ireland. Write the **Office of Australia Affairs** (✉ 59th fl., MLC Centre, 19-29 Martin Pl., Sydney NSW 2000) if you live in Australia. Write the **Office of New Zealand Affairs** (✉ 29 Fitzherbert Terr., Thorndon, Wellington) if you live in New Zealand.

PASSPORT OFFICES

The best time to apply for a passport or to renew is during the fall and winter. Before any trip, check your passport's expiration date, and, if necessary, renew it as soon as possible.

➤ Australian Citizens: **Australian Passport Office** (☎ 131–232).

➤ New Zealand Citizens: **New Zealand Passport Office** (☎ 04/494–0700 for information on how to apply; 04/474–8000 or 0800/225–050 in New Zealand for information on applications already submitted).

➤ U.K. Citizens: **London Passport Office** (☎ 0990/210–410) for fees and documentation requirements and to request an emergency passport.

SIGHTSEEING TOURS

BICYCLE TOURS

Bike the Sites Tours (✉ 3417 Quesada St. NW, ☎ 202/966–8662) leads five tours geared to the occasional exerciser and will customize tours as well. Bicycles (21-speed Trek Hybrids), helmets, and water bottles are included. Licensed guides take groups on tours that range from one hour to a full day; prices are from $25 to $65.

BOAT TOURS

The enclosed boat *The Dandy* (✉ Prince St., between Duke and King Sts., Alexandria, VA, ☎ 703/683–6076 or 703/683–6090) cruises up the Potomac to Georgetown. Lunch cruises board weekdays starting at 10:30 AM and weekends starting at 11:30 AM. Dinner cruises board daily at 6 PM. 🕑 Prices are $26–$32 for lunch and $52–$63 for dinner.

D.C. Ducks (☎ 202/832–9800) offers 90-minute tours in their converted World War II amphibious vehicles. After an hour-long road tour of prominent sights, the tour moves from land to water, as the vehicle is piloted into the waters of the Potomac for a 30-minute boat's-eye view of the city. Tickets are $24.

BUS TOURS

All About Town, Inc. (☎ 202/393–3696) has half-day, all-day, two-day, and twilight bus tours that drive by some sights and stop at others. Tours leave from various downtown locations and hotels. An all-day tour costs $34.

Gray Line Tours (☎ 301/386–8300) has a four-hour tour of Washington, Embassy Row, and Arlington National Cemetery that leaves Union Station at 8:30 AM and 2 PM (at 2 PM only November–March; $25); tours of Mount Vernon and Alexandria depart at 8:30 AM ($25). An all-day trip combining both tours leaves at 8:30 AM (adults $42, children $21).

ORIENTATION TOURS

Old Town Trolley Tours (☎ 202/832–9800), orange-and-green motorized trolleys, take in the main downtown sights and also foray into Georgetown and the upper northwest. Tickets are $24.

Tourmobile buses (☎ 202/554–7950 or 202/554–5100), authorized by the National Park Service, stop at 25 historic sites between the Capitol and Arlington National Cemetery. Tickets are $14.

SPECIAL-INTEREST TOURS
Government buildings and offices that have regularly scheduled tours include the **Government Printing Office** (✉ H and North Capitol Sts. NW, ☎ 202/512–1991), which offers free tours by appointment; and the **Old Executive Office Building** (✉ Pennsylvania Ave. and 17th St. NW, ☎ 202/395–5895), which is open for tours Saturday 9–noon. In addition, tours of the opulent 18th- and early 19th-century **State Department Diplomatic Reception Rooms** (✉ 23rd and C Sts. NW, ☎ 202/647–3241) are given weekdays at 9:30, 10:30, and 2:45; the **Voice of America** (✉ 330 Independence Ave. SW, ☎ 202/619–3919) offers free 45-minute tours weekdays at 10:30, 1:30, and 2:30; and the **Washington, D.C., Post Office** (✉ Brentwood Rd. NE between Rhode Island and New York Aves., ☎ 202/636–2148) has free tours weekdays by appointment, and does not admit children under seven. Reservations are required for tours of all these sites. It's wise to make your reservations a few weeks before your visit.

The Washington Post (✉ 1150 15th St. NW, ☎ 202/334–7969) offers free 50-minute guided tours for ages 11 and up on Monday 10–3.

Every second Saturday in May, a half-dozen embassies in Washington open their doors as stops on a self-guided **Goodwill Embassy Tour** (☎ 202/636–4225). The cost is $30, which includes a tour booklet and free shuttle bus transportation between embassies.

Scandal Tours (☎ 800/758–8687) offers a 90-minute tour of Washington's seamier locales. Tours leave from the Pavilion at the Old Post Office Building on Saturday at 1. The cost is $30 per person.

PERSONAL GUIDES
Personal tour services include **Guide Post, Inc.** (✉ 209 Northwest Terr., Silver Spring, MD 20902, ☎ 301/754–2402), **Guide Service of Washington** (✉ 733 15th St. NW, Suite 1040, Washington, DC 20005, ☎ 202/628–2842), and **A Tour de Force** (✉ Box 2782, Washington, DC 20013, ☎ 703/525–2948). **Sunny Odem** (✉ 2504B S. Walter Reed Dr., Arlington, VA 22206, ☎ 703/379–1633) offers custom photography tours.

THEME TRIPS
➤ LEARNING: **Smithsonian Study Tours and Seminars** (✉ 1100 Jefferson Dr. SW, Room 3045, MRC 702, Washington, DC 20560, ☎ 202/357–4700, FAX 202/633–9250).

➤ PERFORMING ARTS: **Dailey-Thorp Travel** (✉ 330 W. 58th St., #610, New York, NY 10019-

1817, ☎ 212/307–1555 or 800/998–4677, FAX 212/974–1420).

WALKING TOURS

The Black History National Recreation Trail links a group of sights within historic neighborhoods illustrating aspects of African-American history in Washington, from slavery days to the New Deal. A brochure outlining the trail is available from the **National Park Service** (✉ 1100 Ohio Dr. SW, Washington, DC 20242, ☎ 202/619–7222).

The **National Building Museum** (☎ 202/272–2448) sponsors several architecture tours including "Site Seeing" tours (price varies, but includes bus transportation and a boxed lunch), which are led by architectural historians.

The **Smithsonian Resident Associate Program** (☎ 202/357–3030) routinely offers guided walks and bus tours of neighborhoods in Washington and communities outside the city. Many tours are themed.

Capital Entertainment Services (✉ 731 15th St. NW, Washington, DC 20018, ☎ 202/636–9203) offers African-American history tours.

TAXIS

Taxis in the District are not metered; they operate instead on a zone system. **Before you set off, ask your cab driver how much the fare will be.** The basic single rate for traveling within one zone is

$4. There is an extra $1.25 charge for each additional passenger and a $1 surcharge during the 4–6:30 PM rush hour. Bulky suitcases are charged at a higher rate, and a $1.50 surcharge is tacked on when you phone for a cab. Maryland and Virginia taxis are metered but are not allowed to take passengers between points in D.C.

➤ TAXI COMPANIES: **Yellow Cab** (☎ 202/544–1212).

TELEPHONES

The country code for the United States is 1. Competitive long-distance carriers make calling within the United States relatively convenient and let you avoid hotel surcharges. By dialing an 800 number, you can get connected to the long-distance company of your choice.

➤ LONG-DISTANCE CARRIERS: **AT&T** (☎ 800/225–5288). **MCI** (☎ 800/888–8000). **Sprint** (☎ 800/366–2255).

TRAIN TRAVEL

More than 80 trains a day arrive at Washington, D.C.'s **Union Station** on Capitol Hill (✉ 50 Massachusetts Ave. NE).

FARES & SCHEDULES

For information on arrivals, departures, and fares, contact Amtrak, MARC, or the Metro.

➤ TRAIN INFORMATION: **Amtrak** (☎ 800/872–7245). **MARC** (☎ 800/325–7245). **Washington**

Metropolitan Area Transit Authority (WMATA; ☎ 202/637–7000 or 202/638–3780 TDD); open weekdays 6 AM–10:30 PM, weekends 8 AM–10:30 PM.

PAYING
Purchase your ticket in the station before you board.

RESERVATIONS
Reservations are a good idea on Amtrak trains, especially the *Metroliner*. Plan to arrive early if you are traveling during holiday seasons; the trains can be *very* crowded.

VISITOR INFORMATION
➤ CITYWIDE INFORMATION: **Washington, D.C. Convention and Visitors Association** (✉ 1212 New York Ave. NW, Suite 600, Washington, DC 20005, ☎ 202/789–7000, www.washington.org). **D.C. Committee to Promote Washington** (✉ 1212 New York Ave. NW, Suite 200, Washington, DC 20005, ☎ 202/724–5644 or 800/422–8644).

➤ EVENTS AND ATTRACTIONS: **White House Visitor Center** (✉ Baldridge Hall, Dept. of Commerce, 1450 Pennsylvania Ave. NW, ☎ 202/208–1631, www.whitehouse.gov). **Dial-A-Park** (☎ 202/619–7275). **Dial-A-Museum** (☎ 202/357–2020).

➤ NATIONAL PARKS: **National Park Service** (✉ Office of Public Affairs, National Capital Region, 1100 Ohio Dr. SW, Washington, DC 20242, ☎ 202/619–7222, www.nps.gov).

➤ STATE INFORMATION: **State of Maryland** (✉ Office of Tourist Development, 217 E. Redwood St., 9th floor, Baltimore, MD 21202, 410/767–3400 or 800/634–7386, www.mdisfun.org). **Virginia Tourism Corporation** (✉ Headquarters, 901 E. Byrd St., Richmond, VA 23219, ☎ 804/786–4484 or 804/786–2051, www.virginia.org; ✉ Walk-in office, 1629 K St. NW, Washington, DC, ☎ 202/872–0523 or 800/934–9184) for accommodations at Virginia B&Bs.

WEB SITES
Do check out the World Wide Web when you're planning. You'll find everything from up-to-date weather forecasts to virtual tours of famous cities. Fodor's Web site, www.fodors.com, is a great place to start your on-line travels. For more information specifically on Washington, visit the sites listed in the addresses just above or:

www.americanparknetwork.com – Created by the publisher of visitor guide magazines for the national parks, this site has travel and safety tips, as well as environmental primers.

www.dcregistry.com – DC Registry has links to Washington-related sites large and small.

www.vietvet.org – Poems, photographs, and personal stories pay tribute to the Vietnam Veterans Memorial and the lives it memorializes.

www.si.edu – The nation's largest museum provides a comprehensive guide to all things Smithsonian.

www.washingtoncitypaper.com – The *Washington CityPaper*'s site is a nifty and very selective guide to the best of D.C.'s happenings.

sc94.ameslab.gov – At this site, a detailed map shows the capital's major attractions.

www.washingtonpost.com – Like many big city newspapers, the *Washington Post* has an electronic edition.

www.washingtonian.com – *The Washingtonian* magazine's on-line version has upcoming events, restaurant reviews, and more.

WHEN TO GO

Washington has **two delightful seasons: spring and autumn.** In spring, the city's ornamental fruit trees are budding, and its many gardens are in bloom. By autumn, most of the summer crowds have left and you can enjoy the sights in peace. Summers can be uncomfortably hot and humid. Winter weather is often bitter, with a handful of modest snowstorms that somehow bring this southern city to a standstill. If you're interested in government, visit when Congress is in session. When lawmakers break for recess (at Christmas, Easter, July 4, and other holiday periods), the city seems a little less vibrant.

1 Destination: Washington, D.C.

AMERICA'S HOMETOWN

WELCOME to Washington. An ad for a local bank called Washington "the most important city in the world." It's the seat of our government, with some 300,000 federal employees. Our president lives here. Many of the 535 members of Congress who work here also live in the city. Washington is not known for its fashionably dressed inhabitants or its hip arts scene. The main business is politics, and that's probably what most people think of when they think about Washington: politicians, lobbyists, lawyers, public relations firms, government contractors.

So why come to Washington?

Let's start with the simple beauty of the city. As you fly or drive into the city, one of the first things you might notice is the low profile of the city: there are no skyscrapers. (The maximum allowable height of buildings is related to the width of the streets that run in front of those buildings.) And that low profile makes Washington somehow seem more manageable as a tourist destination and a lot less overwhelming than a city where the buildings tower 40 or more stories overhead. Although a New York or Boston skyline is spectacular for its concentration of towering buildings, Washington is just as breathtaking for its open spaces and clean sight lines between some of its most famous attractions. It's almost like an amusement park, with all the best attractions concentrated in a relatively small area.

Washington does have one "skyscraper": the Washington Monument. Awe-inspiring in its own right, it also offers one of Washington's most impressive views—without even going up to the top. Standing at the base of the Washington Monument, you can see some of the most famous and familiar sights in the world. Look along the National Mall to the east and you'll see the Capitol, a short 15 blocks away. Lining the Mall on both sides are many of the Smithsonian Institution's wonderful museums, as well as both buildings of the National Gallery of Art. To the north sits the White House. To the west are the Lincoln Memorial and the reflecting pool. Looking southward, you'll see the Jefferson Memorial and the cherry tree–lined Tidal Basin.

Small parks all around the city function as seasonal flowerpots, their beds replanted with new flowers as the seasons change.

And Washington isn't just the monuments and museums. There are first-class restaurants all around the city. Looking for inexpensive ethnic food? Try Adams-Morgan. Looking for something on the fancy side? Try Georgetown or Downtown. In a city of many immigrants, the cuisine options are plentiful.

As for D.C.'s reputation as a somewhat stuffy, uptight political city: well, that's part of Washington, but it certainly isn't all the city is. Although D.C. is no New York, it actually does having a thriving arts scene. The Kennedy Center, with its full schedule of music and theater programs, is the jewel in Washington's performing arts crown (there's something going on here almost every day, including free nightly music performances), but there is also a thriving local and community theater scene throughout the city. Art galleries abound in Georgetown and Dupont Circle.

One of the nicest things about Washington is how much you can do here for free. The national monuments, as well as many of the museums and parks, are free. A variety of festivals and concerts take place throughout the year. During most evenings in the summer, the various military bands perform. The Smithsonian puts on a week-long Festival of American Folklife with loads of free entertainment. The National Symphony Orchestra performs on the Capitol lawn several times a year. And it's all free.

And, thanks to the small scale of the city, nothing is really too far away from anything else. Your feet will get you around most areas just fine. The Metro—at 25 years old still new by many cities' standards—is clean and safe, and it will get you to most places you'd want to visit. Buses fill in the blanks where the Metro doesn't go (Georgetown and Adams-Morgan, for example).

You might wonder if it's safe to come here. Unfortunately, it's a fact of life that there is crime in America's cities, and the crime you hear about is usually violent crime. Don't let crime statistics give you the wrong impression. Several years ago, Washington was known as the murder capital of the country. What that doesn't say is that almost without exception violent crime is far removed from major attractions. Just use common sense and you'll be fine. If you're out at night in a deserted part of town (Washington is not an all-night city like New York), consider taking a taxi.

Finally, visit Washington to remind yourself that the government does more than just take your money and engage in political infighting. Drop by the National Archives to see the original documents that have created, shaped, and fine-tuned this country. Visit the monuments to our nation's past, and find in them faith in a strong future. See some of the good things your tax dollars do: they protect and preserve our history, promote education and learning, provide parks and gardens. Or, on a more pragmatic note, tour some of the government buildings and find out just what is really done in them.

So, why *not* come to Washington?

–By Bruce Walker

stone and mortar), so you can watch the repair work on the masonry joints and damaged stones. The Washington Monument Interpretive Center, a temporary exhibit area, opened in 1999, near the 15th Street side of the monument, and will remain until the restoration is complete. Interactive touch-screen monitors duplicate the views out the various windows at the monument's top. Other exhibits are about the restoration project and about George Washington.

NEW AND NOTEWORTHY

Two of the Smithsonian's museums, the **National Museum of American Art** and the **National Portrait Gallery,** will close in early 2000 while the building they share, the Old Patent Office Building, undergoes a three-year restoration. During that time, the National Museum of American Art will expand its programs at its Renwick Gallery.

Restoration work continues on the **Washington Monument.** The two-year project began in early 1998 with the installation of a new elevator and other interior improvements and is expected to be completed by July 4, 2000. Currently, the monument is surrounded by scaffolding and a transparent fabric (lines on the fabric mirror the pattern of the

PLEASURES AND PASTIMES

Government and Politics in Action

C-SPAN buffs will want to visit Capitol Hill, where they can observe the House and the Senate in action. The Supreme Court's hearings are also open to visitors. Washington also has many government buildings that you can tour without watching its denizens at work: these include the Pentagon, the FBI Building, the Treasury, and the Federal Reserve. And let's not forget the White House.

Military Memorials

Washington is a fitting spot to honor those who served and fell in defense of our country. More than 200,000 veterans are buried in Arlington National Cemetery, a place where you can trace America's history through the aftermath of its battles. The guard at the Tomb of the Unknowns is changed frequently with a precise ceremony. Near the cemetery is the United States Marine Corps War Memorial, where there's a sunset parade in summer. The Vietnam Veterans Memorial has more than 58,000 names etched in black granite; the Korean War Veterans Memorial consists of a statue and a reflecting pool. Next to the statue that serves as the Navy Memorial is a visitor center and a theater that continuously shows the 30-minute, 70-millimeter film *At Sea,* a visually stunning look at life aboard a modern aircraft carrier.

Architecture and the Decorative Arts

Washington National Cathedral, the sixth-largest cathedral in the world, will impress even the most hardened cathedral viewer with its gothic arches, flying buttresses, and imaginative stonework.

Washington has many buildings of architectural interest, filled with exquisite period furniture, draperies, and china. The White House—with its watered silk–covered walls, Empire settees, and personalized china—is the most obvious example of such a building. You can also visit the DAR Museum, with its 33 period rooms decorated in styles representative of various U.S. states and its 50,000-item collection of Colonial and Federal silver, china, porcelain, and glass; and the Hillwood

Museum, a Georgian mansion that contains a large collection of 18th- and 19th-century French and Russian decorative art, such as gold and silver work, icons, lace, tapestries, china, and Fabergé eggs.

The Renwick Gallery, the Smithsonian's museum of American decorative arts, has exquisitely designed and crafted utilitarian items, as well as objects created out of such traditional crafts materials as fiber and glass. Displays include Shaker furniture, enamel jewelry, and the opulently furnished Victorian-style Grand Salon.

The open interior of the massive redbrick National Building Museum, one of the city's great spaces, has been the site of inaugural balls for more than 100 years. The eight central Corinthian columns are the largest in the world, rising to a height of 75 ft. This enormous edifice is devoted to architecture and the building arts. It outlines the capital's architectural history, from its monuments to its residential neighborhoods.

Many neighborhoods explored in our walking tours cover historic homes and other—formerly commercial—edifices that are open for tours. *See* especially Georgetown and Dupont Circle.

Gardens

The paths of the Constitution Gardens wind through groves of trees, around a lake—a memorial to the signers of the Declaration of

Independence—and past the sobering Vietnam Veterans Memorial. Dumbarton Oaks's 10 acres of formal gardens, in a variety of styles, are some of the loveliest in the city. The grounds of Marjorie Merriweather Post's Georgian-style Hillwood House have a French-style parterre, a rose garden, a Japanese garden, paths through azaleas and rhododendrons, and a greenhouse containing 5,000 orchids.

Parks

C&O Canal National Historical Park has one end in Georgetown and the other in Cumberland, Maryland. Canoeists paddle the canal's "watered" sections, while hikers and bikers use the 12-ft-wide towpath that runs alongside it. In warmer months you can hop a mule-drawn canal boat for a brief trip. You can also walk over a series of bridges to Olmsted Island in the middle of the Potomac for a spectacular view of the falls.

There are playgrounds and picnic tables at the 328-acre East Potomac Park as well as opportunities for tennis, swimming, golf, and miniature golf. Double-blossoming cherry trees line Ohio Drive; they bloom about two weeks after the single-blossoming variety that attracts throngs to the Tidal Basin each spring.

The 1,800 acres of Rock Creek Park have bicycle routes and hiking and equestrian trails, a planetarium, and an 18-hole golf course.

QUICK TOURS

If you're here for just a short period, you need to plan carefully so as to make the most of your time in Washington, D.C. The following itineraries outline major sights throughout the city and will help you structure your visit efficiently. Each is intended to take about four hours—a perfect way to fill a free morning or afternoon. For more information about individual sights, *see* Chapter 2.

D.C. with Kids

Head right to the **Washington Monument.** Not only will children enjoy a bird's-eye view of the city, they'll also enjoy watching the ongoing renovation of this historic landmark. From here head to the **National Air and Space Museum;** on the way, you can stop to ride a painted pony at the **carousel** near the Smithsonian castle. If you still have time, visit either the **National Museum of American History** or the **National Museum of Natural History;** both have hands-on rooms for little ones that are open most afternoons.

Georgetown

Explore trendy **Georgetown.** There are sights to see, but people come here mainly to watch other people, shop, eat, and bar-hop.

The Mall

Start at either end of the **Mall**—at the Capitol or the Lincoln Memorial—and walk to the opposite end. You won't have time to see everything along the way, but you'll walk past or have in sight most of the attractions Washington is famous for: the **Lincoln Memorial**, the **Vietnam Veterans Memorial**, the **Tidal Basin** and **Jefferson Memorial**, the **Washington Monument** (and to the north, the **White House**), most of the **Smithsonian museums**, the **National Gallery of Art**, and the **Capitol**.

The Smithsonian

Spend some time at one or two museums—a few don't-misses are the **National Museum of Natural History**, the **National Air and Space Museum**, and the **United States Holocaust Memorial Museum**.

2 Exploring Washington

By John F.
Kelly

Updated
by Bruce
Walker

THE BYZANTINE WORKINGS of the federal government; the nonsensical, sound-bite-ready oratory of the well-groomed politician; murky foreign policy pronouncements issued from Foggy Bottom; and $600 toilet seats ordered by the Pentagon cause many Americans to cast a skeptical eye on anything that happens "inside the Beltway." Washingtonians take it all in stride, though, reminding themselves that, after all, those responsible for political high jinks don't come *from* Washington; they come *to* Washington. Besides, such ribbing is a small price to pay for living in a city whose charms extend far beyond the bureaucratic. World-class museums and art galleries (nearly all of them free), tree-shaded and flower-filled parks and gardens, bars and restaurants that benefit from a large and creative immigrant community, and nightlife that seems to get better with every passing year are as much a part of Washington as floor debates or filibusters.

The location of the city that calls to mind politicking, back-scratching, and delicate diplomatic maneuvering is itself the result of a compromise. Tired of its nomadic existence after having set up shop in eight locations, Congress voted in 1785 to establish a permanent "Federal town." Northern lawmakers wanted the capital on the Delaware River, in the North; Southerners wanted it on the Potomac, in the South. A deal was struck when Virginia's Thomas Jefferson agreed to support the proposal that the federal government assume the war debts of the colonies if New York's Alexander Hamilton and other Northern legislators would agree to locate the capital on the banks of the Potomac. George Washington himself selected the site of the capital, a diamond-shape, 100-square-mi plot that encompassed the confluence of the Potomac and Anacostia rivers, not far from his estate at Mount Vernon. To give the young city a head start, Washington included the already thriving tobacco ports of Alexandria, Virginia, and Georgetown, Maryland, in the District of Columbia. In 1791, Pierre-Charles L'Enfant, a French engineer who had fought in the Revolution, created the classic plan for the city.

Exploring Washington, D.C. *(Boxes Refer to Detail Maps)*

Georgetown

Dupont Circle
and Foggy Bottom

The White
House Area

California St.

S St.

Decatur Pl.

R St.

Sheridan
Circle

R St.

Q St.

Massachusetts Ave.

P St.

O St.

Rock Creek

M St.

Washington
Circle

Pennsylvania

L St.

K St.

TO ADAMS
MORGAN/
CLEVELAND
PARK

S St.

R St.

Corcoran St.

Q St.

Church St.

Dupont
Circle

P St.

O St.

N St.

Church St.

Rhode Island Ave.

Scott
Circle

Thomas
Circle

New Hampshire Ave.

New Hampshire Ave.

Florida Ave.

Connecticut Ave.

California St.

30th St.

29th St. N

28th St.

27th St.

25th St.

24th St.

23rd St.

22nd St.

21st St.

20th St.

19th St.

18th St.

17th St.

16th St.

15th St.

14th St.

13th St.

H St.

New York

The White
House

G St.

F St.

E St.

D St.

C St.

Virginia Ave.

Constitution Ave.

Lincoln
Memorial

Reflecting Pool

Independence Ave.

Kutz Br.

Washington
Monument

Arlington Memorial Br.

Columbia
Island

Lady Bird Johnson Park

West
Potomac
Park

W. Basin Dr.

Ohio Dr.

Tidal Basin

Outlet Br.

Jefferson
Memorial

Potomac River

TO
ALEXANDRIA

The Monuments

P St.

O St.

M St.

L St.

26th St.

NW ◆ NE

S St.

S St.

Florida Ave.

Vermont Ave.

Rhode Island Ave.

Q St.

Q St.

R St.

Lincoln Rd.

9th St.

8th St.

7th St.

6th St.

5th St.

4th St.

3rd St.

1st St.

O St.

O St.

P St.

New Jersey Ave.

New York Ave.

North Capitol St.

3rd St.

N St.

N St.

M St.

M St.

M St.

L St.

Massachusetts Ave.

14th St.

12th St.

11th St.

10th St.

Mt. Vernon Square

Massachusetts Ave.

I St.

H St.

G St.

F St.

E St.

D St.

Pennsylvania Ave.

Old Downtown and Federal Triangle

2nd St.

Capitol Hill

Union Station

Columbus Memorial Fountain

Stanton Park

Constitution Ave.

Louisiana Ave.

NE

SE

Madison Dr.

National Gallery of Art

Smithsonian Institution

THE   MALL

Jefferson Dr.

National Air and Space Museum

US Capitol

E. Capitol St.

Independence Ave.

Maryland Ave.

Folger Park

C St.

Canal St.

New Jersey Ave.

The Mall

D St.

E St.

Virginia Ave.

G St.

Southwest Fwy.

G St.

Francis Case Memorial Br.

0   550 yards

0   500 meters

I St.

N

Washington Canal

SW ◆ SE

It took the Civil War—and every war thereafter—to ener-gize the city, by attracting thousands of new residents and spurring building booms that extended the capital in all di-rections. Streets were paved in the 1870s, and the first streetcars ran in the 1880s. Memorials to famous Ameri-cans like Lincoln and Jefferson were built in the first decades of the 20th century, along with the massive Federal Trian-gle, a monument to thousands of less-famous government workers.

Despite the growth and the fact that blacks have played an important role in the city's history (black mathematician Benjamin Banneker surveyed the land with Pierre L'Enfant), Washington today remains essentially segregated. Whites—who account for about 30% of the population—reside mostly in northwest Washington. Blacks live largely east of Rock Creek Park and south of the Anacostia River.

It's a city of other unfortunate contrasts: citizens of the cap-ital of the free world couldn't vote in a presidential elec-tion until 1964, weren't granted limited home rule until 1974, and are represented in Congress by a single nonvoting del-egate (though in 1990 residents elected two "shadow" sen-ators, one of whom is political gadfly Jesse Jackson). Homeless people sleep on steam grates next to multimil-lion-dollar government buildings. Violent crime, although it is way down (as it is in many other big cities) from the drug-fueled violent days of the late 1980s and early 1990s, still exists. Though it's little consolation to those affected, most crime is restricted to neighborhoods far from the areas visited by tourists.

Still, there's no denying that Washington, the world's first planned capital, is also one of its most beautiful. And though the federal government dominates the city psy-chologically as much as the Washington Monument dom-inates it physically, there are places where you can leave politics behind. As you explore Washington, look for evi-dence of L'Enfant's hand, still present despite growing pains and frequent deviations from his plan. His Washington was to be a city of vistas—pleasant views that would shift and change from block to block, a marriage of geometry and art. It remains this way today. Like its main industry, politics, Washington's design is a constantly changing kaleidoscope that invites contemplation from all angles.

The Mall

The Mall is the heart of almost every visitor's trip to Washington. With nearly a dozen museums ringing the expanse of green, it's the closest thing the capital has to a theme park (unless you count the federal government itself, which has uncharitably been called "Disneyland on the Potomac"). As at a theme park, you may have to stand in an occasional line, but unlike the amusements at Disneyland, almost everything you'll see here is free. You may, however, need free, timed-entry tickets to some of the more popular traveling exhibitions. These are usually available at the museum information desk or by phone, for a service charge, from Ticketmaster (☎ 202/432–7328).

Of course, the Mall is more than just a front yard for these museums. Bounded on the north and south by Constitution and Independence avenues and on the east and west by 3rd and 14th streets, it's a picnicking park and a jogging path, an outdoor stage for festivals and fireworks, and America's town green. Nine of the Smithsonian Institution's 14 museums in the capital lie within these boundaries.

In the middle of the 19th century, horticulturist Andrew Jackson Downing took a stab at converting the Mall into a large, English-style garden, with carriageways curving through groves of trees and bushes. This was far from the "vast esplanade" L'Enfant had in mind, and by the dawn of the 20th century the Mall had become an eyesore. It was dotted with sheds and bisected by railroad tracks. There was even a railroad station at its eastern end.

In 1900 Senator James McMillan, chairman of the Committee on the District of Columbia, asked a distinguished group of architects and artists to study ways of improving Washington's park system. The McMillan Commission, which included architects Daniel Burnham and Charles McKim, landscape architect Frederick Law Olmsted, and sculptor Augustus Saint-Gaudens, didn't confine its recommendations just to parks; its 1902 report would shape the way the capital looked for decades. The Mall received much of the group's attention and is its most stunning accomplishment. L'Enfant's plan was rediscovered; the sheds, railroad tracks, and carriageways were removed; and Washington finally had the monumental core it had been denied for so long.

Numbers in the margin correspond to numbers on the Mall map.

Sights to See

⑫ **Arthur M. Sackler Gallery.** When Charles Freer endowed the gallery that bears his name, he insisted on a few conditions: objects in the collection could not be lent out, nor could objects from outside the collections be put on display. Because of the latter restriction it was necessary to build a second, complementary museum to house the Asian art collection of Arthur M. Sackler, a wealthy medical researcher and publisher who began collecting Asian art as a student in the 1940s. Sackler allowed Smithsonian curators to select 1,000 items from his ample collection and pledged $4 million toward the construction of the museum. The collection includes works from China, Southeast Asia, Korea, Tibet, and Japan. Articles in the permanent collection include Chinese ritual bronzes, jade ornaments from the 3rd millennium BC, Persian manuscripts, and Indian paintings in gold, silver, lapis lazuli, and malachite. ⊠ *1050 Independence Ave. SW,* ☎ *202/357–2700; 202/357–1729 TDD.* ☞ *Free.* ☉ *Daily 10–5:30. Metro: Smithsonian.*

❷ **Arts and Industries Building.** This was the second Smithsonian museum to be constructed. In 1876, Philadelphia hosted the United States International Exposition in honor of the nation's Centennial. After the festivities, scores of exhibitors donated their displays to the federal government. To house the objects that had suddenly come its way, the Smithsonian commissioned this redbrick-and-sandstone structure. Designed by Adolph Cluss, the building was originally called the United States National Museum, the name that's still engraved in stone above the doorway. It was finished in 1881, just in time to host President James Garfield's inaugural ball.

The Arts and Industries Building housed a variety of artifacts that were eventually moved to other museums as the Smithsonian grew. It was restored to its original appearance and reopened during Bicentennial celebrations in 1976. Today, the building is home to changing exhibits, a working fountain in the rotunda surrounded by seasonal plants and geometric stencils in rich Victorian colors, a museum shop, and Discovery Theater for children. ⊠ *900 Jefferson Dr. SW,* ☎ *202/357–2700; 202/357–1500 Discovery Theater showtimes and ticket information; 202/357–1729 TDD.* ▣ *Free.* ☾ *Daily 10–5:30. Metro: Smithsonian.*

⑨ Bureau of Engraving and Printing. Paper money has been printed here since 1914, when they stopped printing it in the Auditor's Building. Despite the fact that there are no free samples, the guided tour of the bureau—which takes you past presses that turn out some $538 million a day—is one of the city's most popular. In addition to all the paper currency in the United States, stamps, military certificates, and presidential invitations are printed here, too. The tour lasts 40 minutes; the wait to get in, however, can be twice that long. ⊠ *14th and C Sts. SW,* ☎ *202/874–3188.* ▣ *Free.* ☾ *Sept.–May, weekdays 9–2; June–Aug., weekdays 9–2 and 5–6:30. Mar.–Sept. same-day timed-entry passes issued starting at 8 am at Raoul Wallenberg Pl. SW entrance. Metro: Smithsonian.*

⑩ Department of Agriculture. Although there's little of interest inside, this complex is too gargantuan to ignore. The home of a major governmental agency responsible for setting and carrying out the nation's agricultural policies, it comprises two buildings. The older, white-marble building, on the north side of Independence Avenue, was started in 1905 and was the first to be constructed by order of the McMillan Commission on the south side of the Mall. The cornices on the north side depict forests as well as grains, flowers, and fruits—some of the plants the department keeps an eye on. The newer building (built between 1930 and 1936) south of Independence Avenue covers two city blocks—an example, perhaps, of big government. ⊠ *Independence Ave. between 12th and 14th Sts. SW. Metro: Smithsonian.*

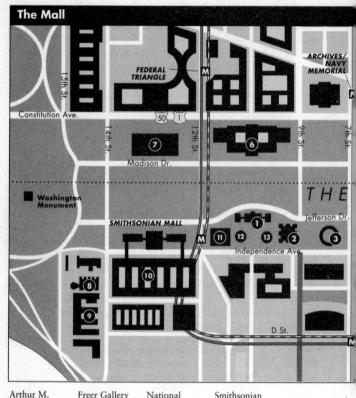

The Mall

Arthur M. Sackler Gallery, **12**

Arts and Industries Building, **2**

Bureau of Engraving and Printing, **9**

Department of Agriculture, **10**

Freer Gallery of Art, **11**

Hirshhorn Museum and Sculpture Garden, **3**

National Air and Space Museum, **4**

National Gallery of Art, **5**

National Museum of African Art, **13**

National Museum of American History, **7**

National Museum of Natural History, **6**

Smithsonian Institution Building, **1**

United States Holocaust Memorial Museum, **8**

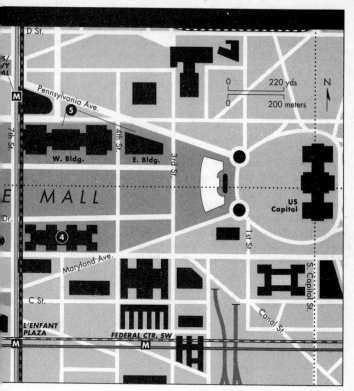

D St.

S/ /Y 4L

M

7th St.

Pennsylvania Ave.

5

4th St.

W. Bldg.

E. Bldg.

3rd St.

E

MALL

Dr.

4

Maryland Ave.

1st St.

US Capitol

S. Capitol St.

C St.

Canal St.

L'ENFANT PLAZA

M

FEDERAL CTR. SW

M

0   220 yds

0   200 meters

N

⓫ **Freer Gallery of Art.** One of the world's finest collections
of masterpieces from Asia, the Smithsonian's Freer Gallery
of Art was made possible by an endowment from Detroit
industrialist Charles L. Freer, who retired in 1900 and devoted the rest of his life to collecting art. Opened in 1923,
four years after its benefactor's death, the collection includes
more than 27,000 works of art from the Far and Near East,
including Asian porcelains, Japanese screens, Chinese paintings and bronzes, Korean stoneware, and examples of Islamic art.

Freer's friend James McNeill Whistler introduced him to
Asian art, and the American painter is represented in the
vast collection. On display is the Peacock Room, a blue-
and-gold dining room decorated with painted leather, wood,
and canvas and designed by Whistler for a British shipping
magnate. Freer paid $30,000 for the entire room and moved
it from London to the United States in 1904. The works of
other American artists Freer felt were influenced by the
Far East also are on display. ⊠ *12th St. and Jefferson Dr.
SW,* ☎ *202/357–2700; 202/357–1729 TTD.* 🖾 *Free.* ☉
Daily 10–5:30. Metro: Smithsonian.

❸ **Hirshhorn Museum and Sculpture Garden.** An architec-
turally striking but aesthetically controversial round building that opened in 1974, the Hirshhorn manages a collection
that includes some 12,000 works of art donated and bequeathed by Joseph H. Hirshhorn, a Latvian-born immigrant who made his fortune in this country running uranium
mines. American artists such as Edward Hopper, Willem
de Kooning, and Richard Diebenkorn are represented, as
are modern European and Latin masters, including Francis Bacon, Piet Mondrian, Jean Dubuffet, and Joan Miró.

The Hirshhorn's impressive sculpture collection is displayed throughout the museum, as well as on the lawns and
granite surfaces of the fountain plaza and across Jefferson
Drive in the sunken Sculpture Garden. Indoors and out, the
display includes works by Henry Moore, Alexander Calder,
and Alberto Giacometti. In the garden, Henri Matisse's *Backs
I–IV* and Auguste Rodin's *Burghers of Calais* are highlights.

Dubbed by its detractors "the Doughnut on the Mall," the
cylindrical, reinforced-concrete building designed by Pritzker

Prize–winning architect Gordon Bunshaft is a fitting home for contemporary art. The severe exterior lines of the museum were softened a bit in 1992 when its plaza was re-landscaped by James Urban. Grass and trees provide a soft setting for such recent work as Juan Munoz's *Conversation Piece*, an intriguing ensemble of five beanbag-like figures in bronze. ⊠ *Independence Ave. and 7th St. SW,* ☎ *202/357–2700; 202/633–8043 TDD.* ☏ *Free.* ☺ *Museum daily 10–5:30, sculpture garden daily 7:30–dusk. Metro: Smithsonian or L'Enfant Plaza (Maryland Ave. exit).*

★ ☝
❹
National Air and Space Museum. Opened in 1976, this museum attracts more than 8 million people each year. Its 23 galleries tell the story of aviation from the earliest human attempts at flight. Suspended from the ceiling like plastic models in a child's room are dozens of aircraft, including the *Wright 1903 Flyer,* which Wilbur Wright piloted over the sands of Kitty Hawk, North Carolina; Charles Lindbergh's *Spirit of St. Louis;* the X-1 rocket plane in which Chuck Yeager broke the sound barrier; and an X-15, the first aircraft to exceed Mach 6.

Other highlights include a backup model of the Skylab orbital workshop that you can walk through; the *Voyager,* which Dick Rutan and Jeana Yeager flew nonstop around the world; and the Lockheed Vega piloted by Amelia Earhart in 1932 in the first solo transatlantic flight by a woman. You can also see a piece of the moon: a 4-billion-year-old slice of rock collected by *Apollo 17* astronauts.

Don't let long lines deter you from seeing a show in the museum's Samuel P. Langley Theater. IMAX films shown on the five-story-high screen—including *Cosmic Voyage, To Fly!* and *Mission to Mir*—usually feature swooping aerial scenes that will convince you you've left the ground. Purchase tickets up to two weeks in advance or as soon as you arrive (prices vary but are inexpensive); then tour the museum. Upstairs, the Albert Einstein Planetarium, which charges a small fee, projects images of celestial bodies on a domed ceiling. Double features are often shown in Langley Theater after the museum has closed. ⊠ *Independence Ave. and 6th St. SW,* ☎ *202/357–2700; 202/357–1729 TDD; 202/357–1686 movie information.* ☏ *Free.* ☺ *Daily 10–5:30. Metro: Smithsonian.*

★ ❺   **National Gallery of Art.** The two buildings of the National Gallery hold one of the world's foremost collections of paintings, sculptures, and graphics. If you want to view the museum's holdings in (more or less) chronological order, it's best to start your exploration in the West Building.

Opened in 1941, the domed **West Building** was a gift to the nation from financier Andrew Mellon, who had long collected great works of art, acquiring some on his frequent trips to Europe. In 1930 and 1931, when the Soviet government was short of cash and selling off many of its art treasures, Mellon bought more than $6 million worth of old masters, including Raphael's *Alba Madonna* and Sandro Botticelli's *Adoration of the Magi.* Mellon promised his collection to America in 1936, the year before his death. He also donated the funds for the construction of the huge gallery and resisted suggestions that it be named after him. The permanent collection includes works from the 13th to the 20th century. A comprehensive survey of Italian paintings and sculpture includes *The Adoration of the Magi,* by Fra Angelico and Filippo Lippi, and *Ginevra de'Benci,* the only painting by Leonardo da Vinci in the Western Hemisphere. Flemish and Dutch works, displayed in paneled rooms, include *Daniel in the Lions' Den,* by Peter Paul Rubens, and a self-portrait by Rembrandt. The Chester Dale Collection comprises works by Impressionist painters such as Edgar Degas, Claude Monet, Auguste Renoir, and Mary Cassatt. Salvador Dalí's *Last Supper* is also in this building.

The **East Building,** designed by I. M. Pei, opened in 1978 in response to the changing needs of the National Gallery. The atrium is dominated by Alexander Calder's mobile *Untitled,* and the galleries display modern art, though you'll also find major temporary exhibitions that span years and artistic styles. Works include Picasso's *The Lovers* and *Family of Saltimbanques,* four of Henri Matisse's cutouts, Miró's *The Farm,* and Pollock's *Lavender Mist.*

The National Gallery **Sculpture Garden** opened in the spring of 1999. Granite walkways take you through the garden, which is planted with shade trees, flowering trees, and perennials. Sculptures on display from the museum's permanent collection include Alexander Archipenko's *Woman*

Combing Her Hair; Miró's *Personnage Gothique, Oiseau-Eclair;* and Isamu Noguchi's *Great Rock of Inner Seeking.* The garden also has works on loan for special exhibitions. The reflecting pool is used as a skating rink during the winter. ⊠ *Constitution Ave. between 3rd and 7th Sts. NW,* ☎ *202/737–4215; 202/842–6176 TDD.* 🎫 *Free.* ⊘ *Mon.–Sat. 10–5, Sun. 11–6. Metro: Archives/Navy Memorial.*

⓭ **National Museum of African Art.** Opened in 1987, this unique underground building houses the museum's galleries, library, photographic archives, and educational facilities. The museum's rotating exhibits present a wide variety of African visual arts, including sculpture, textiles, photography, archaeology, and modern art. Long-term installations explore the sculpture of sub-Saharan Africa, the art of Benin, pottery of Central Africa, the archaeology of the ancient Nubian city of Kerma, and the artistry of utilitarian objects. The museum's educational programs include films showing contemporary perspectives on African life, storytelling programs, festivals, and hands-on workshops for families, all of which bring Africa's oral traditions, literature, and art to life. Workshops and demonstrations offer a chance to meet and talk to practicing African and African-American artists. ⊠ *950 Independence Ave. SW,* ☎ *202/357–2700; 202/357–1729 TDD.* 🎫 *Free.* ⊘ *Daily 10–5:30. Metro: Smithsonian.*

☕ ⓻ **National Museum of American History.** Opened in 1964 as the National Museum of History and Technology and renamed in 1980, the museum explores America's cultural, political, technical, and scientific past. The incredible diversity of artifacts helps the Smithsonian live up to its nickname, "the Nation's attic." This is the museum that displays Muhammad Ali's boxing gloves, the Fonz's leather jacket, Judy Garland's ruby slippers from *The Wizard of Oz,* and the Bunkers' living-room furniture from *All in the Family.*

You can wander for hours on the museum's three floors. Exhibits on the first floor emphasize the history of science and technology and include farm machines, automobiles, and a 280-ton steam locomotive. The permanent "Science in American Life" exhibit shows how science has shaped American life through such breakthroughs as the mass production of penicillin, the development of plastics, and the birth of the environmental movement. Another permanent exhibit looks at 19th-century life in three communities: industrial-era Bridgeport, Connecticut; the Jewish immigrant community in Cincinnati; and African-Americans living in Charleston, South Carolina. Also here are Lewis and Clark's compass and Abraham Lincoln's life mask. The second floor is devoted to U.S. social and political history and has an exhibit on everyday American life just after the Revolution. A permanent exhibit, "First Ladies: Political Role and Public Image," displays gowns worn by presidential wives, but it goes beyond fashion to explore the women behind the satin, lace, and brocade. The third floor has installations on money, musical instruments, and photography. The Armed Forces History exhibit has items from the Revolutionary War (the gunboat *Philadelphia,* George Washington's uniform and tent) through the Vietnam War.

Be sure to check out Horatio Greenough's statue of the first president (near the west-wing escalators on the second floor). Commissioned by Congress in 1832, it was intended to grace the Capitol Rotunda. It was there for only a short while, however, since the toga-clad likeness proved shocking to legislators who grumbled that it looked as if the father of our country had just emerged from a bath. If you want a more interactive visit, check out the Hands on History Room, where you can try some 30 activities, such as pedaling a high-wheeler bike or plucking an old stringed instrument. In the Hands on Science Room you can do one of 25 experiments, including testing a water sample and exploring DNA fingerprinting. ✉ *Constitution Ave. and 14th St. NW,* ☎ *202/357–2700; 202/357–1729 TDD.* 🎫 *Free.* ⏲ *Daily 10–5:30; call for hrs for Hands on History and Hands on Science rooms. Metro: Smithsonian.*

★ 6 **National Museum of Natural History.** This is one of the great natural history museums in the world, filled with bones, fossils, stuffed animals, and other natural delights—122 million specimens in all. Exhibits also explore the many ingenious ways that humans have adapted to their environment. It was constructed in 1910, and two wings were added in the 1960s.

The first-floor rotunda is dominated by a stuffed 8-ton, 13-ft African bull elephant, one of the largest ever found. (The tusks are fiberglass; the original ivory ones were far too heavy for the stuffed elephant to support.) Off to the right is the popular Dinosaur Hall. Fossilized skeletons here range from a 90-ft-long diplodocus to a tiny thescelosaurus neglectus (a small dinosaur so named because its disconnected bones sat for years in a college drawer before being reassembled).

In the west wing are displays of birds, mammals, and sea life. Many of the preserved animal specimens were collected by Teddy Roosevelt during his trips to Africa. The sea-life display features a living coral reef, complete with fish, plants, and simulated waves. The halls north of the rotunda contain tools, clothing, and other artifacts from many cultures. If you've always wished you could get your hands on the objects behind the glass, stop by the **Discovery Room,** in the northwest corner of the first floor. Here elephant tusks, petrified wood, seashells, rocks, feathers, and other items can be handled.

The highlight of the second floor is the **Janet Annenberg Hooker Hall of Geology, Gems and Minerals.** Objects on display include a pair of Marie Antoinette's earrings, the Rosser Reeves ruby, spectacular crystals and minerals, and, of course, the Hope Diamond, a blue gem found in India and reputed to carry a curse (though Smithsonian guides are quick to pooh-pooh this notion).

Also on the second floor is the **O. Orkin Insect Zoo** (named for the pest-control magnate who donated the money to modernize the exhibits), featuring a walk through a rain forest. You can view at least 60 species of live insects, from bees to tarantulas. ⊠ *Constitution Ave. and 10th St. NW,* ☎ *202/357–2700; 202/357–1729 TDD.* ☒ *Free.* ☉ *Daily 10–5:30; Discovery Room Tues.–Fri. noon–2:30, weekends 10:30–3:30; free passes distributed starting at 11:45 weekdays, 10:15 weekends. Metro: Smithsonian.*

❶ Smithsonian Institution Building. The first Smithsonian museum constructed, this red sandstone Norman-style building is better known as the Castle. It was designed by James Renwick, the architect of St. Patrick's Cathedral in New

York City. Although British scientist and founder James Smithson had never visited America, his will stipulated that, should his nephew, Henry James Hungerford, die without an heir, Smithson's entire fortune would go to the United States, "to found at Washington, under the name of the Smithsonian Institution, an establishment for the increase and diffusion of knowledge." The museums on the Mall are the Smithsonian's most visible example of this ideal, but the organization also sponsors traveling exhibitions and maintains research posts in such places as the Chesapeake Bay and the tropics of Panama.

Smithson died in 1829, Hungerford in 1835, and in 1838 the United States received $515,169 worth of gold sovereigns. After eight years of congressional debate over the propriety of accepting funds from a citizen of another country, the Smithsonian Institution was finally established on August 10, 1846. The Castle building was completed in 1855 and originally housed all of the Smithsonian's operations, including the science and art collections, research laboratories, and living quarters for the institution's secretary and his family. The statue in front of the Castle's entrance is not of Smithson but of Joseph Henry, the scientist who served as the institution's first secretary. Smithson's body was brought to America in 1904 and is entombed in a small room to the left of the Castle's Mall entrance.

Today the Castle houses Smithsonian administrative offices and, to help you get your bearings or decide which attractions you want to visit, the **Smithsonian Information Center.** A 24-minute video provides an overview of the Smithsonian museums and the National Zoo and monitors display information on the day's events. Interactive touch-screen displays provide more detailed information on the museums as well as other attractions in the capital. The center opens at 9 AM, an hour before the other museums, so you can plan your day without wasting valuable sightseeing time. ✉ *1000 Jefferson Dr. SW,* ☎ *202/357–2700; 202/357–1729 TDD.* 🎫 *Free.* ⊙ *Daily 9–5:30. Metro: Smithsonian.*

★ ❽ **United States Holocaust Memorial Museum.** Museums usually celebrate the best that humanity can achieve, but this museum, designed by James Ingo Freed, instead illustrates the worst. A permanent exhibition tells the stories of the millions of Jews, Gypsies, Jehovah's Witnesses, homosexuals, political prisoners, and others killed by the Nazis between 1933 and 1945. Striving to give a you-are-there experience, the graphic presentation is as extraordinary as the subject matter: upon arrival, you are issued an "identity card" containing biographical information on a real person from the Holocaust. As you move through the museum, you read sequential updates on your card. The museum recounts the Holocaust with documentary films, video- and audiotaped oral histories, and a collection that includes such items as a freight car like those used to transport Jews from Warsaw to the Treblinka death camp, and the Star of David patches that Jewish prisoners were made to wear. Like the history it covers, the museum can be profoundly disturbing; it's not recommended for visitors under 11. Plan to spend at least four hours here. After this powerful experience, the adjacent Hall of Remembrance provides a space for quiet reflection. In addition to the permanent exhibition, the museum also has a multimedia learning center, a resource center for students and teachers, a survivors' registry, and occasional special exhibitions. ⊠ *100 Raoul Wallenberg Pl. SW (enter from Raoul Wallenberg Pl. or 14th St. SW),* ☎ *202/488–0400; 703/218–6500 Protix.* ⊠ *Free, although same-day timed-entry passes (distributed on a first-come basis at the 14th St. entrance starting at 10 am or available through Protix) are necessary for the permanent exhibition.* ☉ *Daily 10–5:30. Metro: Smithsonian.*

The Monuments

Washington is a city of monuments. In the middle of traffic circles, on tiny slivers of park, and at street corners and intersections, statues, plaques, and simple blocks of marble honor the generals, politicians, poets, and statesmen who helped shape the nation. The monuments dedicated to the most famous Americans are west of the Mall on ground reclaimed from the marshy flats of the Potomac. This is also the location of Washington's cherry trees, gifts from Japan.

Numbers in the margin correspond to numbers on the Monuments map.

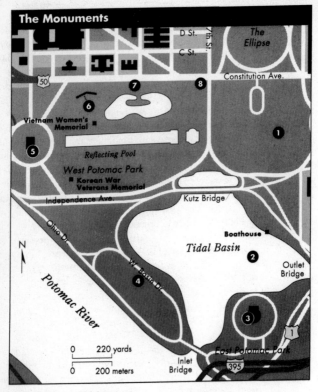

The Monuments

D St.

C St.

The Ellipse

7th St.

Constitution Ave.

50

7

6

8

Vietnam Women's Memorial

5

Reflecting Pool

1

West Potomac Park

■ Korean War Veterans Memorial

Independence Ave.

Kutz Bridge

Ohio Dr.

Boathouse

Tidal Basin

2

Outlet Bridge

W. Basin Dr.

4

Potomac River

3

N

0   220 yards

0   200 meters

East Potomac Park

Inlet Bridge

395

1

Constitution
Gardens, **7**

Franklin
Delano
Roosevelt
Memorial, **4**

Jefferson
Memorial, **3**

Lincoln
Memorial, **5**

Lockkeeper's
House, **8**

Tidal Basin, **2**

Vietnam
Veterans
Memorial, **6**

Washington
Monument, **1**

Sights to See

❼ Constitution Gardens. Many ideas were proposed to develop a 50-acre site that was once home to "temporary" buildings erected by the navy before World War I and not removed until after World War II. President Nixon is said to have favored something resembling Copenhagen's Tivoli Gardens. The final design was a little plainer, with paths winding through groves of trees and, on the lake, a tiny island paying tribute to the signers of the Declaration of Independence, whose signatures are carved into a low stone wall. ✉ *Constitution Ave. between 17th and 23rd Sts. NW. Metro: Foggy Bottom.*

❂ East Potomac Park. This 328-acre tongue of land hangs down from the Tidal Basin between the Washington Channel to the east and the Potomac River to the west. Facilities include playgrounds, picnic tables, tennis courts, swimming pools, a driving range, two 9-hole golf courses, and an 18-hole golf course. Double-blossoming cherry trees line Ohio Drive and bloom about two weeks after the single-blossoming variety that attracts throngs to the Tidal Basin each spring. *The Awakening,* a giant sculpture of a bearded man emerging from the ground, sits on Hains Point, at the tip of the park. ✉ *Maine Ave. SW, heading west, or Ohio Dr., heading south (follow signs carefully),* ☎ *202/619–7222. Ohio Dr. closed to traffic on summer weekends and holidays 3 pm–6 am.*

❹ Franklin Delano Roosevelt Memorial. This is the District's newest monument, unveiled in May 1997. The 7½-acre memorial to the 32nd president features waterfalls and reflection pools, four outdoor gallery rooms—each symbolizing one of his four terms as president—and 10 bronze sculptures. The granite passageways that connect the galleries are engraved with some of Roosevelt's most famous words, including, "The only thing we have to fear is fear itself." As was the case with the Lincoln and Jefferson memorials, the FDR Memorial has had its share of critics. Roosevelt is not portrayed with his omnipresent cigarette; nor is he pictured in a wheelchair, which he used for the last 24 years of his life, after he contracted polio. FDR asked for a simple memorial (in fact, one already sits on a wedge of grass in front of the National Archives), but this memorial is grandiose. ✉ *West side of Tidal Basin,* ☎ *202/619–7222.* 🎟 *Free.* 🕐 *24 hrs; staffed daily 8 am–midnight.*

❸ Jefferson Memorial. The monument honoring the third president of the United States is the southernmost of the District's major monuments. Congress decided that Jefferson deserved a monument positioned as prominently as those in honor of Washington and Lincoln, and this spot directly south of the White House seemed ideal. Jefferson had always admired the Pantheon in Rome—the rotundas he designed for the University of Virginia were inspired by its dome—so the memorial's architect, John Russell Pope, drew from the same source. Dedicated in 1943, it houses a statue of Jefferson, and its walls are lined with inscriptions based on his writings. One of the best views of the White House can be seen from its top steps. ✉ *Tidal Basin, south bank,* ☎ *202/426–6821.* 🎟 *Free.* 🕐 *Daily 8 am–midnight. Metro: Smithsonian.*

★ ❺ Lincoln Memorial. Many people consider the Lincoln Memorial to be the most inspiring monument in the city. This was not always the case. Although today it would be hard to imagine Washington without the Lincoln and Jefferson memorials, both were criticized when first built. The Jefferson Memorial was dubbed "Jefferson's muffin"; critics lambasted the design as outdated and too similar to that of the Lincoln Memorial. Some also complained that the Jefferson Memorial blocked the view of the Potomac from the White House. Detractors of the Lincoln Memorial thought it inappropriate that the humble Lincoln be honored with what amounts to a modified but nonetheless rather grandiose Greek temple. The white Colorado-marble memorial was designed by Henry Bacon and completed in 1922. The 36 Doric columns represent the 36 states in the Union at the time of Lincoln's death; the names of the states appear on the frieze above the columns. Above the frieze are the names of the 48 states in the Union when the memorial was dedicated. (Alaska and Hawaii are noted by an inscription on the terrace leading up to the memorial.)

Daniel Chester French's somber statue of the seated president, in the center of the memorial, gazes out over the Reflecting Pool. Although the 19-ft-high sculpture looks as if it were cut from one huge block of stone, it actually comprises 28 interlocking pieces of Georgia marble. (The memorial's original design called for a 10-ft-high sculpture, but experiments with models revealed that a statue of that size would be lost in the cavernous space.) Inscribed on the south wall is the Gettysburg Address, and on the north wall is Lincoln's second inaugural address. Above each inscription is a mural painted by Jules Guerin: on the south wall is an angel of truth freeing a slave; the unity of North and South are depicted opposite. The memorial served as a fitting backdrop for Martin Luther King's "I Have a Dream" speech in 1963.

Many visitors look only at the front and inside of the Lincoln Memorial, but there is much more to explore. On the lower level is the Lincoln Museum, a small exhibit begun with pennies collected by schoolchildren. There is also a set of windows that overlook the huge structure's foundation. Stalactites (hanging from above) and stalagmites (forming from below) have formed underneath the marble tribute to Lincoln. Although visiting the area around the Lincoln Memorial during the day allows you to take in an impressive view of the Mall to the east, the best time to see the memorial itself is at night. Spotlights illuminate the outside, while inside, light and shadows play across Lincoln's gentle face. ⊠ *West end of Mall,* ☎ *202/426–6895.* ☒ *Free.* ☉ *24 hrs; staffed daily 8 am–midnight. Metro: Foggy Bottom.*

8 **Lockkeeper's House.** The stone Lockkeeper's House is the only remaining monument to Washington's unsuccessful experiment with a canal. The stone building at this corner was the home of the canal's lockkeeper until the 1870s, when the waterway was covered over with B Street, which was renamed Constitution Avenue in 1932. It is not open to visitors. ⊠ *Constitution Ave. and 17th St. Metro: Federal Triangle, 5 blocks east on 12th St.*

2 **Tidal Basin.** This placid pond was part of the Potomac until 1882, when portions of the river were filled in to improve navigation and create additional parkland, including the land upon which the Jefferson Memorial was later built. Paddleboats have been a fixture on the Tidal Basin for years. You can rent one at the boathouse on the east side of the basin, southwest of the Bureau of Engraving.

Walking along the sidewalk that hugs the basin, you'll see two grotesque sculptured heads on the sides of the Inlet Bridge. The inside walls of the bridge also sport two other interesting sculptures: bronze, human-headed fish that spout water from their mouths. The bridge was refurbished in the 1980s at the same time the chief of the park—a Mr. Jack Fish—was retiring. Sculptor Constantine Sephralis played a little joke: these fish heads are actually Fish's head.

Once you cross the bridge, you have a choice: head left, along the Potomac, or continue along the Tidal Basin to the right. The latter route is somewhat more scenic, especially when the cherry trees are in bloom. The first batch of these trees arrived from Japan in 1909. The trees were infected with insects and fungus, however, and the Department of Agriculture ordered them destroyed. A diplomatic crisis was averted when the United States politely asked the Japanese for another batch, and in 1912 Mrs. William Howard Taft planted the first tree. The second was planted by the wife of the Japanese ambassador. About 200 of the original trees still grow near the Tidal Basin. (These cherry trees are the single-flowering Akebeno and Yoshino variety. Double-blossom Fugenzo and Kwanzan trees grow in East Potomac Park and flower about two weeks after their more famous cousins.)

The trees are now the centerpiece of Washington's Cherry Blossom Festival, held each spring. The festivities are kicked off by the lighting of a ceremonial Japanese lantern that rests on the north shore of the Tidal Basin, not far from where the first tree was planted. The once-simple celebration has grown over the years to include concerts, fashion shows, and a parade. Park-service experts try their best to predict exactly when the buds will pop. The trees are usually in bloom for about 10–12 days at the beginning of April. When winter refuses to release its grip, the parade and festival are held anyway, without the presence of blossoms, no matter how inclement the weather. And when the weather complies and the blossoms are at their peak at the time of the festivities, Washington rejoices. ⊠ *Boathouse: Northeast bank of Tidal Basin,* ☎ *202/479–2426. Paddleboat rental $7 per hr, $1.75 each additional 15 mins.* ☉ *Mid-Mar.–Oct., daily 10–6 (until 5 Mar.–Apr.), weather permitting. Metro: Smithsonian.*

❻ **Vietnam Veterans Memorial.** Renowned for its power to evoke poignant reflection, the Vietnam Veterans Memorial was conceived by Jan Scruggs, a former infantry corporal who had served in Vietnam. The stark design by Maya Ying Lin, a 21-year-old Yale architecture student, was selected in a 1981 competition. Upon its completion in 1982, the memorial was decried by some veterans as a "black gash of shame." With the addition of Frederick Hart's statue of three soldiers and a flagpole, south of the wall, most critics were won over.

The wall is one of the most-visited sites in Washington, its black granite panels reflecting the sky, the trees, and the faces of those looking for the names of friends or relatives who died in the war. The names of more than 58,000 Americans are etched on the face of the memorial in the order of their deaths. Directories at the entrance and exit to the wall list the names in alphabetical order. (It was discovered that because of a clerical error the names of some two dozen living vets are carved into the stone as well.) For help in finding a name, ask a ranger at the blue-and-white hut near the entrance. Thousands of offerings are left at the wall each year: letters, flowers, medals, uniforms, snapshots. The National Park Service collects these and stores them in a warehouse in Lanham, Maryland, where they are fast becoming another memorial. Tents are often set up near the wall by veterans' groups; some provide information on soldiers who remain missing in action, and others are on call to help fellow vets deal with the sometimes overwhelming emotions that grip them when they visit the wall for the first time. ✉ *Constitution Gardens, 23rd St. and Constitution Ave. NW,* ☎ *202/634–1568.* 🎫 *Free.* 🕐 *24 hrs; staffed daily 8 am–midnight. Metro: Foggy Bottom.*

Vietnam Women's Memorial. After years of debate over its design and necessity, the Vietnam Women's Memorial, honoring the women who served in that conflict, was finally dedicated on Veterans Day 1993. It is a stirring sculpture group consisting of two uniformed women caring for a wounded male soldier while a third woman kneels nearby. ✉ *Constitution Gardens, southeast of Vietnam Veterans Memorial. Metro: Foggy Bottom.*

☝ **❶** **Washington Monument.** At the western end of the Mall, the 555-ft, 5-inch Washington Monument punctuates the capital like a huge exclamation point. Visible from nearly everywhere in the city, it is truly a landmark.

In 1833, after years of quibbling in Congress, a private National Monument Society was formed to select a designer and to search for funds to construct this monument. Robert Mills's winning design called for a 600-ft-tall decorated obelisk rising from a circular colonnaded building. The building at the base was to be an American pantheon, adorned with statues of national heroes and a massive statue of Washington riding in a chariot pulled by snorting horses.

Because of the marshy conditions at L'Enfant's original site, the position of the monument was shifted to firmer ground 100 yards southeast. (If you walk a few steps north of the monument you can see the stone marker that denotes L'Enfant's original axis.) The cornerstone was laid in 1848 with the same Masonic trowel Washington himself had used to lay the Capitol's cornerstone 55 years earlier. The National Monument Society continued to raise funds after construction was begun, soliciting subscriptions of $1 from citizens across America. It also urged states, organizations, and foreign governments to contribute memorial stones for the construction. Problems arose in 1854, when members of the anti-Papist "Know Nothing" party stole a block donated by Pope Pius IX, smashed it, and dumped its shards into the Potomac. This action, a lack of funds, and the onset of the Civil War kept the monument at a fraction of its final height, open at the top, and vulnerable to the rain. A clearly visible ring about a third of the way up the obelisk testifies to this unfortunate stage of the monument's history: although all of the marble in the obelisk came from the same Maryland quarry, the stone used for the second phase of construction came from a different stratum and is of a slightly different shade.

In 1876 Congress finally appropriated $200,000 to finish the monument, and the Army Corps of Engineers took over construction, simplifying Mills's original design. Work was finally completed in December 1884, when the monument was topped with a 7½-pound piece of aluminum, then one of the most expensive metals in the world. Four years later the monument was opened to visitors, who rode to the top in a steam-operated elevator. (Only men were allowed to take the 20-minute ride; it was thought too dangerous for women, who as a result had to walk up the stairs if they wanted to see the view.)

The monument's heating and cooling systems were replaced and the elevator was serviced in 1998. In 1999, work was begun on the exterior, including a close inspection and cleaning of the surfaces and replacement of the mortar between the 36,000 slabs of marble. These renovations should be finished by July 2000, or possibly sooner. During that time the monument will be wrapped in transparent blue fabric that masks the scaffolding.

The Washington Monument is the world's tallest masonry structure. The view from the top takes in most of the District and parts of Maryland and Virginia. You are no longer permitted to climb the 897 steps leading to the top. (Incidents of vandalism and a disturbing number of heart attacks on the steps convinced the park service that letting people walk up on their own wasn't a good idea.) Most spring and summer weekends there are walk-down tours at 10 and 2, with a guide describing the monument's construction and showing the 193 stone and metal plaques that adorn the inside. (The tours are sometimes canceled owing to lack of staff. Call the day of your visit to confirm.)

To avoid the formerly long lines of people waiting for the minute-long elevator ride up the monument's shaft, the park service now uses a free timed-ticket system. A limited number of tickets are available at the kiosk on 15th Street daily beginning at 8 AM April–Labor Day and 9 AM September–March, with a limit of six tickets per person. Tickets are good during a specified half-hour period. No tickets are required after 8 PM (3 PM in the off-season). Advance tickets are available from Ticketmaster (call 202/432–7328; $1.50 per ticket service charge).While the Washington Monument undergoes its renovation, there is an interactive tourist center on the 15th Street side. Video screens display the views from the four windows at the top of the monument. Other exhibits tell the story of George Washington and explain the restoration process. There's even a photo opportunity: have your picture taken hanging from a replica of the aluminum lightning-deflector tip of the monument. The center will remain open until the renovation project is finished (probably the summer of 2000). ⊠ *Constitution Ave. and 15th St. NW,* ☎ *202/426–6840.* ✆ *Free.* ⊘ *Apr.–Labor Day, daily 8 am–midnight; Labor Day–Mar., daily 9–5. Metro: Smithsonian.*

West Potomac Park. Between the Potomac and the Tidal Basin, West Potomac Park is best known for its flowering cherry trees, which bloom for only two weeks in April. During the rest of the year, West Potomac Park is just a nice place to relax, play ball, or admire the views at the Tidal Basin.

The White House Area

In a world full of recognizable images, few are better known than the whitewashed, 32-room, Irish-country-house–like mansion at 1600 Pennsylvania Avenue. The residence of arguably the single most powerful person on the planet, the White House has an awesome majesty, having been the home of every U.S. president except, ironically, the father of our country, George Washington. This is where the buck stops in America and where the nation turns in times of crisis. In the wake of recent political scandal, however, America has been reminded that for all the power and majesty that come with the title and the address, the house is still inhabited by imperfect humans. After joining the more than 1.5 million people who visit the White House each year, strike out into the surrounding streets to explore the president's neighborhood, which includes some of the city's oldest houses.

Numbers in the margin correspond to numbers on the White House Area map.

Sights to See

⑬ Art Museum of the Americas. Changing exhibits in this small gallery highlight 20th-century Latin American artists. ⊠ *201 18th St. NW,* ☎ *202/458–6016.* ✆ *Free.* ⊘ *Tues.–Sun. 10–5. Metro: Farragut West.*

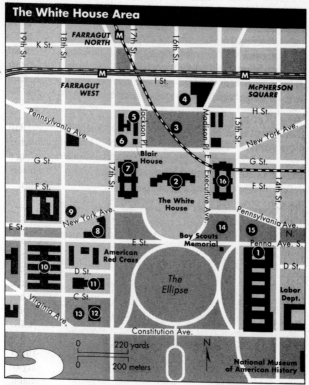

The White House Area

Art Museum of the Americas, **13**

Corcoran Gallery of Art, **8**

DAR Museum, **11**

Decatur House, **5**

Department of the Interior, **10**

Lafayette Square, **3**

Octagon, **9**

Old Executive Office Building, **7**

Organization of American States, **12**

Pershing Park, **15**

Renwick Gallery, **6**

St. John's Episcopal Church, **4**

Treasury Building, **16**

White House, **2**

White House Visitor Center, **1**

William Tecumseh Sherman Monument, **14**

Blair House. A green canopy marks the entrance to Blair House, the residence used by heads of state visiting Washington. Harry S. Truman lived here from 1948 to 1952 while the White House was undergoing much-needed renovations. A plaque on the fence honors White House policeman Leslie Coffelt, who died in 1950 when Puerto Rican separatists attempted to assassinate President Truman at this site. ⊠ *1651 Pennsylvania Ave. Metro: McPherson Square.*

Boy Scouts Memorial. Near the Ellipse stands this statue of a uniformed Boy Scout flanked by a male figure representing Patriotism and a female figure who holds the light of faith. ⊠ *East of Ellipse, near 15th St. NW. Metro: McPherson Square.*

❽ **Corcoran Gallery of Art.** The Corcoran is one of the few large museums in Washington outside the Smithsonian family. The Beaux Arts–style building, its copper roof green with age, was designed by Ernest Flagg and completed in 1897. The gallery's permanent collection numbers more than 14,000 works, including paintings by the first great American portraitists John Copley, Gilbert Stuart, and Rembrandt Peale. The Hudson River School is represented by such works as *Mount Corcoran* by Albert Bierstadt and Frederic Church's *Niagara.* There are also portraits by John Singer Sargent, Thomas Eakins, and Mary Cassatt. European art is seen in the Walker Collection (late 19th- and early 20th-century paintings, including works by Gustave Courbet, Claude Monet, Camille Pissarro, and Pierre-Auguste Renoir) and the Clark Collection (Dutch, Flemish, and French Romantic paintings, and the restored entire 18th-century Salon Doré of the Hotel de Clermont in Paris). Be sure to see Samuel Morse's *Old House of Representatives* and Hiram Powers's *Greek Slave,* which scandalized Victorian society. (The latter, a statue of a nude woman with her wrists chained, was considered so shocking by Victorian audiences that separate viewing hours were established for men and women; children under 16 weren't allowed to see it at all.) Photography and works by contemporary American artists are also among the Corcoran's strengths. The adjacent Corcoran School is the only four-year art college in the Washington area. ⊠ *500 17th St. NW,* ☎ *202/639–1700.* ⊠ *Suggested donation $3.* ⊘ *Mon., Wed., and Fri.–Sun. 10–5;*

Thurs. 10–9; tours of permanent collection Mon.–Wed. and Fri. at noon; weekends at 10:30 am, noon, and 2:30 pm; Thurs. at 7:30 pm. Metro: Farragut West or Farragut North.

🕐 ⓫   **DAR Museum.** A Beaux Arts building serving as headquarters of the Daughters of the American Revolution, Memorial Continental Hall was the site each year of the DAR's congress until the larger Constitution Hall was built around the corner. An entrance on D Street leads to the DAR Museum. Its 33,000-item collection includes fine examples of Colonial and Federal furniture, textiles, quilts, silver, china, porcelain, stoneware, earthenware, and glass. Thirty-three period rooms are decorated in styles representative of various U.S. states, ranging from an 1850 California adobe parlor to a New Hampshire attic filled with toys from the 18th and 19th centuries. Two galleries—one a permanent exhibition, the other a rotating one—display decorative arts. Docents are available for tours weekdays 10–2:30 and Sunday 1–5. Youngsters will especially love the "Colonial Adventure" tours, which are usually held the first and third Sundays of the month. Costumed docents lead children ages five to seven through the museum, explaining the exhibits and describing life in Colonial America. Make reservations at least 10 days in advance. ⊠ *1776 D St. NW,* ☎ *202/879–3241.* 🎟 *Free.* ☉ *Weekdays 8:30–4, Sun. 1–5. Closed Sat. Metro: Farragut West.*

❺   **Decatur House.** Designed by Benjamin Latrobe, Decatur House was built for naval hero Stephen Decatur and his wife, Susan, in 1819. A redbrick Federal-style building on the corner of H Street and Jackson Place, it was the first private residence on President's Park (the White House doesn't really count as *private*). Decatur had earned the affection of the nation in battles against the British and the Barbary pirates. Planning to start a political career, he used the money Congress awarded him for his exploits to build this home near the White House. Tragically, only 14 months after he moved in, Decatur was killed in a duel with James Barron, a disgruntled former navy officer who held Decatur responsible for his court-martial. Later occupants of the house included Henry Clay, Martin Van Buren, and the Beales, a prominent family from the West whose modifications of the building include a parquet floor showing the state seal of California. The house is now operated by the National Trust for Historic Preservation. The first floor is furnished as it was in Decatur's time. The second floor is furnished in the Victorian style favored by the Beale family, who owned it until 1956 (thus making Decatur House both the first and the last private residence on Lafayette Square). The museum shop around the corner (entrance on H Street) sells books, postcards, and gifts.

Many of the row houses along Jackson Place date from the pre–Civil War or Victorian period; even the more modern additions, though—such as those at 718 and 726—are designed to blend with their more historic neighbors. Count Rochambeau, aide to General Lafayette, is honored with a statue at Lafayette Square's southwest corner. ⊠ *748 Jackson Pl. NW,* ☎ *202/842–0920.* ☎ *$4.* ☉ *Tues.–Fri. 10–3, weekends noon–4; tours on the hr and ½ hr. Metro: Farragut West.*

❿ Department of the Interior. Designed by Waddy B. Wood, the Department of the Interior was the most modern government building in the city and the first large federal building with escalators and central air-conditioning at the time of its construction in 1937. The outside of the building is somewhat plain, but much of the inside is decorated with art that reflects the department's work. Hallways feature heroic oil paintings of dam construction, gold panning, and cattle drives. You'll pass several of these if you visit the **Department of the Interior Museum** on the first floor. (You can enter the building at its E Street or C Street door; adults must show photo ID.) The museum tour will take you past more of the three dozen murals throughout the building. Soon after it opened in 1938, the museum became one of the most popular attractions in Washington; evening hours were maintained even during World War II. The small museum tells the story of the Department of the Interior, a huge agency dubbed "the Mother of Departments" because from it grew the Departments of Agriculture, Labor, Education, and Energy.

Today the department oversees most federally owned land and natural resources, and exhibits in the museum outline the work of the Bureau of Land Management, the U.S. Geological Survey, the Bureau of Indian Affairs, the National Park Service, and other department branches. The museum retains a New Deal–era flavor—including meticulously created dioramas depicting historic events and American locales—and is, depending on your tastes, either quaint or outdated. The Indian Craft Shop across the hall from the museum sells Native American pottery, dolls, carvings, jewelry, baskets, and books. Call at least two weeks ahead to schedule a tour of the building's architecture and murals. ⊠ *C and E Sts. between 18th and 19th Sts. NW,* ☎ *202/208–4743.* 🎫 *Free.* ☉ *Weekdays 8:30–4:30. Metro: Farragut West.*

Ellipse. From the Ellipse you can see the Washington Monument and the Jefferson Memorial to the south and the red-tile roof of the Department of Commerce to the east, with the tower of the Old Post Office Building sticking up above it. To the north you have a good view of the rear of the White House (the Ellipse was once part of its backyard); the rounded portico and Harry Truman's second-story porch are clearly visible. The **Boy Scouts Memorial** (☞ *above*) is nearby. ⊠ *Bounded by Constitution Ave. and E, 15th, and 17th Sts. Metro: Farragut West or McPherson Square.*

❸ Lafayette Square. With such an important resident living across the street, National Capital Park Service gardeners lavish extra attention on this square's trees and flower beds. It's an intimate oasis in downtown Washington.

When Pierre L'Enfant proposed the location for the Executive Mansion, the only building north of what is today Pennsylvania Avenue was the Pierce family farmhouse, which stood at the northeast corner of the present square. An apple orchard and a family burial ground were the area's two other features. During the construction of the White House, workers' huts and a brick kiln were set up, and soon residences began popping up around the square (though sheep would continue to graze on it for years). Soldiers camped in the square during the War of 1812 and the Civil War, turning it into a muddy pit. Today, protesters set their placards up in Lafayette Square, jockeying for positions that face the White House. Although the National Park Service can't restrict the protesters' freedom of speech, it does try to restrict the size of their signs.

In the center of the park—and dominating the square—is a large **statue of Andrew Jackson.** Erected in 1853 and cast from bronze cannons that Jackson captured during the War of 1812, this was the first equestrian statue made in America. (There's a duplicate in front of St. Louis Cathedral in New Orleans's Jackson Square.) In the southeast corner is the park's namesake, the **Marquis de Lafayette,** the young French nobleman who came to America to fight in the Revolution. When Lafayette returned to the United States in 1824 he was given a rousing welcome: he was wined and dined in the finest homes and showered with gifts of cash and land. The colonnaded building across Madison Place at the corner of Pennsylvania Avenue is an annex to the Treasury Department. The modern redbrick building farther on, at 717 Madison Place, houses a variety of judicial offices. Its design—with squared-off bay windows—is echoed in the taller building that rises behind it and is mirrored in the **New Executive Office Building** on the other side of Lafayette Square. The next house down, yellow with a second-story ironwork balcony, was built in 1828 by Benjamin Ogle Tayloe. During the McKinley administration, Ohio senator Marcus Hanna lived here, and the president's frequent visits earned it the nickname "Little White House."

9   **The Octagon.** This octagon actually has six, rather than eight, sides. Designed by Dr. William Thornton (the Capitol's architect), it was built for John Tayloe III, a wealthy Virginia plantation owner, and was completed in 1801. Thornton chose the unusual shape to conform to the acute angle formed by L'Enfant's intersection of New York Avenue and 18th Street. After the White House was burned in 1814 the Tayloes invited James and Dolley Madison to stay in the Octagon. It was in a second-floor study that the Treaty of Ghent, ending the War of 1812, was signed. It is now the Museum of the American Architectural Foundation. The galleries inside host changing exhibits on architecture, city planning, and Washington history and design. ✉ *1799 New York Ave. NW,* ☎ *202/638–3105; 202/638–1538 TDD.* 🖼 *$3.* ☉ *Tues.–Sun. 10–4. Metro: Farragut West.*

7   **Old Executive Office Building.** Once one of the most detested buildings in the city, the Old Executive Office Building is now one of the most beloved. It was built between 1871 and 1888 as the State, War, and Navy Building, headquarters of those three executive-branch offices. Its architect, Alfred B. Mullett, patterned it after the style of the Louvre, but detractors quickly criticized the busy French Empire design—with its mansard roof, tall chimneys, and 900 freestanding columns—as an inappropriate counterpoint to the Greek Revival Treasury Building that sits on the other side of the White House. Numerous plans to alter the facade foundered because of lack of money. The granite edifice may look like a wedding cake, but its high ceilings and spacious offices make it popular with occupants, who include members of the executive branch. Several presidents, including both Roosevelts, Richard Nixon, and George Bush, have served here during their careers. The former office of the secretary of the navy, restored in the 1980s, shows the opulent style of that office at the turn of the 20th century and has been an office for every vice president (except Hubert Humphrey) since Lyndon B. Johnson. The Old Executive Office Building has hosted numerous historic events. It was here that Secretary of State Cordell Hull met with Japanese diplomats after the bombing of Pearl Harbor, and it was here that Oliver North and Fawn Hall shredded Iran-Contra documents. ⊠ *East side of 17th St., west of White House,* ☎ *202/395–5895; 202/395–9103 TDD. Tours available certain Saturdays; reservations and security clearance required. Metro: Farragut West.*

⑫ Organization of American States. The headquarters of the Organization of American States, which is made up of nations from North, South, and Central America, contains a patio adorned with a pre-Columbian–style fountain and lush tropical plants. This tiny rain forest is a good place to rest when Washington's summer heat is at its most oppressive. The upstairs Hall of the Americas contains busts of generals and statesmen from the 34 OAS member nations, as well as each country's flag. ⊠ *17th St. and Constitution Ave. NW,* ☎ *202/458–3000.* ▭ *Free.* ☉ *Weekdays 9–5:30. Metro: Farragut West.*

⑮ Pershing Park. A quiet sunken garden honors General "Blackjack" Pershing, famous for failing to capture the Mexican revolutionary Pancho Villa in 1916–17 and then for commanding the American expeditionary force in World War I, among other military exploits. Engravings on the stone walls recount pivotal campaigns from that war. Ice-skaters glide on the square pool in winter. ⊠ *15th St. and Pennsylvania Ave. Metro: McPherson Square.*

⑥ Renwick Gallery. The Renwick Gallery of the National Museum of American Art has been at the forefront of the crafts movement, and its collection includes exquisitely designed and made utilitarian items, as well as objects created out of such traditional crafts media as fiber and glass. The words "Dedicated to Art" are engraved above the entrance to the French Second Empire–style building, designed by Smithsonian Castle architect James Renwick in 1859 to house the art collection of Washington merchant and banker William Wilson Corcoran.

In 1874 the Corcoran, as it was then called, opened as the first private art museum in the city. Corcoran's collection quickly outgrew the building, and in 1897 it was moved to a new gallery a few blocks south on 17th Street (☞ Corcoran Gallery of Art, *above*). After a stint as the U.S. Court of Claims, this building was restored, renamed after its architect, and opened in 1972 as the Smithsonian's Museum of American Crafts. Although crafts were once the poor relations of the art world—handwoven rugs and delicately carved tables were considered somehow less "artistic" than, say, oil paintings and sculptures—they have since come into their own. Not everything in the museum is Shaker furniture and enamel jewelry, though. The second-floor Grand Salon is still furnished in the opulent Victorian style Corcoran favored when his collection adorned its walls. ⊠ *Pennsylvania Ave. and 17th St. NW,* ☎ *202/357–2700; 202/357–1729 TDD.* 🖾 *Free.* ☉ *Daily 10–5:30. Metro: Farragut West.*

❹ St. John's Episcopal Church. The golden-domed so-called Church of the Presidents sits across Lafayette Park from the White House. Every president since Madison has visited the church, and many worshiped here regularly. Built in 1816, the church was the second building on the square. Benjamin Latrobe, who worked on both the Capitol and the White House, designed it in the form of a Greek cross, with a flat dome and a lantern cupola. The church has been altered somewhat since then; later additions include the Doric portico and the cupola tower. You can best sense the intent of Latrobe's design while standing inside under the saucer-shape dome of the original building. Not far from the center of the church is Pew 54, where visiting presidents are seated. The prie-dieux of many of the pews are embroidered with the presidential seal and the names of several chief executives. If you want to take a self-guided tour, brochures are available inside. ⊠ *16th and H Sts. NW,* ☎ *202/347–8766.* ✆ *Free.* ☉ *Weekdays 9–3; guided tours by appointment. Metro: McPherson Square.*

16 **Treasury Building.** Once used as a repository for currency, this is the largest Greek Revival edifice in Washington. Robert Mills, the architect responsible for the Washington Monument and the Patent Office (now the National Museum of American Art; ☞ Old Downtown and Federal Triangle, *below*), designed the grand colonnade that stretches down 15th Street. Construction of the Treasury Building started in 1836 and, after several additions, was finally completed in 1869. Its southern facade has a **statue of Alexander Hamilton,** the department's first secretary. Guided 90-minute tours—given every Saturday at 10, 10:20, 10:40, and 11—take you past the Andrew Johnson Suite, used by Johnson as the executive office while Mrs. Lincoln moved out of the White House; the two-story marble Cash Room; and a 19th-century burglarproof vault lining that saw duty when the building stored currency. Register at least one week ahead for the tour; you must provide name, date of birth, and Social Security number and show a photo ID at the start of the tour. ⊠ *15th St. and Pennsylvania Ave. NW,* ☎ *202/622–0896; 202/622–0692 TDD.* ✆ *Free. Metro: McPherson Square or Metro Center.*

★ ☝ **White House.** This "house" surely has the best-known address in the United States: 1600 Pennsylvania Avenue. Pierre L'Enfant called it the President's House; it was known formally as the Executive Mansion; and in 1902 Congress officially proclaimed it the White House. Irishman James Hoban's plan, based on the Georgian design of Leinster Hall in Dublin and of other Irish country houses, was selected in a 1792 contest. The building wasn't ready for its first occupant, John Adams, the second U.S. president, until 1800, and so, in a colossal irony, George Washington, who seems to have slept everyplace else, never slept here. Completed in 1829, it has undergone many structural changes since then. Andrew Jackson installed running water. James Garfield put in the first elevator. Between 1948 and 1952, Harry Truman had the entire structure gutted and restored, adding a second-story porch to the south portico. Each family that has called the White House home has left its imprint on the 132-room mansion. George Bush installed a horseshoe pit. Most recently, a jogging track was installed for Bill Clinton.

Tuesday through Saturday mornings (except holidays), from 10 AM to noon, selected public rooms on the ground floor and first floor are open to visitors. There are two ways to visit the White House. The most popular (and easiest) way is to pick up timed tickets from the **White House Visitor Center** (☞ *below*). Your ticket will tell you where and when your tour begins. Plan on being there 5–10 minutes before your tour is scheduled to begin. The other option is to write to your representative or senator's office 8–10 weeks in advance of your trip to request special VIP passes for tours between 8 and 10 AM, but these tickets are extremely limited. (Keep in mind that the White House is occasionally closed without notice for official functions.) Baby strollers are not allowed on the tour. On selected weekends in April and October, the White House is open for garden tours. In December it's decorated for the holidays.

You'll enter the White House through the East Wing lobby on the ground floor, walking past the Jacqueline Kennedy Rose Garden. You can view several rooms on the ground floor, then proceed to the State Floor and enter the large white-and-gold **East Room,** the site of presidential social events. In 1814 Dolley Madison saved the room's full-length portrait of George Washington from torch-carrying British soldiers by cutting it from its frame, rolling it up, and spiriting it out of the White House. (No fool she, Dolley also rescued her own portrait.) One of Abraham Lincoln's sons once harnessed a pet goat to a chair and went for a ride through the East Room during a reception.

The Federal-style **Green Room,** named for the moss-green watered silk that covers its walls, is used for informal receptions and "photo opportunities" with foreign heads of state. Notable furnishings here include a New England sofa that once belonged to Daniel Webster and portraits of Benjamin Franklin, John Quincy Adams, and Abigail Adams. The president and his guests are often shown on TV sitting in front of the Green Room's English Empire mantel, engaging in what are invariably described as "frank and cordial" discussions.

The elliptical **Blue Room,** the most formal space in the White House, is furnished with a gilded Empire-style settee and chairs that were ordered by James Monroe. (Monroe asked for plain wooden chairs, but the furniture manufacturer thought such unadorned furnishings too simple for the White House and took it upon himself to supply chairs more in keeping with their surroundings.) The White House Christmas tree is placed in this room each year. (Another well-known elliptical room, the president's **Oval Office,** is in the West Wing of the White House, along with other executive offices, and is not part of the tour.)

The **Red Room** is decorated as an American Empire–style parlor of the early 19th century, with furniture by the New York cabinetmaker Charles-Honoré Lannuier. The marble mantel is the twin of the mantel in the Green Room.

The **State Dining Room,** second in size only to the East Room, can seat 140 guests. It's dominated by G. P. A. Healy's portrait of Abraham Lincoln, painted after the president's death. The stone mantel is inscribed with a quotation from one of John Adams's letters: "I pray heaven to bestow the best of blessings on this house and all that shall hereafter inhabit it. May none but honest and wise men ever rule under this roof." In Teddy Roosevelt's day a stuffed moose head hung over the mantel. ✉ *1600 Pennsylvania Ave. NW,* ☎ *202/456–7041 or 202/208–1631.* ✉ *Free.* ☉ *Tues.–Sat. 10–noon. Metro: Federal Triangle.*

❶ **White House Visitor Center.** If you're visiting the White House, you need to stop by the visitor center for free tickets from March to September and December. Tickets are dispensed on a first-come, first-served basis. (They're usually gone by 9 AM.) Your ticket will show the starting point and time of your tour. Also at the center are exhibits pertaining to the White House's construction, its decor, and the families who have lived there. Photographs, artifacts, and videos relate the house's history to those who don't have the opportunity to tour the building; if you're taking the tour, they help you better appreciate and understand what you'll see. *Official address:* ⊠ *1450 Pennsylvania Ave. NW; entrance:* ⊠ *Department of Commerce's Baldrige Hall, E St. between 14th and 15th Sts.,* ☎ *202/208–1631.* ☜ *Free.* ☉ *Daily 7:30–4. Metro: Federal Triangle.*

⑭ William Tecumseh Sherman Monument. Sherman, whose Atlanta Campaign in 1864 cut a bloody swath of destruction through the Confederacy, was said to be the greatest Civil War general, as the sheer size of this massive monument, set in a small park, would seem to attest. ⊠ *Bounded by E and 15th Sts., East Executive Ave., and Alexander Hamilton Pl. Metro: Federal Triangle.*

Capitol Hill

The people who live and work on "the Hill" do so in the shadow of the edifice that lends the neighborhood its name: the gleaming white Capitol. More than just the center of government, however, the Hill also includes charming residential blocks lined with Victorian row houses and a fine assortment of restaurants, bars, and shops. Capitol Hill's boundaries are disputed: it's bordered to the west, north, and south by the Capitol, Union Station, and I Street, respectively. Some argue that Capitol Hill extends east to the Anacostia River, others that it ends at 11th Street near Lincoln Park. The neighborhood does in fact seem to grow as members of Capitol Hill's active historic-preservation movement restore more and more 19th-century houses.

Numbers in the margin correspond to numbers on the Capitol Hill map.

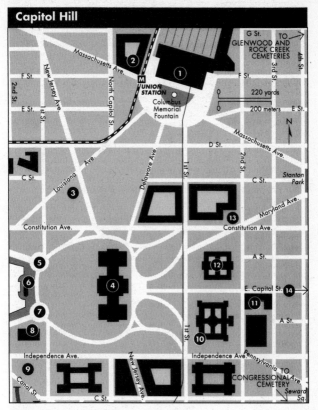

Capitol Hill

Bartholdi
Fountain, **9**

Capitol, **4**

Folger
Shakespeare
Library, **11**

Grant
Memorial, **6**

James Garfield
Memorial, **7**

Library of
Congress, **10**

National Postal
Museum, **2**

Peace
Monument, **5**

Robert A. Taft
Memorial, **3**

Sewall-Belmont
House, **13**

South Side of
East Capitol
Street, **14**

Supreme Court
Building, **12**

Union Station, **1**

United States
Botanic
Garden, **8**

Sights to See

9 **Bartholdi Fountain.** Frédéric-Auguste Bartholdi, sculptor of the more famous—and much larger—Statue of Liberty, created this delightful fountain, some 25 ft tall, for the Philadelphia Centennial Exhibition of 1876. With its aquatic monsters, sea nymphs, tritons, and lighted globes (once gas, now electric), the fountain represents water and light. The U.S. Government purchased the fountain after the exhibition and placed it on the grounds of the old Botanic Garden on the Mall. It was moved to its present location in 1932. ⊠ *1st St. and Independence Ave. SW. Metro: Federal Center.*

★ 4 **Capitol.** As beautiful as the building itself are the Capitol grounds, landscaped in the late 19th century by Frederick Law Olmsted, who, along with Calvert Vaux, created New York City's Central Park. On these 68 acres you will find both the city's tamest squirrels and the highest concentration of TV news correspondents, jockeying for a good position in front of the Capitol for their "stand-ups." A few hundred feet northeast of the Capitol are two cast-iron car shelters, left from the days when horse-drawn trolleys served the Hill. Olmsted's six pinkish, bronze-top lamps directly east from the Capitol are a treat, too.

The design of this monument was the result of a competition held in 1792; the winner was William Thornton, a physician and amateur architect from the West Indies. The cornerstone was laid by George Washington in a Masonic ceremony on September 18, 1793; and in November 1800, both the Senate and the House of Representatives moved down from Philadelphia to occupy the first completed section: the boxlike portion between the central rotunda and today's north wing. By 1807 the House wing had been completed, just to the south of what is now the domed center, and a covered wooden walkway joined the two wings.

The Congress House grew slowly and suffered a grave setback on August 24, 1814, when British troops led by Sir George Cockburn marched on Washington and set fire to the Capitol, the White House, and numerous other government buildings. (Cockburn reportedly stood on the House Speaker's chair and asked his men, "Shall this harbor of Yankee democracy be burned?" The question was rhetorical; the building was torched.) The wooden walkway was destroyed and the two wings were gutted, but the walls were left standing after a violent rainstorm doused the flames. Architect Benjamin Henry Latrobe supervised the rebuilding, adding such American touches as the corncob-and-tobacco-leaf capitals to columns in the east entrance of the Senate wing. He was followed by Boston-born Charles Bulfinch, and in 1826 the Capitol, its low wooden dome sheathed in copper, was finished.

North and south wings were added in the 1850s and '60s to accommodate a growing government trying to keep pace with a growing country. The elongated edifice extended farther north and south than Thornton had planned, and in 1855, to keep the scale correct, work began on a tall cast-iron dome. President Lincoln was criticized for continuing this expensive project while the country was in the throes of the Civil War, but he called the construction "a sign we intend the Union shall go on." This twin-shell dome, a marvel of 19th-century engineering, rises 285 ft above the ground and weighs 9 million pounds. It expands and contracts up to 4 inches a day, depending on the outside temperature. The figure atop the dome, often mistaken for Pocahontas, is called *Freedom*.

The Capitol has continued to grow. In 1962 the east front was extended 33½ ft, creating 100 additional offices. Preservationists have fought to keep the west front from being extended, since it is the last remaining section of the Capitol's original facade. A compromise was reached in 1983, when it was agreed that the facade's crumbling sandstone blocks would simply be replaced with stronger limestone.

Guided tours of the Capitol usually start beneath the **Rotunda's** dome, but during the busy season, lines form outside along the east-front drive. If you want to forego the tour, which is brief but informative, you may look around on your own. Enter through one of the lower doors to the right or left of the main steps. Start your exploration under Constantino Brumidi's 1865 fresco, *Apotheosis of Washington*, in the center of the dome. The figures in the inner circle represent the 13 original states; those in the outer ring symbolize arts, sciences, and industry. The flat, sculpture-style frieze around the Rotunda's rim depicts 400 years of American history and was started by Brumidi in 1877. While painting Penn's treaty with the Indians, the 74-year-old artist slipped on the 58-ft-high scaffold and almost fell off. Brumidi managed to hang on until help arrived, but he died a few months later from the shock of the incident. The work was continued by another Italian, Filippo Costaggini, but the frieze wasn't finished until American Allyn Cox added the final touches in 1953.

Notice the Rotunda's eight immense oil paintings of scenes from American history. The four scenes from the Revolutionary War are by John Trumbull, who served alongside George Washington and painted the first president from life. Twenty-nine people have lain in state or in honor in the Rotunda, including nine presidents, from Abraham Lincoln to Lyndon Baines Johnson. Underneath the Rotunda, above an empty crypt that was designed to hold the remains of George and Martha Washington (though they both were buried at their beloved Mount Vernon), is an exhibit chronicling the construction of the Capitol.

South of the Rotunda is **Statuary Hall,** once the legislative chamber of the House of Representatives. The room has an interesting architectural feature that maddened early legislators: a slight whisper uttered on one side of the hall can be heard on the other. (Don't be disappointed if this parlor trick doesn't work when you're visiting the Capitol; sometimes the hall is just too noisy.)

To the north, on the Senate side, you can look into the chamber once used by the Supreme Court and into the splendid Old Senate Chamber above it, both of which have been restored. Also be sure to see the Brumidi Corridor on the ground floor of the Senate wing. Frescoes and oil paintings of birds, plants, and American inventions adorn the walls and ceilings, and intricate, Brumidi-designed bronze stairways lead to the second floor. The Italian artist also memorialized several American heroes, painting them inside trompe l'oeil frames. Some frames were left blank. The most recent one to be filled, in 1987, honors the crew of the space shuttle *Challenger.*

If you want to watch some of the legislative action in the **House or Senate chambers** while you're on the Hill, you'll have to get a gallery pass from the office of your representative or senator. To find out where those offices are, ask any Capitol police officer, or call 202/224–3121. In the chambers you'll notice that Democrats sit to the right of the presiding officer, Republicans to the left—the opposite, it's often noted, of their political leanings. You may be disappointed by watching from the gallery. Most of the day-to-day business is conducted in the legislative committees, many of which meet in the congressional office buildings. The *Washington Post*'s daily "Today in Congress" lists when and where the committees are meeting. To get to a House or Senate office building, go to the Capitol's basement and ride the miniature subway used by legislators.

When you're finished exploring the inside of the Capitol, make your way to the **west side.** In 1981, Congress broke with tradition and moved the presidential swearing-in ceremony to this side of the Capitol, which offers a dramatic view of the Mall and monuments below and can accommodate more guests than the east side, where most previous presidents took the oath of office. ✉ *East end of Mall,* ☎ *202/224–3121; 202/225–6827 guide service.* ✆ *Free.* ☉ *Sept.–Feb., daily 9–4:30; Mar.–Aug., daily 9–8. Metro: Capitol South or Union Station.*

Congressional Cemetery. Dating from 1807, the Congressional Cemetery was the first national cemetery created by the government. Notables buried here include U.S. Capitol architect William Thornton, Marine Corps march composer John Philip Sousa, Civil War photographer Mathew Brady, and FBI director J. Edgar Hoover. There are also 76 members of Congress, many of them beneath ponderous markers. A brochure for a self-guided walking tour is available at the office. ✉ *1801 E St. SE,* ☎ *202/543–0539.* ☉ *Daily dawn–dusk; office Sat. 10–4.*

⑪ **Folger Shakespeare Library.** The Folger Library's collection of works by and about Shakespeare and his times is second to none. The white-marble Art Deco building, designed by architect Paul Philippe Cret, is decorated with scenes from the Bard's plays. Inside is a reproduction of an inn-yard theater—the setting for performances of chamber music, Baroque opera, and other events appropriate to the surroundings—and a gallery, designed in the manner of an Elizabethan Great Hall, which hosts rotating exhibits from the library's collection. ✉ *201 E. Capitol St. SE,* ☎ *202/544–4600.* ✉ *Free.* ☉ *Mon.–Sat. 10–4. Metro: Capitol South.*

Glenwood Cemetery. Not far from Catholic University, Glenwood has its share of notable residents, including the artists Constantino Brumidi, responsible for much of the Capitol building's beauty (among other things, he painted the frescoes adorning the inside of the great dome), and Emanuel Leutze, painter of *Washington Crossing the Delaware,* one of the most famous paintings in American history. More striking are the tombstones of two more-obscure citizens: Benjamin Greenup was the first firefighter killed on duty in Washington, and he's honored with an obelisk carved with his death scene. Teresina Vasco, a child who died at age two after playing with matches, is immortalized sitting in her favorite rocking chair. ✉ *2219 Lincoln Rd. NE,* ☎ *202/667–1016.* ☉ *Daily dawn–dusk; office weekdays 9:30–3:30.*

➏ Grant Memorial. The 252-ft-long memorial to the 16th American president and commander in chief of the Union forces during the Civil War is the largest sculpture group in the city. The statue of Ulysses S. Grant on horseback is flanked by Union artillery and cavalry. ✉ *Near 1st St. and Maryland Ave. SW. Metro: Federal Center.*

➐ James Garfield Memorial. Near the Grant Memorial and the United States Botanic Garden is a memorial to the 20th president of the United States. James Garfield was assassinated in 1881 after only a few months in office. His bronze statue stands on a pedestal with three other bronze figures seated around it; one bears a tablet inscribed with the words "Law," "Justice," and "Prosperity," which the figures presumably represent. Grand though this may seem, Garfield's two primary claims to fame were that he was the last log-cabin president and that his was the second presidential assassination (Lincoln's was first), ending the second-shortest presidency. ✉ *1st St. and Maryland Ave. SW. Metro: Federal Center.*

⑩ Library of Congress. One of the world's largest libraries, the Library of Congress contains some 115 million items, of which only a quarter are books. The remainder includes manuscripts, prints, films, photographs, sheet music, and the largest collection of maps in the world. Also part of the library is the Congressional Research Service, which, as the name implies, works on special projects for senators and representatives.

Provisions for a library to serve members of Congress were originally made in 1800, when the government set aside $5,000 to purchase and house books that legislators might need to consult. This small collection was housed in the Capitol but was destroyed in 1814, when the British burned the city. Thomas Jefferson, then in retirement at Monticello, offered his personal library as a replacement, noting that "there is, in fact, no subject to which a Member of Congress may not have occasion to refer." Jefferson's collection of 6,487 books, for which Congress eventually paid him $23,950, laid the foundation for the great national library. (Sadly, another fire in 1851 destroyed two-thirds of Jefferson's books.) By the late 1800s it was clear the Capitol could no longer contain the growing library, and the copper-domed **Thomas Jefferson Building** was constructed. The **Adams Building,** on 2nd Street behind the Jefferson, was added in 1939. A third structure, the **James Madison Building,** opened in 1980; it's just south of the Jefferson Building, between Independence Avenue and C Street.

The Jefferson Building's Great Hall is richly adorned with mosaics, paintings, and curving marble stairways. The grand, octagonal Main Reading Room, its central desk surrounded by mahogany readers' tables, is either inspiring or overwhelming to researchers. Computer terminals have replaced the wood card catalogs, but books are still retrieved and dispersed the same way: readers (18 years or older) hand request slips to librarians and wait patiently for their materials to be delivered. Researchers aren't allowed in the stacks, and only members of Congress and other special borrowers can check books out.

But books are only part of the story. Family trees are explored in the Local History and Genealogy Reading Room.

In the Folklife Reading Room, researchers can listen to LP recordings of Native American music or hear the story of B'rer Rabbit read in the Gullah dialect of coastal Georgia and South Carolina. Items from the library's collection—which includes a Gutenberg Bible—are on display in the Jefferson Building's second-floor Southwest Gallery and Pavilion. ⊠ *Jefferson Bldg., 1st St. and Independence Ave. SE,* ☎ *202/707–4604 taped exhibit information; 202/707–5000 Library of Congress operator; 202/707–6400 taped schedule of general and reading-room hrs.* 🎟 *Free.* ☼ *Mon.–Sat. 10–5:30. Tours Mon.–Sat. at 11:30, 1, 2:30, and 4 from Great Hall. Metro: Capitol South.*

🖐 ❷ **National Postal Museum.** The museum is home to, among other things, the Smithsonian's priceless stamp collection, consisting of a whopping 11 million stamps. Exhibits underscore the important part the mail has played in the development of America and include horse-drawn mail coaches, railway mail cars, airmail planes, and a collection of philatelic rarities. The National Museum of Natural History may have the Hope Diamond, but the National Postal Museum has the container used to mail the priceless gem to the Smithsonian. The family-oriented museum has more than 40 interactive and touch-screen exhibits. The museum takes up only a portion of what is the old Washington City Post Office, designed by Daniel Burnham and completed in 1914. Nostalgic odes to the noble mail carrier are inscribed on the exterior of the marble building; one of them eulogizes the "Messenger of sympathy and love, servant of parted friends, consoler of the lonely, bond of the scattered family, enlarger of the common life." ⊠ *2 Massachusetts Ave. NE,* ☎ *202/357–2700; 202/357–1729 TDD.* 🎟 *Free.* ☼ *Daily 10–5:30. Metro: Union Station.*

❺ **Peace Monument.** A white-marble memorial depicts America in the form of a woman grief-stricken over sailors lost at sea during the Civil War; she is weeping on the shoulder of a second female figure representing History. The plaque inscription refers movingly to navy personnel who "fell in defence of the union and liberty of their country 1861–1865." ⊠ *Traffic circle at 1st St. and Pennsylvania Ave. Metro: Union Station.*

❸ **Robert A. Taft Memorial.** Rising above the trees in the triangle formed by Louisiana, New Jersey, and Constitution avenues, a monolithic carillon pays tribute to the longtime Republican senator and son of the 27th president. ⊠ *Constitution and New Jersey Aves. Metro: Union Station.*

Rock Creek Cemetery. Rock Creek, the city's oldest cemetery, is administered by the city's oldest church, St. Paul's Episcopal, which erected its first building in 1775. (What remains of the original structure is a single brick wall.) Many beautiful and imposing monuments are in the cemetery. The best known and most moving honors Marion Hooper "Clover" Adams, wife of historian Henry Adams; she committed suicide in 1885. Sculptor Augustus Saint-Gaudens created the enigmatic figure of a seated, shroud-draped woman, calling it *The Peace of God That Passeth Understanding*, though it's best known by the nickname "Grief." It is thought by many to be the most moving sculpture in the city. ⊠ *Rock Creek Church Rd. and Webster St. NW,* ☎ *202/829–0585.* ◷ *Daily 7:30–dusk.*

❸ **Sewall-Belmont House.** The oldest home on Capitol Hill is now the headquarters of the National Woman's Party. It has a museum that chronicles the early days of the women's movement and the history of the house. The house is filled with period furniture and portraits and busts of such suffragist leaders as Lucretia Mott, Elizabeth Cady Stanton, and Alice Paul. The redbrick house was built in 1800 by Robert Sewall. Part of the structure dates from about 1750. From 1801 to 1813 Secretary of the Treasury Albert Gallatin, who finalized the details of the Louisiana Purchase in his front-parlor office, lived here. The house was the only residence burned in Washington during the British invasion of 1814, after a resident fired on advancing British troops from an upper-story window. (This was, in fact, the only armed resistance the British met that day.) ⊠ *144 Constitution Ave. NE,* ☎ *202/546–3989.* ▧ *Free.* ◷ *Jan.–Feb. and Apr.–Oct., Tues.–Fri. 10–3, Sat. noon–4; Mar. and Nov.–Dec., Tues.–Fri. 10–3, Sat. noon–4, Sun. 1–4. Metro: Union Station.*

❹ **South Side of East Capitol Street.** Walk along East Capitol Street, the border between the northeast and southeast

quadrants of the city, for a sample of the residential area
of the Hill. The house on the corner of East Capitol Street,
No. 329, has a striking tower with a bay window and
stained glass. Next door are two Victorian houses with iron
trim below the second floor. A pre–Civil War Greek Revival
frame house sits behind a tidy garden at No. 317. ⊠ *E. Capitol St. between 3rd and 4th Sts. Metro: Capitol South.*

⑫ **Supreme Court Building.** It wasn't until 1935 that the
Supreme Court got its own building: a white-marble temple with twin rows of Corinthian columns designed by
Cass Gilbert. In 1800, the justices arrived in Washington
along with the rest of the government but were for years
shunted around various rooms in the Capitol; for a while
they even met in a tavern. William Howard Taft, the only
man to serve as both president and chief justice, was instrumental in getting the Court a home of its own, though
he died before it was completed.

The Supreme Court convenes on the first Monday in October and remains in session until it has heard all of its cases
and handed down all of its decisions (usually the end of June).
On Monday through Wednesday of two weeks in each
month, the justices hear oral arguments in the velvet-
swathed court chamber. Visitors who want to listen can
choose to wait in either of two lines. One, the "three-to-
five-minute" line, shuttles visitors through, giving them a
quick impression of the court at work. If you choose the
other, for those who'd like to stay for the whole show, it's
best to be in line by 8:30 AM. The main hall of the Supreme
Court is lined with busts of former chief justices; the court-
room itself is decorated with allegorical friezes. Perhaps the
most interesting appurtenance in the imposing building, however, is a basketball court on one of the upper floors (it's
been called the highest court in the land). ⊠ *1st and E. Capitol Sts. NE,* ☎ *202/479–3000.* ▣ *Free.* ☉ *Weekdays 9–
4:30. Metro: Capitol South.*

❶ **Union Station.** With its 96-ft-high coffered ceiling gilded with
8 pounds of gold leaf, the city's train station is one of the
capital's great spaces and is used for inaugural balls and
other festive events. In 1902 the McMillan Commission—
charged with suggesting ways to improve the appearance

of the city—recommended that the many train lines that sliced through the capital share one main depot. Union Station was opened in 1908 and was the first building completed under the commission's plan. Chicago architect and commission member Daniel H. Burnham patterned the station after the Baths of Diocletian in Rome.

For many visitors to Washington, the capital city is first seen framed through the grand station's arched doorways. In its heyday, during World War II, more than 200,000 people swarmed through the building daily. By the '60s, however, the decline in train travel had turned the station into an expensive white-marble elephant. It was briefly, and unsuccessfully, transformed into a visitor center for the Bicentennial; but by 1981 rain was pouring in through its neglected roof, and passengers boarded trains at a ramshackle depot behind the station.

The Union Station you see today is the result of a restoration, completed in 1988, that was intended to begin a revival of Washington's east end. Between train travelers and visitors to the shops, restaurants, and nine-screen movie theater, 70,000 people a day pass through the Beaux Arts building. The jewel of the structure is its main waiting room. Forty-six statues of Roman legionnaires, one for each state in the Union when the station was completed, ring the grand room. The statues were a subject of controversy when the building was first opened. Pennsylvania Railroad president Alexander Cassatt (brother of artist Mary) ordered sculptor Louis Saint-Gaudens (brother of sculptor Augustus) to alter the statues, convinced that the legionnaires' skimpy outfits would upset female passengers. The sculptor obligingly added a shield to each figure, obscuring any offending body parts.

The east hall, now filled with vendors, was once an expensive restaurant. It's decorated with Pompeiian-style tracery and plaster walls and columns painted to look like marble. At one time the station also had a secure presidential waiting room, now restored. This room was by no means frivolous: 20 years before Union Station was built, President Garfield was assassinated in the public waiting room of the old Baltimore and Potomac terminal on 6th Street.

The **Columbus Memorial Fountain,** designed by Lorado Taft, sits in the plaza in front of Union Station. A caped, steely-eyed Christopher Columbus stares into the distance, flanked by a hoary, bearded figure (the Old World) and a Native American brave (the New). ⊠ *Massachusetts Ave. north of Capitol,* ☎ *202/289–1908. Metro: Union Station.*

On Union Station's lower level you'll find more than 20 food stalls offering everything from pizza to sushi. There are several restaurants throughout the station, one of the best being **America** (☎ 202/682–9555), with a menu of regional foods that lives up to its expansive name.

↻ ❽ **United States Botanic Garden.** The rather cold exterior belies the peaceful, plant-filled oasis within. The conservatory includes a cactus house, a fern house, and a subtropical house filled with orchids. Seasonal displays include blooming plants at Easter, chrysanthemums in the fall, and Christmas greens and poinsettias in December and January. Brochures just inside the doorway offer helpful gardening tips. The conservatory closed in late 1997 for renovation of the building and exhibits. In early 1998, work was begun on the new **National Garden,** which will occupy the 3 acres of lawn adjacent to the conservatory. The conservatory and the garden are scheduled to open in the year 2000. ⊠ *1st St. and Maryland Ave. SW,* ☎ *202/225–8333.* ▭ *Free.* ☉ *Daily 9–5. Metro: Federal Center SW.*

Old Downtown and Federal Triangle

The fact that Washington is a planned city doesn't mean the plan was executed flawlessly. Pierre L'Enfant's design has been alternately shelved and rediscovered several times in the past 200 years. Nowhere have the city's imperfections been more visible than on L'Enfant's grand thoroughfare, Pennsylvania Avenue. By the early '60s it had become a national disgrace, the dilapidated buildings that lined it home to pawnshops and cheap souvenir stores. While riding up Pennsylvania Avenue in his inaugural parade, a disgusted John F. Kennedy is said to have turned to an aide and said, "Fix it!" Washington's downtown—once within the diamond formed by Massachusetts, Louisiana, Pennsylvania, and New York avenues—had its problems, too, many the result of riots that rocked the capital in 1968 after the assassination of Martin Luther King, Jr. In their wake, many businesses left the area and moved north of the White House.

In recent years developers have rediscovered "old downtown," and buildings are now being torn down or remodeled at an amazing pace. After several false starts Pennsylvania Avenue is shining once again.

Numbers in the margin correspond to numbers on the Old Downtown and Federal Triangle map.

Sights to See

13 **Canadian Embassy.** A spectacular edifice constructed of stone and glass, the Canadian Embassy was designed by Arthur Erickson and completed in 1988. Inside, a gallery periodically has exhibits on Canadian culture and history. ⊠ *501 Pennsylvania Ave. NW,* ☎ *202/682–1740.* ☞ *Free.* ☉ *Weekdays 10–5 during exhibitions only. Metro: Archives/Navy Memorial.*

Chinatown. You know you're entering Washington's compact Chinatown when you notice the Chinese characters on the street signs. The area is somewhat down-at-the-heels—you'll find boarded-up buildings and graffiti-covered walls—but this is the place to go for Chinese food in the District. Cantonese, Szechuan, Hunan, and Mongolian are among the delectable culinary styles you'll find. Nearly every restaurant has a roast duck hanging in the window, and the shops here sell a wide variety of Chinese goods. Most interesting are traditional pharmacies purveying folk medicines such as dried eels, powdered bones, and a variety of unusual herbs for teas and broths believed to promote health, longevity, and sexual potency. ⊠ *Bounded by G, H, 5th, and 8th Sts. Metro: Gallery Place/Chinatown.*

Federal Triangle. To the south of Freedom Plaza, Federal Triangle consists of a mass of government buildings constructed between 1929 and 1938. Notable are the Department of Commerce (with the National Aquarium inside), the District Building, the Old Post Office Building, the Internal Revenue Service Building, the Department of Justice, the National Archives, and the Apex Building, which houses the Federal Trade Commission.

Old Downtown and Federal Triangle

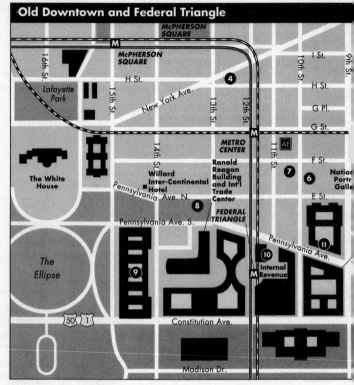

Canadian Embassy, **13**

Ford's Theatre, **6**

Freedom Plaza, **8**

Friendship Arch, **3**

J. Edgar Hoover Federal Bureau of Investigation Building, **11**

National Aquarium, **9**

National Archives, **12**

National Building Museum, **1**

National Law Enforcement Officers Memorial, **2**

National Museum of Women in the Arts, **4**

Old Patent Office Building/ National Museum of American Art and National Portrait Gallery, **5**

Old Post Office Building, **10**

Petersen House, **7**

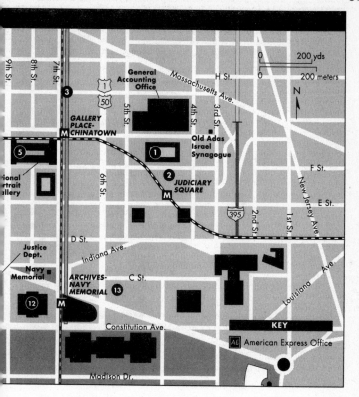

9th St.
8th St.
7th St.

3

GALLERY
PLACE-
M **CHINATOWN**

5

rional
rtrait
allery

Justice
Dept.

Navy
Memorial ■

12

M

General
Accounting
Office

5th St.

H St.

Massachusetts Ave.

4th St.
3rd St.

1

Old Adas
Israel
Synagogue

2

JUDICIARY
M **SQUARE**

395

D St.

Indiana Ave.

ARCHIVES-
NAVY
MEMORIAL **13**

C St.

Constitution Ave.

Madison Dr.

N

0   200 yds
0   200 meters

F St.

E St.

New Jersey Ave.

2nd St.
1st St.

Louisiana Ave.

KEY

A₤ American Express Office

Before Federal Triangle was developed, government workers were scattered throughout the city, largely in rented offices. Looking for a place to consolidate this workforce, city planners hit on the area south of Pennsylvania Avenue known, at the time, as "Murder Bay," a notorious collection of rooming houses, taverns, tattoo parlors, and brothels. A uniform classical architectural style, with Italianate red-tile roofs and interior plazas reminiscent of the Louvre, was chosen for the building project. Federal Triangle's planners envisioned interior courts filled with plazas and parks, but the needs of the motorcar foiled any such grand plans. A park was planned for the spot of land between 13th and 14th streets across from the Department of Commerce, but for years it was an immense parking lot; today it is a federal office building and the Ronald Reagan Building and International Trade Center. The trade center houses U.S. Customs, U.S. AID, EPA, and others and has a food court and a few shops. ✉ *15th St. and Pennsylvania and Constitution Aves. Metro: Federal Triangle.*

🖐 ❻ **Ford's Theatre.** In 1861, Baltimore theater impresario John T. Ford leased the First Baptist Church building that stood on this site and turned it into a successful music hall. The building burned down late in 1862, and Ford rebuilt it. The events of April 14, 1865, would shock the nation and close the theater. On that night, during a production of *Our American Cousin,* John Wilkes Booth entered the presidential box and shot Abraham Lincoln. The stricken president was carried across the street to the house of tailor William Petersen. Charles Augustus Leale, a 23-year-old doctor, attended to the president. To let Lincoln know that someone was nearby, Leale held his hand throughout the night. Lincoln died the next morning.

The federal government bought Ford's Theatre in 1866 for $100,000 and converted it into office space. It was remodeled as a Lincoln museum in 1932 and was restored to its 1865 appearance in 1968. The basement museum displays artifacts such as Booth's pistol and the clothes Lincoln was wearing when he was shot. The theater itself continues to present a complete schedule of plays. *A Christmas Carol* is an annual holiday favorite. ✉ *511 10th St. NW,* ☎ *202/426–6924.* ▣ *Free.* ☉ *Daily 9–5; theater*

closed when rehearsals or matinees are in progress (gener-
ally Thurs. and weekends); Lincoln Museum in basement
remains open at these times. Metro: Metro Center.

8 **Freedom Plaza.** In 1988, Western Plaza was renamed Freedom Plaza in honor of Martin Luther King, Jr. Its east end
is dominated by a statue of General Casimir Pulaski, the
Polish nobleman who led an American cavalry corps during the Revolutionary War and was mortally wounded in
1779 at the Siege of Savannah. He gazes over a plaza that
is inlaid in bronze with a detail from L'Enfant's original
1791 plan for the Federal City. Bronze outlines the President's Palace and the Congress House; the Mall is represented by a green lawn. Cut into the edges are quotations
about the capital city, not all of them complimentary. To
compare L'Enfant's vision with today's reality, stand in the
middle of the map's Pennsylvania Avenue and look west.
L'Enfant had planned an unbroken vista from the Capitol
to the White House, but the Treasury Building, begun in
1836, ruined the view. Turning to the east, you'll see the
U.S. Capitol sitting on Jenkins Hill like an American Taj
Mahal.

There's a lot to see and explore in the blocks near Freedom
Plaza. The Beaux Arts **Willard Inter-Continental Hotel** (☞
below) is on the corner of 14th Street and Pennsylvania Avenue NW. Just north of Freedom Plaza, on F Street between
13th and 14th streets, are the **Shops,** a collection of stores
in the National Press Building, itself home to dozens of media
organizations. The Shops' upstairs Food Hall has sit-down
restaurants and fast-food places. Washington's oldest stage,
the **National Theatre,** also overlooks the plaza. ⊠ *Bounded*
by 13th, 14th, and E Sts. and Pennsylvania Ave. Metro: Fed-
eral Triangle.

3 **Friendship Arch.** A colorful and ornate 75-ft-wide arch is
a reminder of Washington's sister-city relationship with
Beijing. ⊠ *Spanning H St. at 7th St. Metro: Gallery*
Place/Chinatown.

☾ **11** **J. Edgar Hoover Federal Bureau of Investigation Building.**
The one-hour tour of the FBI building is one of the most
popular activities in the city. A brief film outlines the bureau's work, and exhibits describe famous past cases and

illustrate the FBI's fight against organized crime, terrorism, bank robbery, espionage, extortion, and other criminal activities. There's everything from gangster John Dillinger's death mask to a poster display of the 10 Most Wanted criminals. (Look carefully: two bad guys were apprehended as a result of tips from tour takers!) You'll also see the laboratories where the FBI painstakingly studies evidence. The high point of the tour comes right at the end: an agent gives a live-ammo firearms demonstration in the indoor shooting range.

Although it overlooks Federal Triangle, the FBI building is on the wrong side of Pennsylvania Avenue to be part of it. (The main Department of Justice Building, however, *is* part of it; like the rest of Federal Triangle, this building is sprinkled with Art Deco details, including cylindrical aluminum torches outside the doorways and bas-relief figures of bison, dolphins, and birds.) A hulking presence on the avenue, the FBI building was decried from birth as hideous. Even Hoover himself is said to have called it the "ugliest building I've ever seen." Opened in 1974, it hangs over 9th Street like a poured-concrete Big Brother. One thing is certain—it is secure. At peak times there may be a three- to four-hour wait for a tour. ⊠ *10th St. and Pennsylvania Ave. NW (tour entrance on E St. NW),* ☎ *202/324–3447.* ⊠ *Free.* ⊙ *Tours weekdays every 20 mins, 8:45–4:15 (note: line for tours can be closed on short notice when it gets crowded). Metro: Federal Triangle or Gallery Place/Chinatown.*

👌 ❾ **National Aquarium.** The western base of Federal Triangle between 14th and 15th streets is the home of the Department of Commerce, charged with promoting U.S. economic development and technological advancement. When it opened in 1932 it was the world's largest government office building. It's a good thing there's plenty of space; incongruously, the National Aquarium is housed inside. Established in 1873, it's the country's oldest public aquarium, with more than 1,200 fish and other creatures representing 270 species of fresh- and saltwater life. Its 80 tanks are alive with brilliantly colored tropical fish, fire-hose-thick moray eels, curious frogs and turtles, silvery schools of flesh-chomping piranhas, and even more fearsome sharks. A "touch tank" lets you handle more-hospitable sea creatures, such as crabs and oysters. ⊠ *14th St. and Pennsylvania Ave. NW,* ☎ *202/482–2825.* 🎫 *$2.* ☉ *Daily 9–5; sharks fed Mon., Wed., and Sat. at 2; piranhas fed Tues., Thurs., and Sun. at 2. Metro: Federal Triangle.*

⓬ **National Archives.** If the Smithsonian Institution is the nation's attic, the Archives is the nation's basement, and it bears responsibility for important government documents and other items. The Declaration of Independence, the Constitution, and the Bill of Rights are on display in the building's rotunda, in a case made of bulletproof glass, equipped with green filters, and filled with helium gas (to protect the irreplaceable documents). At night and on Christmas—the only day the archives are closed—the cases and documents are lowered into a vault. Other objects in the Archives' vast collection include bureaucratic correspondence, veterans and immigration records, treaties, Richard Nixon's resignation letter, and the rifle Lee Harvey Oswald used to assassinate John F. Kennedy.

The Archives fills the area between 7th and 9th streets and Pennsylvania and Constitution avenues on Federal Triangle. Beside it is a small park with a modest memorial to Franklin Roosevelt. The desk-size piece of marble on the sliver of grass is exactly what the president asked for (though this hasn't stopped fans of the 32nd president from building a grand memorial at the Tidal Basin; ☞ **Franklin Delano Roosevelt Memorial** *in* The Monuments, *above*). Designed by John Russell Pope, the Archives was erected in 1935 on the site of the old Center Market. This large block had been a center of commerce since the early 1800s, when barges plying the City Canal (which flowed where Constitution Avenue is now) were loaded and unloaded here. A vestige of this mercantile past lives on in the name given to the two semicircular developments across Pennsylvania Avenue from the Archives—Market Square. City planners hope that the residential development will enliven this stretch of Pennsylvania Avenue.

Turn right onto 9th Street and head to the Constitution Avenue side of the Archives. All the sculpture that adorns the building was carved on the site, including the two statues that flank the flight of steps facing the Mall, *Heritage* and

Guardianship, by James Earle Fraser. Fraser also carved the scene on the pediment, which represents the transfer of historic documents to the recorder of the Archives. (Like nearly all pediment decorations in Washington, this one is bristling with electric wires designed to thwart the advances of destructive starlings.) Call at least three weeks in advance to arrange a behind-the-scenes tour. ⊠ *Constitution Ave. between 7th and 9th Sts. NW,* ☎ *202/501–5000; 202/501–5205 tours.* 🖀 *Free.* ☉ *Apr.–Labor Day, daily 10– 9; Labor Day–Mar., daily 10–5:30; tours weekdays at 10:15 and 1:15. Metro: Archives/Navy Memorial.*

☾ ❶ **National Building Museum.** The open interior of this mammoth redbrick edifice is one of the city's great spaces and has been the site of inaugural balls for more than 100 years. (The first ball was for Grover Cleveland in 1885; because the building wasn't finished at the time, a temporary wooden roof and floor were erected.) The eight central Corinthian columns are among the largest in the world, rising to a height of 75 ft. Although they look like marble, each is made of 70,000 bricks, covered with plaster and painted to resemble Siena marble. For years, NBC has taped its *Christmas in Washington* TV special in this breathtaking hall.

Formerly known as the Pension Building, it was erected between 1882 and 1887 to house workers who processed the pension claims of veterans and their survivors, an activity that intensified after the Civil War. The architect was U.S. Army Corps of Engineers general Montgomery C. Meigs, who took as his inspiration the Italian Renaissance–style Palazzo Farnese in Rome. The museum is devoted to architecture and the building arts. "Washington: Symbol and City" is a permanent exhibit that outlines the capital's architectural history, from monumental core to residential neighborhoods. Recent temporary exhibits have explored the massive World War II building campaign and the history of roads in our national parks.

Before entering the building, walk down its F Street side. The terra-cotta frieze by Caspar Buberl between the first and second floors depicts soldiers marching and sailing in an endless procession around the building. Architect Meigs lost his oldest son in the Civil War, and, though the frieze depicts Union troops, he intended it as a memorial to all who were killed in the bloody war. Meigs designed the Pension Building with workers' comfort in mind long before anyone knew that cramped, stuffy offices could cause "sick building syndrome." Note the three "missing" bricks under each window that helped keep the building cool by allowing air to circulate.

For a nice view of the building, head west on F Street, cross 5th Street, and look back. The **Old Adas Israel Synagogue** (☞ *below*) is nearby. ✉ *401 F St. NW (between 4th and 5th Sts.),* ☎ *202/272–2448.* 🎟 *Free.* ☉ *Mon.–Sat. 10–4, Sun. noon–4; tour weekdays at 12:30, weekends at 11:30, 12:30, and 1:30. Metro: Judiciary Square.*

② **National Law Enforcement Officers Memorial.** The National Law Enforcement Officers Memorial is a 3-ft-high wall that bears the names of more than 15,000 American police officers killed in the line of duty since 1794. On the third line of panel 13W are the names of six officers killed by William Bonney, better known as Billy the Kid. J. D. Tippit, the Dallas policeman killed by Lee Harvey Oswald, is honored on the ninth line of panel 63E. Given the dangerous nature of police work, it will be one of the few memorials to which names will continue to be added. Two blocks away is a visitor center with exhibits on the history of the memorial and computers that allow you to look up officers by name, date of death, state, and department. A small shop sells souvenirs. Call to arrange for a free tour. ✉ *E St. between 4th and 5th Sts.; visitor center, 605 E St. NW,* ☎ *202/737–3400.* 🎟 *Free.* ☉ *Weekdays 9–5, Sat. 10–5, Sun. noon–5. Metro: Judiciary Square.*

National Museum of American Art. The first floor of the National Museum of American Art, which is in the **Old Patent Office Building** (☞ *below*) has displays of Early American art and art of the West, as well as a gallery of painted miniatures. Be sure to see *The Throne of the Third Heaven of the Nations' Millennium General Assembly,* by James Hampton. Discarded materials, such as chairs, bottles, and lightbulbs, are sheathed in aluminum and gold foil in this strange and moving work of religious art. On the second floor are works by the American impressionists, including

Childe Hassam and Mary Cassatt. Plaster models and marble sculptures by Hiram Powers are on display, including the plaster cast of his famous work *The Greek Slave*. Also on this floor are massive landscapes by Albert Bierstadt and Thomas Moran, including three panoramic views of the Grand Canyon. The third floor is filled with modern art, including works by Leon Kroll and Edward Hopper that were commissioned during the '30s by the federal government. A major renovation of the Old Patent Office Building is scheduled to begin in early January 2000 and last approximately three years. During the renovation, NMAA will continue its public presence through its Web site (www.nmaa.si.edu) and a full program at its Renwick Gallery, but the museum and the National Portrait Gallery, which shares the building, will be closed. ⊠ *8th and G Sts. NW,* ☎ *202/357–2700; 202/357–1729 TDD.* ⊠ *Free.* ☉ *Daily 10–5:30. Metro: Gallery Place/Chinatown.*

❹ National Museum of Women in the Arts. Works by female artists from the Renaissance to the present are showcased at one of the larger non-Smithsonian museums. The beautifully restored 1907 Renaissance Revival building was designed by Waddy Wood; ironically, it was once a men-only Masonic temple. In addition to displaying traveling shows, the museum has a permanent collection that includes paintings, drawings, sculpture, prints, and photographs by such artists as Georgia O'Keeffe, Mary Cassatt, Élisabeth Vigée-Lebrun, Frida Kahlo, and Camille Claudel. ⊠ *1250 New York Ave. NW,* ☎ *202/783–5000.* ⊠ *Suggested donation $3.* ☉ *Mon.–Sat. 10–5, Sun. noon–5. Metro: Metro Center.*

National Portrait Gallery. This museum is in the **Old Patent Office Building** (☞ *below*) along with the **National Museum of American Art** (☞ *above*). The best place to start a circuit of the Portrait Gallery is on the restored third floor. The Renaissance-style gallery, with its colorful tile flooring and stained-glass skylight, was the site of the receiving line at Abraham Lincoln's 1865 inaugural ball. Highlights of the Portrait Gallery's second floor include the Hall of Presidents (featuring a portrait or sculpture of each chief executive), the George Washington "Lansdowne" portrait, and a portrait of Pocahontas. The first floor features portraits of well-known American athletes and performers. *Time* magazine gave the museum its collection of original art commissioned for the magazine covers and many other photos and paintings that the magazine has commissioned over the years. Parts of this collection are periodically on display. A major renovation of the Old Patent Office Building is scheduled to begin in early January 2000 and last approximately three years. During the renovation, the National Portrait Gallery will be closed. ⊠ *8th and F Sts. NW,* ☎ *202/357–2700; 202/357–1729 TDD.* ⊠ *Free.* ☉ *Daily 10–5:30. Metro: Gallery Place/Chinatown.*

Navy Memorial. A huge outdoor plaza, this memorial includes a granite map of the world and a 7-ft statue, *The Lone Sailor.* In summer, its concert stage is the site of military band performances. Next to the memorial, in the Market Square East Building, is the Naval Heritage Center, which has a gift shop and the Navy Log Room, where you can use computers to look up the service records of navy veterans entered into the log. There's also the 250-seat, widescreen Arleigh & Roberta Burke Theater, home of continuous screenings of the 30-minute, 70-millimeter film *At Sea.* Produced by the same company that made the IMAX hit *To Fly, At Sea* is a visually stunning look at life aboard a modern aircraft carrier. A memorial to General Winfield Scott is in the park adjacent to the Navy Memorial. ⊠ *701 Pennsylvania Ave. NW,* ☎ *202/737–2300.* ⊠ *Film $4.* ☉ *Naval Heritage Center Mar.–Nov., Mon.–Sat. 9:30–5, Sun. noon–5; Dec.–Feb., Tues.–Sat. 10:30–4. Metro: Archives/Navy Memorial.*

Old Adas Israel Synagogue. This is the oldest synagogue in Washington. Built in 1876 at 6th and G streets NW, the redbrick Federal Revival–style building was moved to its present location in 1969 to make way for an office building. Exhibits in the Lillian and Albert Small Jewish Museum inside explore Jewish life in Washington. ⊠ *701 3rd St. NW,* ☎ *202/789–0900.* ⊠ *Suggested donation $2.* ☉ *Museum Sun.–Thurs. noon–4. Metro: Judiciary Square.*

❺ Old Patent Office Building. Two Smithsonian museums now share the Old Patent Office Building. The **National Portrait Gallery** (☞ *above*), with its Civil War photographs, paintings, and prints, presidential portraits, and *Time* magazine covers, is on the south side. The **National Museum of American Art** (☞ *above*), with displays on Early American and western art, is on the north. Construction on the south wing, which was designed by Washington Monument architect Robert Mills, started in 1836. When the huge Greek Revival quadrangle was completed in 1867, it was the largest building in the country. Many of its rooms housed glass display cabinets filled with the models that inventors were required to submit with their patent applications.

During the Civil War, the Patent Office, like many other buildings in the city, was turned into a hospital. Among those caring for the wounded here were Clara Barton and Walt Whitman. In the 1950s the building was threatened with demolition to make way for a parking lot, but the efforts of preservationists saved it. The Smithsonian opened it to the public in 1968. ⊠ *G St. between 7th and 9th Sts.*

👆 **❿** **Old Post Office Building.** When it was completed in 1899, this Romanesque structure on Federal Triangle was the largest government building in the District, the first with a clock tower, and the first with an electric power plant. Despite these innovations, it earned the sobriquet "old" after only 18 years, when a new District post office was constructed near Union Station. When urban planners in the '20s decided to impose a uniform design on Federal Triangle, the Old Post Office was slated for demolition. The fanciful granite building was saved first because of a lack of money during the Depression, then thanks to the intercession of preservationists. Major renovation was begun in 1978, and in 1984 the public areas in the Old Post Office Pavilion—an assortment of shops and restaurants inside the airy central courtyard—were opened. Park service rangers who work at the Old Post Office consider the observation deck in the clock tower to be one of Washington's best-kept secrets. Although not as tall as the Washington Monument, it offers nearly as impressive a view. Even better, it's usually not as crowded, and the windows are bigger, and—unlike the monument's windows—they're open, allowing cool breezes to waft through. (The tour is about 15 minutes long.) ⊠ *Pennsylvania Ave. and 12th St. NW,* ☎ *202/ 606–8691 tower; 202/289–4224 pavilion.* 🎟 *Free.* ☉ *Tower Easter–Labor Day, daily 8 am–11 pm (last tour at*

*10:45); Labor Day–Mar., daily 10–6 (last tour at 5:45).
Metro: Federal Triangle.*

Pennsylvania Avenue. The capital's most historically important thoroughfare will repeatedly thread through your sightseeing walks. Newly inaugurated presidents travel west on Pennsylvania Avenue en route to the White House. Thomas Jefferson started the parade tradition in 1805 after taking the oath of office for his second term. He was accompanied by a few friends and a handful of congressmen. Four years later James Madison made things official by instituting a proper inaugural celebration. The flag holders on the lampposts are clues that Pennsylvania Avenue remains the city's foremost parade route. With the Capitol at one end and the White House at the other, the avenue symbolizes both the distance and the connection between these two branches of government.

❼ Petersen House. Lincoln died in the house of William Petersen, a tailor, on the morning of April 15, 1865. You can see the restored front and back parlors of the house, as well as the bedroom where the president died. Most of the furnishings are not original, but the pillow and bloodstained pillowcases are those used on that fateful night. ⊠ *516 10th St. NW, ☎ 202/426–6830. ☞ Free. ☉ Daily 9–5. Metro: Metro Center.*

Ronald Reagan Building and International Trade Center. This $818 million, 3.1-million-square-ft colossus is the largest federal building to be constructed in the Washington area since the Pentagon. A blend of classical and modern architecture, the Indiana limestone structure with its huge domed corner piece replaced what for 50 years had been an enormous parking lot, an eyesore that interrupted the flow of the buildings of Federal Triangle. At present, the Reagan Building is home to the Environmental Protection Agency, an odd irony considering the building's namesake's dislike for that agency. The building also houses the U.S. Customs Service, U.S. AID, a food court, and space for public functions. Public accessibility has been questioned recently amid new security concerns. ⊠ *1300 Pennsylvania Ave. NW. Metro: Federal Triangle.*

Willard Inter-Continental Hotel. There was a Willard Hotel (☞ Chapter 4) on this spot long before this ornate structure was built in 1901. The original Willard was *the* place to stay in Washington if you were rich or influential (or wanted to give that impression). Abraham Lincoln stayed there while waiting to move into the nearby White House. Julia Ward Howe stayed there during the Civil War and wrote "The Battle Hymn of the Republic" after gazing down from her window to see Union troops drilling on Pennsylvania Avenue. It's said the term "lobbyist" was coined to describe the favor seekers who would buttonhole President Ulysses S. Grant in the hotel's public rooms. The second Willard, its mansard roof dotted with circular windows, was designed by Henry Hardenbergh, architect of New York's Plaza Hotel. Although it was just as opulent as the hotel it replaced, it fell on hard times after World War II. In 1968 it closed, standing empty until 1986, when it reopened, amid much fanfare, after an ambitious restoration. ⊠ *1401 Pennsylvania Ave. NW,* ☎ *202/628–9100.*

Georgetown

Long before the District of Columbia was formed, Georgetown, Washington's oldest neighborhood, was a separate city with a harbor full of ships and warehouses filled with tobacco. Washington has filled in around Georgetown over the years, but the former tobacco port retains an air of aloofness. Its narrow streets, which do not conform to Pierre L'Enfant's plan for the Federal City, make up the capital's wealthiest neighborhood and are the nucleus of its nightlife.

The area that would come to be known as George (after George II), then George Towne, and finally Georgetown, was part of Maryland when it was settled in the early 1700s by Scottish immigrants, many of whom were attracted to the region's tolerant religious climate. Georgetown's position at the farthest point up the Potomac accessible by boat made it an ideal transit and inspection point for farmers who grew tobacco in Maryland's interior. In 1789 the state granted the town a charter, but two years later Georgetown—along with Alexandria, its counterpart in Virginia—was included by George Washington in the Territory of Columbia, site of the new capital.

Finally, a travel companion that doesn't snore on the plane or eat all your peanuts.

123 456 7891 2345
J.D. SMITH

When traveling, your MCI WorldCom Card is the best way to keep in touch. Our operators speak your language, so they'll be able to connect you back home—no matter where your travels take you. Plus, your MCI WorldCom Card is easy to use, and even earns you frequent flyer miles every time you use it. When you add in our great rates, you get something even more valuable: peace-of-mind. So go ahead. Travel the world. MCI WorldCom just brought it a whole lot closer.

You can even sign up today at www.mci.com/worldphone or ask your operator to make a collect call to 1-410-314-2938.

EASY TO CALL WORLDWIDE

1 Just dial the WorldPhone access number of the country you're calling from.
2 Dial or give the operator your MCI WorldCom Card number.
3 Dial or give the number you're calling.

Argentina	
To call using Telefonica	0-800-222-6249
To call using Telecom	0-800-555-1002
Brazil	000-8012
France ◆	0-800-99-0019
Ireland	1-800-55-1001
United Kingdom	
To call using BT	0800-89-0222
To call using CWC	0500-89-0222
United States	1-800-888-8000

For your complete WorldPhone calling guide, dial the WorldPhone access number for the country you're in and ask the operator for Customer Service. In the U.S. call 1-800-431-5402.

◆ Public phones may require deposit of coin or phone card for dial tone.

EARN FREQUENT FLYER MILES

AmericanAirlines®
AAdvantage®

Continental Airlines
OnePass®

▲ Delta Air Lines
SkyMiles®

✈ MILEAGE PLUS®
United Airlines

U·S AIRWAYS
DIVIDEND MILES

MCI WorldCom, its logo and the names of the products referred to herein are proprietary marks of MCI WorldCom, Inc. All airline names and logos are proprietary marks of the respective airlines. All airline program rules and conditions apply.

Distinctive guides packed with up-to-date expert
advice and smart choices for every type of traveler.

Fodor's. For the world of ways you travel.

While Washington struggled, Georgetown thrived. Wealthy traders built their mansions on the hills overlooking the river; merchants and the working class lived in modest homes closer to the water's edge. In 1810 a third of Georgetown's population was black—both free people and slaves. The Mt. Zion United Methodist Church on 29th Street is the oldest black church in the city and was a stop on the Underground Railroad. Georgetown's rich history and success instilled in citizens of both colors a sense of superiority that many feel lingers today. (When Georgetowners thought the dismal capital was dragging them down, they asked to be given back to Maryland, the way Alexandria was given back to Virginia in 1845.) Tobacco eventually became a less important commodity, and Georgetown became a milling center, using water power from the Potomac. When the Chesapeake & Ohio (C&O) Canal was completed in 1850, the city intensified its milling operations and became the eastern end of a waterway that stretched 184 mi to the west. The canal took up some of the slack when Georgetown's harbor began to fill with silt and the port lost business to Alexandria and Baltimore, but the canal never became the success it was meant to be.

In the years that followed, Georgetown was a far cry from the fashionable spot it is today. Clustered near the water were a foundry, a fish market, paper and cotton mills, and a power station for the city's streetcar system, all of which made Georgetown a smelly industrial district. It still had its Georgian, Federal, and Victorian homes, though, and when the New Deal and World War II brought a flood of newcomers to Washington, Georgetown's tree-shaded streets and handsome brick houses were rediscovered. Pushed out in the process were Georgetown's blacks, most of whom rented the houses they lived in.

Today some of Washington's most famous citizens call Georgetown home, including *Washington Post* matriarch Katharine Graham, former *Post* editor Ben Bradlee, and celebrity biographer Kitty Kelley. Georgetown's historic preservationists are among the most vocal in the city. Part of what the activists want protection from is the crush of people who descend on their community every night. This is Washington's center for restaurants, bars, nightclubs, and trendy boutiques. On M Street and Wisconsin Avenue, you can indulge just about any taste and take home almost any upscale souvenir. Harder to find is a parking place.

Georgetown owes some of its charm and separate growth to geography. This town-unto-itself is separated from Washington to the east by Rock Creek. On the south it's bordered by the Potomac, on the west by Georgetown University. How far north does Georgetown reach? Probably not much farther than the large estates and parks above R Street, though developers and real estate agents would be happy to take Georgetown right up to the Canadian border if it increased the value of property along the way.

The lack of a Metro station in Georgetown means you'll have to take a bus or taxi or walk to this part of Washington. It's about a 15-minute walk from the Dupont Circle or Foggy Bottom Metro station. (If you'd rather take a bus, the G2 Georgetown University bus goes from Dupont Circle west along P Street. The 34 and 36 Friendship Heights buses leave from 22nd and Pennsylvania and deposit you at 31st and M.)

Numbers in the margin correspond to numbers on the Georgetown map.

Sights to See

③ C&O Canal. This waterway kept Georgetown open to shipping after its harbor had filled with silt. George Washington was one of the first to advance the idea of a canal linking the Potomac with the Ohio River across the Appalachians. Work started on the C&O Canal in 1828, and when it opened in 1850, its 74 locks linked Georgetown with Cumberland, Maryland, 184 mi to the northwest (still short of its intended destination). Lumber, coal, iron, wheat, and flour moved up and down the canal, but it was never as successful as its planners had hoped it would be. Many of the bridges spanning the canal in Georgetown were too low to allow anything other than fully loaded barges to pass underneath, and competition from the Baltimore & Ohio Railroad eventually spelled an end to profitability. Today the canal is a part of the National Park System, and walkers follow the towpath once used by mules while canoeists paddle the canal's calm waters. Between April and November you can go on a leisurely (about an hour), mule-drawn

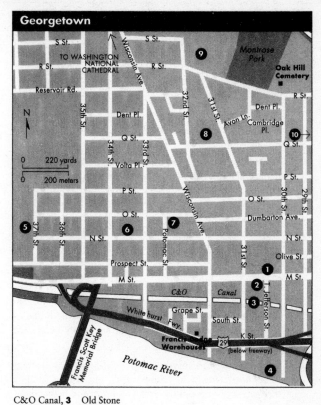

Georgetown

TO WASHINGTON NATIONAL CATHEDRAL

Montrose Park

Oak Hill Cemetery

S St.
R St.
Reservoir Rd.
Wisconsin Ave.
S St.
R St.
R St.
Dent Pl.
Dent Pl.
Cambridge Pl.
32nd St.
31st St.
Avon Ln.
N
0 220 yards
0 200 meters
35th St.
34th St.
33rd St.
30th St.
29th St.
Dent Pl.
Q St.
Volta Pl.
Q St.
P St.
P St.
O St.
O St.
Dumbarton Ave.
N St.
N St.
Olive St.
M St.
M St.
Prospect St.
Potomac St.
Wisconsin Ave.
31st St.
Jefferson St.
37th St.
36th St.
C&O Canal
White hurst Fwy.
Grape St.
South St.
K St.
(below freeway)
Francis Scott Key Memorial Bridge
Potomac River
Francis Scott Key Warehouse
29

C&O Canal, **3**

Cox's Row, **6**

Dumbarton House, **10**

Dumbarton Oaks, **9**

Georgetown University, **5**

Masonic Lodge, **2**

Old Stone House, **1**

St. John's Church, **7**

Tudor Place, **8**

Washington Harbour, **4**

trip aboard the *Georgetown* canal barge. Tickets are available across the canal, next to the Foundry Mall. Barge rides also are available at Great Falls, at the end of MacArthur Boulevard, in nearby Potomac, Maryland. ✉ *1057 Thomas Jefferson St. NW,* ☎ *202/653–5190;* ✉ *11710 MacArthur Blvd., Potomac, MD,* ☎ *301/299–3613.* 🎟 *Barge trip $7.50.* ☉ *June 17–Sept. 7, Wed.–Fri 11, 1, and 2:30, weekends 11, 1, 2:30, and 4. Barge trips Mid-Apr.–June 14 and Sept. 9–Nov. 1, Wed.–Fri. 11 and 2:30, weekends 11, 1, 2:30, and 4.*

❻ Cox's Row. Architecture buffs, especially those interested in Federal and Victorian houses, enjoy wandering along the redbrick sidewalks of upper Georgetown. The average house here has two signs on it: a brass plaque notifying passersby of the building's historic interest and a window decal that warns burglars of its state-of-the-art alarm system. To get a representative taste of the houses in the area, walk along the 3300 block of N Street. The group of five Federal houses between 3339 and 3327 N Street is known collectively as Cox's Row, after John Cox, a former mayor of Georgetown, who built them in 1817. The flat-front redbrick Federal house at 3307 N Street was the home of then-Senator John F. Kennedy and his family before the White House beckoned.

❿ Dumbarton House. Its symmetry and the two curved wings on its north side make Dumbarton, built around 1800, a distinctive example of Georgian architecture. Eight rooms inside Dumbarton House have been restored to Federal-period splendor, with period furnishings such as mahogany American Chippendale chairs, hallmark silver, Persian rugs, and a breakfront cabinet filled with rare books. ✉ *2715 Q St. NW,* ☎ *202/337–2288.* 🎟 *Suggested donation $3.* ☉ *Tues.–Sat. 10–12:15.*

❾ Dumbarton Oaks. In 1944 one of the most important events of the 20th century took place in Dumbarton Oaks, when representatives of the United States, Great Britain, China, and the Soviet Union met in the music room here to lay the groundwork for the United Nations. Career diplomat Robert Woods Bliss and his wife, Mildred, bought the property in 1920 and set about taming the sprawling grounds and removing 19th-century additions that had marred the Federal lines of the 1801 mansion. In 1940 the Blisses conveyed the estate to Harvard University, which maintains world-renowned collections of Byzantine and pre-Columbian art there. Both are small but choice, reflecting the enormous skill and creativity going on at roughly the same time on two sides of the Atlantic. The Byzantine collection includes beautiful examples of both religious and secular items executed in mosaic, metal, enamel, and ivory. Pre-Columbian works—artifacts and textiles from Mexico and Central and South America by such peoples as the Aztec, Maya, and Olmec—are arranged in an enclosed glass pavilion designed by Philip Johnson. Also on view to the public are the lavishly decorated music room and selections from Mrs. Bliss's collection of rare illustrated garden books.

Dumbarton Oaks's 10 acres of formal gardens, one of the loveliest spots in Washington, incorporate elements of traditional English, Italian, and French styles. A full-time crew of a dozen gardeners toils to maintain the stunning collection of terraces, geometric gardens, tree-shaded brick walks, fountains, arbors, and pools. Plenty of well-positioned benches make this a good place for resting weary feet, too. Enter via R Street. ⊠ *Art collections, 1703 32nd St. NW,* ☎ *202/339–6401 or 202/339–6400;* ⊠ *gardens, 31st and R Sts. NW.* 🖅 *Art collections, suggested donation $1; gardens Apr.–Oct. $4, Nov.–Mar. free.* ☉ *Art collections Tues.–Sun. 2–5; gardens Apr.–Oct., daily 2–6; Nov.–Mar., daily 2–5.*

Francis Dodge Warehouses. The last three buildings at the foot of the west side of Wisconsin Avenue are reminders of Georgetown's mercantile past. They were built around 1830 by trader and merchant Francis Dodge. Note the heavy stone foundation of the southernmost warehouse, its star-end braces, and the broken hoist in the gable end. According to an 1838 newspaper ad, Georgetown shoppers could visit Dodge's grocery to buy such items as "Porto Rico Sugar, Marseilles soft-shelled Almonds and Havanna Segars." Although the dry goods of yesteryear have been replaced by small nonprofit organizations, the buildings don't look as if they house modern offices, and their facades make an interesting snapshot.

⑤ Georgetown University. Founded in 1789 by John Carroll, first American bishop and first archbishop of Baltimore, Georgetown is the oldest Jesuit school in the country. About 12,000 students attend Georgetown, known now as much for its perennially successful basketball team as for its fine programs in law, medicine, foreign service, and the liberal arts. When seen from the Potomac or from Washington's high ground, the Gothic spires of Georgetown's older buildings give the university an almost medieval look. ⊠ *37th and O Sts.,* ☎ *202/687–5055.*

② Masonic Lodge. A two-story brick structure, Georgetown's Masonic Lodge, which is not open to visitors, was built around 1810. Freemasonry, the world's largest secret society, was started by British stonemasons and cathedral builders as early as the 14th century; the fraternal order now has a much broader international membership that has included U.S. presidents—among them George Washington—as well as members of Congress. It's no accident that the Freemasons chose Georgetown to be the site of a lodge. Although Georgetown today is synonymous with affluence, for most of its history it was a working-class city, and the original names of its streets—Water Street, the Keys, Fishing Lane—attest to the past importance of traditional trades to the region's economy. Among the lodge's interesting details are a pointed facade and recessed central arch, features that suggest the society's traditional attachment to the building arts. ⊠ *1058 Thomas Jefferson St.*

Oak Hill Cemetery. Oak Hill Cemetery's funerary obelisks, crosses, and gravestones spread out like an amphitheater of the dead on a hill overlooking Rock Creek. Near the entrance is an 1850 Gothic-style chapel designed by Smithsonian Castle architect James Renwick. Across from the chapel is the resting place of actor, playwright, and diplomat John H. Payne, who is remembered today primarily for his song "Home Sweet Home." A few hundred feet to the north is the circular tomb of William Corcoran, founder of the Corcoran Gallery of Art. Cameras and backpacks are not allowed in the cemetery. ⊠ *30th and R Sts. NW,* ☎ *202/337–2835.* ▣ *Free.* ☾ *Weekdays 10–4.*

❶ Old Stone House. What was early American life like? Here's the capital's oldest window into the past. Work on this field-stone house, thought to be Washington's only surviving pre-Revolutionary building, was begun in 1764 by a cabinetmaker named Christopher Layman. The house, now a museum, was used as both a residence and a place of business by a succession of occupants. Five of the house's rooms are furnished with the simple, sturdy artifacts—plain tables, spinning wheels, and so forth—of 18th-century middle-class life. The National Park Service maintains the house and its lovely gardens in the rear, which are planted with fruit trees and perennials. ⊠ *3051 M St. NW,* ☎ *202/426–6851.* 🎟 *Free.* ☉ *Wed.–Sun. 10–4.*

❼ St. John's Church. West of Wisconsin Avenue, a stretch of O Street several blocks long has remnants from an earlier age: cobblestones and streetcar tracks. Residents are so proud of the cobblestones that newer concrete patches have been scored to resemble them. Prominent in this section of Georgetown is St. John's Church, built in 1809 and attributed to Dr. William Thornton, architect of the Capitol. Later alterations have left it looking more Victorian than Federal. St. John's is also noted for its stained-glass windows, including a small Tiffany. ⊠ *3240 O St. NW,* ☎ *202/338–1796.* ☉ *Services Sun. 9 and 11.*

❽ Tudor Place. Stop at Q Street between 31st and 32nd streets; look through the trees to the north, at the top of a sloping lawn; and you'll see the neoclassical Tudor Place, designed by Capitol architect Dr. William Thornton and completed in 1816. On a house tour you'll see items that belonged to George Washington, Francis Scott Key's desk, and spurs belonging to members of the Peter family who were killed in the Civil War. The grounds contain many specimens planted in the early 19th century. The house was built for Thomas Peter, son of Georgetown's first mayor, and his wife, Martha Custis, Martha Washington's granddaughter. It was because of this connection to the president's family that Tudor Place came to house many items from Mount Vernon. The yellow stucco house is interesting for its architecture—especially the dramatic two-story domed portico on the south side—but its familial heritage is even more remarkable: Tudor

Place stayed in the same family for 178 years, until 1983, when Armistead Peter III died. Before his death, Peter established a foundation to restore the house and open it to the public. Tour reservations are advised. ⊠ *1644 31st St. NW,* ☎ *202/965–0400.* 🖃 *Suggested donation $6.* ☽ *House tours Tues.–Fri. at 10, 11:30, 1, and 2:30; Sat. hourly 10–4 (last tour at 3); garden Mon.–Sat. 10–4 (also Apr.–May and Sept.–Oct., Sun. noon–4).*

❹ **Washington Harbour.** Stately columns and the liberal use of glass as a construction material are hallmarks of Washington Harbour, a glittering postmodern riverfront development designed by Arthur Cotton Moore. Included are such restaurants as the two-story Sequoia, Tony & Joe's Seafood Place, and the Riverside Grille, as well as offices, apartments, and upscale shops. Highlights of the central plaza are a large fountain and a futuristic, lighthouselike structure made up of four towering white columns. Several restaurants offer outdoor dining. From the edge of Washington Harbour you can see the Watergate complex and Kennedy Center to the east while the waters of the Potomac gently lap at the edge of the dock. Those who prefer the water to the streets often arrive by boat, docking just yards from outdoor diners. At night, the area sparkles like a Christmas scene with hundreds of twinkling white lights. ⊠ *3000 K St. NW.*

Washington National Cathedral. Construction of Washington National Cathedral, a stunning Gothic church—the sixth-largest cathedral in the world—started in 1907 and was finished on September 30, 1990, when the building was consecrated. Like its 14th-century counterparts, the National Cathedral (officially Washington's Cathedral Church of St. Peter and St. Paul) has a nave, flying buttresses, transepts, and vaults that were built stone by stone. It's adorned with fanciful gargoyles created by skilled stone carvers. The tomb of Woodrow Wilson, the only president buried in Washington, is on the south side of the nave. The expansive view of the city from the Pilgrim Gallery is exceptional. The cathedral is under the governance of the Episcopal Church but has hosted services of many denominations. ⊠ *Wisconsin and Massachusetts Aves. NW,* ☎ *202/537–6200; 202/537–6207 tour information.* 🖃 *Suggested tour donation $3.* ☽ *Labor Day–Memorial Day, daily 10–4:30;*

*Memorial Day–Labor Day, weekdays 10–9, weekends 10–
4:30; Sun. services at 8, 9, 10, 11, and 6:30; evensong at
4; tours every 15 mins Mon.–Sat. 10–11:30 and 12:45–3:15,
Sun. 12:30–2:45.*

Dupont Circle

Three of Washington's main thoroughfares intersect at
Dupont Circle: Connecticut, New Hampshire, and Massachusetts avenues. With a small, handsome park and a
splashing fountain in the center, Dupont Circle is more than
a deserted island around which traffic flows, making it an
exception among Washington circles. The activity spills
over into the surrounding streets, one of the liveliest, most
vibrant neighborhoods in D.C.

Development near Dupont Circle started during the post–
Civil War boom of the 1870s. As the city increased in
stature, the nation's wealthy and influential citizens began
building their mansions near the circle. The area underwent
a different kind of transformation in the middle of the
20th century, when the middle and upper classes deserted
Washington for the suburbs, and in the 1960s the circle became the starting point for rowdy, litter-strewn marches sponsored by countercultural groups. Today the neighborhood
is once again fashionable, and its many restaurants, offbeat
shops, and specialty bookstores lend it a distinctive, cosmopolitan air. Stores and clubs catering to the neighborhood's large gay community are abundant.

*Numbers in the margin correspond to numbers on the
Dupont Circle and Foggy Bottom map.*

Sights to See

❷ **Anderson House.** A palatial home that's a mystery even to
many longtime Washingtonians, who assume it's just another embassy, Anderson House is not an embassy, though
it does have a link to the diplomatic world. Larz Anderson
was a diplomat whose career included postings to Japan
and Belgium. Anderson and his heiress wife, Isabel, toured
the world, picking up objects that struck their fancy. They
filled their residence, which was constructed in 1905, with
the booty of their travels, including choir stalls from an Italian Renaissance church, Flemish tapestries, and a large—

Dupont Circle and Foggy Bottom

KEY

Ⓐ American Express Office

Anderson
House, **2**

Bison Bridge, **3**

B'nai B'rith
Klutznick
Museum, **9**

Council
House, **10**

Department
of State, **15**

Federal
Reserve
Building, **16**

George
Washington
University, **13**

Heurich House
Museum, **1**

Metropolitan
African
Methodist
Episcopal
Church, **11**

National
Academy of
Sciences, **17**

National
Geographic
Society, **12**

National
Museum of
American
Jewish Military
History, **7**

Phillips
Collection, **6**

St. Matthew's
Cathedral, **8**

Textile
Museum, **5**

Watergate, **14**

Woodrow
Wilson
House, **4**

if spotty—collection of Asian art. All this remains in the house for you to see.

In accordance with the Andersons' wishes, the building also serves as the headquarters of a group to which Larz belonged: the Society of the Cincinnati. The oldest patriotic organization in the country, the society was formed in 1783 by a group of officers who had served with George Washington during the Revolutionary War. The group took the name Cincinnati from Cincinnatus, a distinguished Roman who, circa 500 BC, led an army against Rome's enemies and later quelled civil disturbances in the city. After each success, rather than seek political power that could have easily been his, he returned to the simple life on his farm. The story impressed the American officers, who saw in it a mirror of their own situation: they, too, would leave the battlefields to get on with the business of forging a new nation. (One such member went on to name the city in Ohio.) Today's members are direct descendants of those American revolutionaries.

Many of the displays in the society's museum focus on the Colonial period and the Revolutionary War. One room—painted in a marvelous trompe l'oeil style that deceives you into thinking the walls are covered with sculpture—is filled with military miniatures from the United States and France. (Because of the important role France played in defeating the British, French officers were invited to join the society. Pierre L'Enfant, "Artist of the Revolution" and planner of Washington, designed the society's eagle medallion.)

The house is often used by the federal government to entertain visiting dignitaries. Amid the glitz, glamour, beauty, and patriotic spectacle of the mansion are two delightful painted panels in the solarium that depict the Andersons' favorite motorcar sightseeing routes around Washington. ⊠ 2118 Massachusetts Ave. NW, ☎ 202/785–2040. ▣ Free. ☉ Tues.–Sat. 1–4. Metro: Dupont Circle.

Australian Embassy. Many foreign embassies in Washington host art exhibits or cultural programs open to the public. One of the best galleries is at the Australian Embassy, which periodically displays masterpieces from Down Under. If you're lucky, you'll see Aboriginal artifacts and dot paintings of striking originality and beauty, as well as contemporary landscapes and portraits with a uniquely Australian character. ✉ *1601 Massachusetts Ave. NW,* ☎ *202/797–3000.* 🎟 *Free.* ☉ *Weekdays 9–5. Metro: Dupont Circle.*

③ Bison Bridge. Tour guides at the Smithsonian's National Museum of Natural History (☞ The Mall, *above*) are quick to remind you that America never had buffalo; the big, shaggy animals that roamed the plains were bison. (True buffalo are African and Asian animals of the same family.) Although many maps and guidebooks call this the Buffalo Bridge, the four bronze statues by A. Phimister Proctor are of bison. Officially called the Dumbarton Bridge, the structure stretches across Rock Creek Park into Georgetown. Its sides are decorated with busts of Native Americans, the work of architect Glenn Brown, who, along with his son Bedford, designed the bridge in 1914. The best way to see the busts is to walk the footpath along Rock Creek. ✉ *23rd and Q Sts. NW. Metro: Dupont Circle.*

⑨ B'nai B'rith Klutznick Museum. Devoted to the history of Jewish people, this museum's permanent exhibits span 20 centuries and highlight Jewish festivals and the rituals employed to mark the stages of life. A wide variety of Jewish decorative art, adorning such items as spice boxes and Torah covers, is on display. Changing exhibits highlight the work of contemporary Jewish artists. ✉ *1640 Rhode Island Ave. NW,* ☎ *202/857–6583.* 🎟 *Suggested donation $2.* ☉ *Sun.–Fri. 10–4:30. Metro: Dupont Circle or Farragut North.*

Cameroon Embassy. The westernmost of the Beaux Arts–style mansions built along Massachusetts Avenue in the late-19th and early 20th centuries today houses the Cameroon Embassy. The building is a fanciful castle with a conical tower, bronze weather vane, and intricate detailing around the windows and balconies. ✉ *2349 Massachusetts Ave. Metro: Dupont Circle.*

Charles Sumner School. Built in 1872 for the education of black children, the Charles Sumner School takes its name from the Massachusetts senator who delivered a blistering attack against slavery in 1856 and was savagely caned as a result by a congressman from South Carolina. The build-

ing was designed by Adolph Cluss, who created the Arts and
Industries Building on the Washington Mall. It's typical of
the District's Victorian-era public schools. Beautifully restored
in 1986, the school serves mainly as a conference center,
though it hosts changing art exhibits and houses a permanent collection of memorabilia relating to the city's public
school system. ⊠ *1201 17th St. NW,* ☎ *202/727–3419.* ▤
Free. ⊙ *Tues.–Fri. 10–5; often closed for conferences. Metro:
Farragut North.*

⑩ Council House. Exhibits in this museum focus on the achieve-
ments of black women, including Mary McLeod Bethune,
who founded Florida's Bethune-Cookman College, established the National Council of Negro Women, and served
as an adviser to President Franklin D. Roosevelt. ⊠ *1318
Vermont Ave. NW,* ☎ *202/673–2402.* ▤ *Free.* ⊙ *Mon.–
Sat. 10–4. Metro: McPherson Square.*

Dupont Circle. Originally known as Pacific Circle, this hub
was the westernmost circle in Pierre L'Enfant's original design for the Federal City. The name was changed in 1884,
when Congress authorized construction of a bronze statue
honoring Civil War hero Admiral Samuel F. Dupont. The
statue fell into disrepair, and Dupont's family—who had
never liked it anyway—replaced it in 1921. The marble fountain—with allegorical figures of Sea, Stars, and Wind—that
stands in its place was created by Daniel Chester French,
the sculptor of Lincoln's statue in the Lincoln Memorial.

As you look around the circumference of the circle, you'll
see the special constraints within which architects in Washington must work. Since a half dozen streets converge on
Dupont Circle, the buildings around it are, for the most part,
wedge-shape and set on plots of land shaped like massive
slices of pie. Only two of the great houses that stood on
the circle in the early 20th century remain today. The Renaissance-style house at **15 Dupont Circle,** next to P Street,
was built in 1903 for Robert W. Patterson, publisher of the
Washington Times-Herald. Patterson's daughter, Cissy,
who succeeded him as publisher, was known for hosting
parties that attracted such notables as William Randolph
Hearst, Douglas MacArthur, and J. Edgar Hoover. In 1948
Cissy willed the house to the American Red Cross, and the

Washington Club, a private club, bought it from the organization in 1951. The **Sulgrave Club,** at the corner of Massachusetts Avenue, was also once a private home and is now likewise a private club. *Metro: Dupont Circle.*

Fondo Del Sol Visual Arts Center. A nonprofit museum devoted to the cultural heritage of the Americas, the Fondo Del Sol Visual Arts Center has changing exhibitions covering contemporary, pre-Columbian, and folk art. The museum also offers a program of lectures, concerts, poetry readings, exhibit tours, and an annual summer festival featuring salsa and reggae music. ✉ *2112 R St. NW,* ☎ *202/483–2777.* 🎫 *$3.* ◷ *Wed.–Sat. 12:30–5:30. Metro: Dupont Circle.*

❶ **Heurich House Museum.** Currently housing the Historical Society of Washington, D.C., this opulent Romanesque Revival was the home of Christian Heurich, a German orphan who made his fortune in this country in the beer business. Heurich's brewery was in Foggy Bottom, where the Kennedy Center stands today. Brewing was a dangerous business in the 19th century, and fires more than once reduced Heurich's brewery to ashes. Perhaps because of this he insisted that his home, completed in 1894, be fireproof. Although 17 fireplaces were installed—some with onyx facings, one with the bronze image of a lion staring out from the back—not a single one ever held a fire.

After Heurich's widow died in 1955, the house was turned over to the historical society and today houses a research library and museum. Most of the furnishings in the house were owned and used by the Heurichs. The interior is an eclectic Victorian treasure trove of plaster detailing, carved wooden doors, and painted ceilings. The downstairs breakfast room, in which Heurich, his wife, and their three children ate most of their meals, is decorated like a rathskeller and is adorned with such German sayings as "A good drink makes old people young." Heurich must have taken the German proverbs seriously. He drank his beer every day, had three wives (not all at once), and lived to be 102. Tours are self-guided, or you can make an advance request for a guided tour. The docents who give these tours are also adept at answering questions about other Washington landmarks. ⊠ *1307 New Hampshire Ave. NW,* ☎ *202/785–2068.* ⛁ *$3.* ⊙ *Mon.–Sat. 10–4. Metro: Dupont Circle.*

Islamic Mosque and Cultural Center. The Muslim faithful are called to prayer five times a day from atop the 162-ft-high minaret of the Islamic Mosque and Cultural Center. Each May, the Muslim Women's Association sponsors a bazaar, with crafts, clothing, and food for sale. Visitors wearing shorts will not be admitted to the mosque; women must wear scarves to cover their heads. ⊠ *2551 Massachusetts Ave. NW,* ☎ *202/332–8343.* ⊙ *Center daily 10–5; mosque open for all 5 prayers, dawn–after sunset.*

⑪ **Metropolitan African Methodist Episcopal Church.** Completed in 1886, the Gothic-style Metropolitan African Methodist Episcopal Church became one of the most influential black churches in the city. Abolitionist orator Frederick Douglass worshiped here, and Bill Clinton chose the church as the setting for both of his inaugural prayer services. ⊠ *1518 M St. NW,* ☎ *202/331–1426. Metro: Farragut North.*

☝ ⑫ **National Geographic Society.** Founded in 1888, the society is best known for its yellow-border magazine, found in doctor's offices, family rooms, and attics across the country. The society has sponsored numerous expeditions throughout its 100-year history, including those of Admirals Peary and Byrd and underwater explorer Jacques Cousteau. Explorers Hall, entered from 17th Street, is the magazine come to life. It invites you to learn about the world in a decidedly interactive way: you can experience everything from a minitornado to video touch-screens that explain geographic concepts and then quiz you on what you've learned. The most dramatic events take place in Earth Station One, a 72-seat amphitheater that sends the audience on a journey around the world. The centerpiece is a hand-painted globe, 11 ft in diameter, that floats and spins on a cushion of air, showing off different features of the planet. ⊠ *17th and M Sts.,* ☎ *202/857–7588; 202/857–7689 group tours.* ⛁ *Free.* ⊙ *Mon.–Sat. 9–5, Sun. 10–5. Metro: Farragut North.*

⑦ **National Museum of American Jewish Military History.** The museum's focus is on American Jews who have served in every war the nation has fought. On display are their weapons, uniforms, medals, recruitment posters, and other military memorabilia. The few specifically religious items—a camouflage yarmulke, rabbinical supplies fashioned from shell casings and parachute silk—underscore the strange demands placed on religion during war. ⊠ *1811 R St. NW,* ☎ *202/265–6280.* ⊡ *Free.* ☉ *Weekdays 9–5, Sun. 1–5. Metro: Dupont Circle.*

❻ Phillips Collection. The first permanent museum of modern art in the country, the masterpiece-filled Phillips Collection is unique in both origin and content. In 1918 Duncan Phillips, grandson of a founder of the Jones and Laughlin Steel Company, started to collect art for a museum that would stand as a memorial to his father and brother, who had died within 13 months of each other. Three years later what was first called the Phillips Memorial Art Gallery opened in two rooms of this Georgian Revival home near Dupont Circle.

Not interested in a painting's market value or its faddishness, Phillips searched for works that impressed him as outstanding products of a particular artist's unique vision. Holdings include works by Georges Braque, Paul Cézanne, Paul Klee, Henri Matisse, and John Henry Twachtman, and the largest museum collection in the country of the work of Pierre Bonnard. The exhibits change regularly. The collection's best-known paintings include Renoir's *Luncheon of the Boating Party, Repentant Peter* by both Goya and El Greco, *A Bowl of Plums* by 18th-century artist Jean-Baptiste Siméon Chardin, Degas's *Dancers at the Bar,* Vincent van Gogh's *Entrance to the Public Garden at Arles,* and Cézanne's self-portrait, the painting Phillips said he would save first if his gallery caught fire. During the '20s, Phillips and his wife, Marjorie, started to support American Modernists such as John Marin, Georgia O'Keeffe, and Arthur Dove. On Thursday, the museum stays open late, enticing people with live jazz, gallery talks, and a cash bar. ⊠ *1600 21st St. NW,* ☎ *202/387–2151.* ⊡ *$6.50; Thurs. night $5; some exhibitions may require an additional charge.* ☉ *Tues.–Wed. and Fri.–Sat. 10–5; Thurs. 10–8:30; Sun. noon–7 (noon–5 June–Aug.); tour Wed. and Sat. at 2; gallery talks 1st and 3rd Thurs. of month at 12:30. Metro: Dupont Circle.*

Russian Embassy. Here's where some of the Cold War's most famous spies were based and where some of the most notorious American traitors sought sanctuary. For example, John A. Walker Jr., the onetime navy warrant officer who eventually enlisted the help of his son, his brother, and his best friend in his spying activities, walked into the embassy in October 1967 with a list of codes for U.S. military cipher machines. The ornate mansion was originally built for the widow of George Pullman of railroad-car fame. It first did diplomatic duty as the Imperial Russian Embassy, then became the Soviet Embassy, and now is the Russian once again. The rest of the former Soviet republics were left scrambling for their own embassies after the breakup of the USSR in 1991. ⊠ *1125 16th St. NW. Metro: Farragut North.*

❽ St. Matthew's Cathedral. St. Matthew's is the seat of Washington's Catholic archbishop. John F. Kennedy frequently worshiped in this Renaissance-style church, and in 1963 his funeral mass was held within its richly decorated walls. Set in the floor, directly in front of the main altar, is a memorial to the slain president: "Here rested the remains of President Kennedy at the requiem mass November 25, 1963, before their removal to Arlington, where they lie in expectation of a heavenly resurrection." A memorial to nuns who served as nurses during the Civil War is across Rhode Island Avenue. ⊠ *1725 Rhode Island Ave. NW,* ☎ *202/ 347–3215.* 🎟 *Free.* ☉ *Weekdays and Sun. 7–6:30, Sat. 8–6:30; tour usually Sun. at 2:30. Metro: Farragut North.*

❺ Textile Museum. In the 1890s, founder George Hewitt Myers purchased his first Oriental rug for his dorm room at Yale. An heir to the Bristol-Myers fortune, Myers and his wife lived two houses down from Woodrow Wilson, at 2310 S Street, in a home designed by John Russell Pope, architect of the National Archives and the Jefferson Memorial. Myers bought the Waddy Wood–designed house next door, at No. 2320, and opened his museum to the public in 1925. Today the collection includes more than 15,500 rugs and textiles. Rotating exhibits are taken from a permanent collection of historic and ethnographic items that include Coptic and pre-Columbian textiles, Kashmir embroidery, and Turkman tribal rugs. At least one show of modern textiles—such as quilts or fiber art—is mounted each year. The Activity Gallery in the new Textile Learning Center has hands-on exhibits and activities. You can look at several textile techniques, then try your hand at doing them yourself. ⊠ *2320 S St. NW,* ☎ *202/667–0441.* ☞ *Suggested donation $5.* ☼ *Mon.–Sat. 10–5, Sun. 1–5; highlight tour Sept.–May, Wed. and weekends at 1:30. Metro: Dupont Circle.*

❹ Woodrow Wilson House. Wilson is the only president who stayed in D.C. after leaving the White House. (He's also the only president buried in the city, inside the National Cathedral.) He and his second wife, Edith Bolling Wilson, retired in 1920 to this Georgian Revival designed by Washington architect Waddy B. Wood. President Wilson suffered a stroke toward the end of his second term, in 1919, and he lived out the last few years of his life on this quiet street.

Wilson died in 1924. Edith survived him by 37 years. After she died in 1961, the house and its contents were bequeathed to the National Trust for Historic Preservation. On view inside are such items as a Gobelin tapestry, a baseball signed by King George V, and the shell casing from the first shot fired by U.S. forces in World War I. The house also contains memorabilia related to the history of the short-lived League of Nations, including the colorful flag Wilson hoped would be adopted by that organization. ⊠ *2340 S St. NW,* ☎ *202/387–4062.* ☞ *$5.* ☼ *Tues.–Sun. 10–4. Metro: Dupont Circle.*

Foggy Bottom

The Foggy Bottom area of Washington—bordered roughly by the Potomac and Rock Creek to the west, 20th Street to the east, Pennsylvania Avenue to the north, and Constitution Avenue to the south—has three main claims to fame: the State Department, the Kennedy Center, and George Washington University. In 1763 a German immigrant named Jacob Funk purchased this land, and a community called Funkstown sprang up on the Potomac. This nickname is only slightly less amusing than the present one, an appellation derived from the wharves, breweries, lime kilns, and glassworks that were near the water. Smoke from these factories combined with the swampy air of the low-lying ground to produce a permanent fog along the waterfront.

The smoke-belching factories ensured work for the hundreds of German and Irish immigrants who settled in Foggy Bottom in the 19th century. By the 1930s, however, industry was on the way out, and Foggy Bottom had become a poor part of Washington. The opening of the State Department headquarters in 1947 reawakened middle-class interest in the neighborhood's modest row houses. Many of them are now gone, and Foggy Bottom today suffers from a split personality as tiny, one-room-wide row houses sit next to large, mixed-use developments.

Although the Foggy Bottom neighborhood has its own Metro stop, many attractions are a considerable distance away. If you don't relish long walks or time is limited, check the Foggy Bottom map to see if you need to make alternate travel arrangements to visit specific sights.

Numbers in the margin correspond to numbers on the Dupont Circle and Foggy Bottom map.

Sights to See

American Pharmaceutical Association. You might think the American Pharmaceutical Association is a rather odd sightseeing recommendation, even just for a casual glance as you're passing. But aside from the fact that the white-marble building was designed in 1934 by noted architect John Russell Pope, who also designed the Lincoln Memorial and the National Gallery of Art, the American Pharmaceutical Association is as much a symbol of modern Washington as any government edifice. It's the home of one of more than 3,000 trade and professional associations (as obscure as the Cast Iron Soil Pipe Institute and as well known as the National Association of Broadcasters) that have chosen the capital for their headquarters, eager to represent their members' interests before the government. ⊠ *Constitution Ave. and 23rd St. Metro: Foggy Bottom.*

⓯ Department of State. The foreign policy of the United States is formulated and administered by battalions of brainy analysts in the huge Department of State Building (often referred to as the State Department), which also serves as the headquarters of the United States Diplomatic Corps. All is presided over by the secretary of state, who is fourth in line for the presidency (after the vice president, speaker of the House, and president *pro tempore* of the Senate, respectively) should the president be unable to serve. On the top floor are the opulent Diplomatic Reception Rooms, decorated in the manner of great halls of Europe, and the rooms of Colonial American plantations. The museum-quality furnishings include a Philadelphia highboy, a Paul Revere bowl, and the desk on which the Treaty of Paris was signed. The largest room has a specially loomed carpet so heavy and large it had to be airlifted in by helicopter. The rooms are used 15–20 times a week to entertain foreign diplomats and heads of state; you can see them, too, but you need to register for a tour well ahead of your visit. Summer tours must be booked up to three months in advance. ⌧ *23rd and C Sts. NW,* ☎ *202/647–3241; 202/736–4474 TDD.* ⌧ *Free.* ☉ *Tours weekdays at 9:30, 10:30, and 2:45. Metro: Foggy Bottom.*

⓰ Federal Reserve Building. Whether interest rates are raised or lowered in attempts to control the economy is decided in this imposing marble edifice, its bronze entryway topped by a massive eagle. Designed by Folger Library architect Paul Cret, "the Fed" is on Constitution Avenue between 21st and 20th streets. It seems to say, "Your money's safe with us." Even so, there isn't any money here: Ft. Knox holds most of the government's gold. The stolid Fed is a bit more human inside, with a varied collection of art and four special art exhibitions every year. A 45-minute tour includes a film that attempts to explain exactly what it is that the Fed does. ⌧ *Enter on C St. between 20th and 21st Sts.,* ☎ *202/452–3000; 202/452–3149 building tours; 202/452–3686 art tours.* ⌧ *Free.* ☉ *Weekdays 11–2 during art exhibitions (tours of permanent art collection by appointment only); building tour Thurs. at 2:30. Metro: Foggy Bottom.*

⓭ George Washington University. George Washington had always hoped the capital would be home to a world-class university. He even left 50 shares of stock in the Patowmack Canal Co. to endow it. Congress never acted upon his wishes, however, and it wasn't until 1822 that the university that would eventually be named after the first president began to take shape. The private Columbian College in the District of Columbia opened that year with the aim of training students for the Baptist ministry. In 1904 the university shed its Baptist connections and changed its name to George Washington University. In 1912 it moved to its present location and since that time has become the second largest landholder in the District (after the federal government). Students have ranged from J. Edgar Hoover to Jacqueline Bouvier. In addition to its modern university buildings, GWU occupies many 19th-century houses. ⊠ *Downtown campus covers much of Foggy Bottom south of Pennsylvania Ave. between 19th and 24th Sts. Metro: Foggy Bottom.*

John F. Kennedy Center for the Performing Arts. The opening of the Kennedy Center in 1971 instantly established the capital as a cultural mecca on an international scale. Concerts, ballets, opera, musicals, and drama are presented in the center's five theaters, and movies are screened almost every night in the theater of the American Film Institute. In addition to the regular performances in the five theaters, each year the Kennedy Center also produces a variety of festivals highlighting different musical traditions and cultures. The hugely popular annual open house is a free daylong extravaganza of theater, dance, and music, with nonstop entertainment both indoors and outdoors. There also are free performances every evening at 6 on the Millennium Stage.

Some critics have called the center's square design unimaginative—it has been dubbed the cake box that the more decorative Watergate came in—but no one can deny that the building is immense. The Grand Foyer, lighted by 18 one-ton Orrefors crystal chandeliers, is 630 ft long. (Even at this size it's mobbed at intermission.) Many of the center's furnishings were donated by foreign countries: the chandeliers came from Sweden; the tapestries on the walls came from Brazil, France, and Mexico; and the 3,700 tons of white Carrara marble for the interior and exterior of the building were a gift from Italy. Flags fly in the Hall of Nations and the Hall of States, and in the center of the foyer is a 7-ft-high bronze bust of Kennedy by sculptor Robert Berks. ⊠ *New Hampshire Ave. and Rock Creek Pkwy. NW,* ☎ *202/467–4600.* 🎫 *Free.* ☉ *Daily 10–9 (or until last show lets out); box office Mon.–Sat. 10–9, Sun. noon–9; tours daily 10–1. Metro: Foggy Bottom.*

⑰ **National Academy of Sciences.** Inscribed in Greek under the cornice is a quotation from Aristotle on the value of science—appropriate for a building that houses the offices of the National Academy of Sciences, the National Academy of Engineering, the Institute of Medicine, and the National Research Council. There are often free art exhibits—not all of them relating to science—and weekend concerts. In front of the academy is Robert Berks's sculpture of Albert Einstein, done in the same lumpy, mashed-potato style as the artist's bust of JFK in the Kennedy Center. ⊠ *2101 Constitution Ave. NW,* ☎ *202/334–2000.* 🎫 *Free.* 🕐 *Weekdays 8:30–5. Metro: Foggy Bottom.*

⑭ **Watergate.** Thanks to the events that took place on the night of June 17, 1972, the Watergate is possibly the world's most notorious apartment-office complex. As Nixon aides E. Howard Hunt Jr. and G. Gordon Liddy sat in the Howard Johnson Motor Lodge across the street, five of their men were caught trying to bug the Democratic National Committee headquarters on the building's sixth floor, in an attempt to subvert the democratic process on behalf of the then-president of the United States. A marketing company occupies the space today. ⊠ *2600 Virginia Ave. Metro: Foggy Bottom.*

Adams-Morgan/Cleveland Park

Cleveland Park, a tree-shaded neighborhood in northwest Washington, owes its name to onetime summer resident Grover Cleveland, who established a summer White House on Newark Street between 35th and 36th streets. Many prominent Washingtonians followed suit. Today the neighborhood's attractive houses and suburban character are popular with Washington professionals.

Southeast of Cleveland Park, Adams-Morgan (roughly, the blocks north of Florida Avenue, between Connecticut Avenue and 16th Street NW) is Washington's most ethnically diverse neighborhood. And as is so often the case, that means it's one of Washington's most interesting areas—home to a veritable United Nations of cuisines, offbeat shops, and funky bars and clubs. There's no Metro stop in Adams-Morgan; it's a 15-minute walk from the Woodley Park/Zoo Metro station: walk south on Connecticut, then turn left on Calvert Street, and cross over Rock Creek Park on the Duke Ellington Bridge. Or you can get off at the Dupont Circle Metro stop and walk east to (and turn left onto) 18th Street. The heart of Adams-Morgan is at the crossroads of Adams Mill Road, Columbia Road, and 18th Street.

Numbers in the margin correspond to numbers on the Adams-Morgan/Cleveland Park map.

Sights to See

❹ District of Columbia Arts Center. A combination art gallery and performance space, the DCAC exhibits the cutting-edge work of local artists and is the host of offbeat plays, including that uncategorizable category known as performance art. ⊠ *2438 18th St. NW,* ☎ *202/462–7833.* ☞ *Gallery free, performance costs vary.* ⊙ *Wed.–Thurs. 2–6, Fri.–Sun. 2–10, and during performances (generally Thurs.–Sun. 7 pm–midnight).*

❶ Hillwood Museum and Gardens. Hillwood House, cereal heiress Marjorie Merriweather Post's 40-room Georgian mansion, contains a large collection of 18th- and 19th-century French and Russian decorative art that includes gold and silver work, icons, lace, tapestries, china, and Fabergé eggs. The grounds are composed of lawns, formal French and Japanese gardens, and paths that wind through plantings of azaleas, laurels, and rhododendrons. Make reservations for the house tour well in advance. Hillwood is one or two Metro stops from the zoo, depending on which station you use. The house and gardens are closed for renovation until the spring of 2000, but lecture, music, and travel programs will continue. ⊠ *4155 Linnean Ave. NW,* ☎ *202/686–5807 or 202/686–8500.* ☞ *House and grounds $10; grounds only $2.* ⊙ *House tours Mar.–Jan., Tues.–Sat. 9:30–3; grounds Mar.–Jan., Tues.–Sat. 9–5. Metro: Van Ness/UDC.*

❷ Kennedy-Warren. Art Deco lovers won't want to miss the Kennedy-Warren. The apartment house is a superb example of the style, with such period detailing as decorative alu-

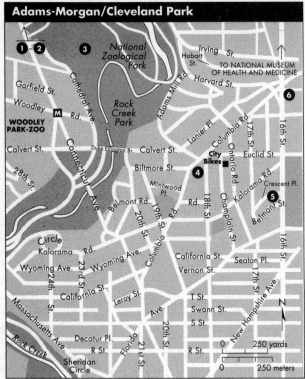

Adams-Morgan/Cleveland Park

National Zoological Park

Rock Creek Park

TO NATIONAL MUSEUM OF HEALTH AND MEDICINE

Irving St.
Hobart St.
Harvard St.

Garfield St.
Woodley
WOODLEY PARK-ZOO
Cathedral Ave.
Rd.
Calvert St.
28th St.
Connecticut Ave.
Duke Ellington Br.
Calvert St.
Biltmore St.
Mintwood Pl.
Belmont Rd.
20th St.
19th St.

Lanier Pl.
Columbia Rd.
17th St.
16th St.
Ontario Rd.
Euclid St.
City Bikes
18th St.
Champlain St.
Kalorama Rd.
Crescent Pl.
Belmont St.

Circle
Kalorama
Rd.
Wyoming Ave.
23rd St.
24th St.
Wyoming Ave.
Columbia
California St.
Rd.
Ave.
18th St.
California St.
Vernon St.
Seaton Pl.
17th St.
16th St.

Massachusetts Ave.
Rock Creek
Leroy St.
California St.
Decatur Pl.
R St.
Florida
21st St.
Sheridan Circle
20th St.
T St.
Swann St.
S St.
R St.
New Hampshire Ave.

N

0   250 yards
0   250 meters

District of
Columbia Arts
Center, **4**

Hillwood
Museum and
Gardens, **1**

Kennedy-
Warren, **2**

Meridian House
and the
White-Meyer
House, **5**

Mexican
Cultural
Institute, **6**

National
Zoological
Park, **3**

minum panels and a streamlined entryway, stone griffins under the pyramidal copper roof, and stylized carved eagles flanking the driveways. Perhaps in keeping with its elegant architecture, this is one of the last apartment buildings in town still to have a doorman. ⊠ *3133 Connecticut Ave. NW. Metro: Cleveland Park.*

❺ Meridian House and the White-Meyer House. Meridian International Center, a nonprofit institution promoting international understanding, owns two handsome mansions designed by John Russell Pope. The 30-room Meridian House was built in 1920 by Irwin Boyle Laughlin, scion of a Pittsburgh steel family and former ambassador to Spain. The Louis XVI–style home features parquet floors, ornamental iron grillwork, handsome moldings, period furniture, tapestries, and a garden planted with European linden trees. Next door is the Georgian-style house built for Henry White (former ambassador to France) that was later the home of the Meyer family, publishers of the *Washington Post.* The first floors of both houses are open to the public and are the scene of periodic art exhibits with an international flavor. ⊠ *1630 and 1624 Crescent Pl. NW,* ☎ *202/ 667–6800.* ⊑ *Free.* ⊙ *Wed.–Sun. 2–5.*

❻ Mexican Cultural Institute. In a glorious 1911 Italianate house that was once the mbassy of Mexico, the Mexican Cultural Institute's exhibits have included works by 19th- and 20th-century Mexican artists such as Diego Rivera, José Clemente Orozco, David Alfaro, and Juan O'Gorman. ⊠ *2829 16th St. NW,* ☎ *202/728–1628.* ⊑ *Free.* ⊙ *Tues.–Sat. 11–5.*

☙ ❸ National Zoological Park. Part of the Smithsonian Institution, the National Zoo is one of the foremost zoos in the world. Created by an Act of Congress in 1889, the 163-acre park was designed by landscape architect Frederick Law Olmsted, the man who designed the U.S. Capitol grounds. (Before the zoo opened in 1890, live animals used as taxidermists' models had been kept on the Mall.) For years the zoo's most famous residents were giant pandas Hsing-Hsing and Ling-Ling, gifts from China in 1972. But female Ling-Ling died of heart failure in 1993 at age 23. Sympathy cards poured in from all over the country, the zoo tried in vain to fertilize some of Ling-Ling's extracted eggs, and her body was donated to the Museum of Natural History.

The zoo has had success breeding numerous other species, however, including red pandas, Pere David's deer, golden lion tamarins, and pygmy hippopotamuses. The National Zoo was the first non-Indonesian zoo to successfully breed Komodo dragons. Innovative compounds show many animals in naturalistic settings, including the Great Flight Cage—a walk-in aviary in which birds fly unrestricted during May–October (they're moved indoors during the colder months). Zoolab, the Reptile Discovery Center, and the Bird Resource Center all offer activities that teach young visitors about biology. The most ambitious addition to the zoo is Amazonia, a reproduction of a South American rain-forest ecosystem. Fish swim behind glass walls, while overhead, monkeys and birds flit from tree to tree. The temperature is a constant 85° F, with 85% humidity. The Cheetah Conservation Area is a grassy compound that's home to a family of the world's fastest cats. Amazonia and the Cheetah Conservation Area, as well as the Gorilla Outdoor Yard and the Sea Lion Exhibit, are the most visible attempts by the zoo to show animals in more naturalistic settings and heighten your appreciation of those environments. ⊠ *3000 block of Connecticut Ave. NW,* ☎ *202/673–4800 or 202/ 673–4717.* 🎟 *Free.* ⏰ *May 1–Sept. 15, grounds daily 6 am– 8 pm, animal buildings daily 10–6 (may be open later in summer); Sept. 16–Apr. 30, grounds daily 6–6, animal buildings daily 10–4:30. Metro: Cleveland Park or Woodley Park/Zoo.*

🔄 **Rock Creek Park.** The 1,800 acres of park on either side of Rock Creek have provided a cool oasis for D.C. residents ever since Congress set them aside in 1890. Bicycle routes and hiking and equestrian trails wind through the groves of dogwoods, beeches, oaks, and cedar, and 30 picnic areas are scattered about. Rangers at the **Nature Center and Planetarium** (⊠ South of Military Rd. at 5200 Glover Rd. NW, ☎ 202/426–6829) introduce the park and list daily events; guided nature walks leave from the center weekends at 2. A highlight of the park is **Pierce Mill** (⊠ Rock Creek Park at Tilden St. and Beach Dr., ☎ 202/426–6908). The mill has been undergoing restoration and is expected to be open soon. Other park features include remnants of the orig-

inal ring of forts that guarded Washington during the Civil
War, and the Rock Creek Park Golf Course, an 18-hole public course. **Meridian Hill Park,** which is part of Rock Creek
Park, contains elements of parks in France, Italy, and
Switzerland. It's also unofficially known as Malcolm X Park,
renamed by the D.C. Council in the 1970s in honor of Malcolm X, who once spoke here. Drug activity once made it
unwise to visit this park alone. It's somewhat safer now,
but avoid it after dark. ✉ *16th and Euclid Sts. NW,* ☎ *202/
282–1063.*

Woodley Park. The stretch of Connecticut Avenue south
of the **National Zoological Park** (☞ *above*) is bordered by
venerable apartment buildings. Passing Cathedral Avenue
(the first cross street south of the zoo), you enter a part of
town known as Woodley Park. Like Cleveland Park to the
north, Woodley Park grew as the streetcar advanced into
this part of Washington. In 1800 Philip Barton Key, uncle
of Francis Scott Key, built **Woodley,** a Georgian mansion
on Cathedral Avenue between 29th and 31st streets. The
white stucco mansion was the summer home of four presidents: Van Buren, Tyler, Buchanan, and Cleveland. It's
now owned by the private Maret School. *Metro: Woodley
Park/Zoo.*

Around Washington, D.C.

The Virginia suburb of Arlington County was once part of
the District of Columbia. Carved out of the Old Domin-
ion when Washington was created, it was returned to Virginia along with the rest of the land west of the Potomac
in 1845. Washington hasn't held a grudge, though, and there
are three attractions in Arlington—each linked to the military—that should be a part of any complete visit to the nation's capital: Arlington National Cemetery, the U.S. Marine
Corps War Memorial, and the Pentagon. All are accessible by Metro, and a trip across the Potomac makes an en-
joyable half day of sightseeing.

Just a short Metro ride (or bike ride) from Washington, Old
Town Alexandria attracts those who seek a break from the
monuments and hustle-and-bustle of the District and who
are interested in an encounter with America's Colonial

heritage. Founded in 1749 by Scottish merchants eager to capitalize on the booming tobacco trade, Alexandria emerged as one of the most important Colonial ports. The city's history is linked to the most significant events and personages of the Colonial and Revolutionary periods. This colorful past is still alive in restored 18th- and 19th-century homes, churches, and taverns; on the cobbled streets; and on the revitalized waterfront, where clipper ships dock and artisans display their wares. The quickest way to get to Old Town is to take the Metro to the King Street stop (about 25 minutes from Metro Center). If you're driving, you can take either the George Washington Memorial Parkway or Jefferson Davis Highway (Route 1) south from Arlington.

Arlington

Arlington House. The somber plot of land composing Arlington Cemetery hasn't always been a cemetery. It was in Arlington that the two most famous names in Virginia history—Washington and Lee—became intertwined. George Washington Parke Custis—raised by Martha and George Washington, his grandmother and step-grandfather—built Arlington House (also known as the Custis-Lee Mansion), one of the area's best examples of Greek Revival architecture, between 1802 and 1817 on his 1,100-acre estate overlooking the Potomac. After his death, the property went to his daughter, Mary Anna Randolph Custis. In 1831, Mary married Robert E. Lee, a graduate of West Point. For the next 30 years the Custis-Lee family lived at Arlington House.

In 1861, Lee was offered command of the Union forces. He declined, insisting that he could never take up arms against his native Virginia. The Lees left Arlington House that spring, never to return. Union troops soon occupied the estate, making it the headquarters of the officers who were charged with defending Washington. When Mrs. Lee was unable to appear in person to pay a $92.07 government property tax, the Lees forfeited the property. The government purchased the house and land at open auction in 1863. In June 1864 a portion of the property was set aside as a military cemetery. In 1955 Arlington House was designated a memorial to Robert E. Lee. It looks much as it did in the 19th century, and a quick tour will take you past objects once owned by the Custises and the Lees. ⊠ *Between Lee and Sherman Drs.,* ☎ *703/557–0613.* ✉ *Free.* ⊙ *Daily 9:30–4:30.*

Arlington National Cemetery. Some 250,000 American war dead, as well as many notable Americans (among them Presidents William Howard Taft and John F. Kennedy, General John Pershing, and Admiral Robert E. Peary), are interred in these 612 acres across the Potamac River from Washington, established as the nation's cemetery in 1864. While you're at Arlington you'll probably hear the clear, doleful sound of a trumpet playing taps or the sharp reports of a gun salute. Approximately 15 funerals are held daily (it's projected that the cemetery will be filled in 2020). Although not the largest cemetery in the country, Arlington is certainly the best known, a place where you can trace America's history through the aftermath of its battles.

To get here, you can take the Metro, travel on a Tourmobile bus, or walk across Memorial Bridge from the District (southwest of the Lincoln Memorial). If you're driving, there's a large paid parking lot at the skylit visitor center on Memorial Drive. Stop at the center for a free brochure with a detailed map of the cemetery. If you're looking for a specific grave, the staff will consult microfilm records and give you directions on how to find it. You should know the deceased's full name and, if possible, his or her branch of service and year of death.

Tourmobile tour buses leave from just outside the visitor center April 1–September 30, daily 8:30–6:30; and October 1–March 31, daily 8:30–4:30. You can buy tickets here for the 40-minute tour of the cemetery, which includes stops at the Kennedy grave sites, the Tomb of the Unknowns, and Arlington House. Touring the cemetery on foot means a fair bit of hiking, but it will give you a closer look at some of the thousands of graves spread over these rolling Virginia hills. If you decide to walk, head west from the visitor center on Roosevelt Drive and then turn right on Weeks Drive. ⊠ *West end of Memorial Bridge, Arlington, VA,* ☎ *703/697–2131; 703/607–8052 to locate a grave.* ✉ *Cemetery free; tours $4.* ⊙ *Apr.–Sept., daily 8–7; Oct.–Mar., daily 8–5.*

Kennedy graves. A highlight of any visit to Arlington National Cemetery is a visit to the graves of John F. Kennedy and other members of his family. JFK is buried under an eternal flame near two of his children, who died in infancy, and his wife, Jacqueline Bouvier Kennedy Onassis. The graves are just west of the visitor center. Across from them is a low wall engraved with quotations from Kennedy's inaugural address. JFK's grave was opened to the public in 1967 and since that time has become the most-visited grave site in the country. Nearby, marked by a simple white cross, is the grave of his brother Robert Kennedy. ⊠ *Sheridan and Weeks Drs.*

Netherlands Carillon. A visit to Arlington National Cemetery affords the opportunity for a lovely and unusual musical experience, thanks to a 49-bell carillon presented to the United States by the Dutch people in 1960 in gratitude for aid received during World War II. A performance season featuring guest carillonneurs usually runs through the spring and summer. For one of the most inclusive views of Washington, look to the east across the Potomac. From this vantage point, the Lincoln Memorial, the Washington Monument, and the Capitol appear bunched together in a side-by-side formation. ⊠ *Mead and Marshall Drs.,* ☎ *703/289–2552.*

Pentagon. To call the colossal edifice that serves as headquarters of the United States Department of Defense "mammoth" is an understatement. This is, quite simply, the largest office building in the world. Actually, the Pentagon is not one but five concentric buildings, collectively as wide as three Washington Monuments laid end to end, covering 34 acres. The buildings are connected by 17½ mi of corridors through which 23,000 military and civilian personnel pass each day. There are 685 drinking fountains, 7,748 windows, and a blizzard of other eye-popping statistics. Astonishingly, all this was completed in 1943 after just two years of construction.

The escalator from the Pentagon Metro station surfaces right into the gargantuan office building. The 75-minute tour takes you past only those areas that are meant to be seen by outside visitors. In other words, you won't see situation rooms, communications centers, or gigantic maps outlining U.S. and foreign troop strength. A uniformed serviceman or -woman (who conducts the entire tour walking backward, lest anyone slip away down a corridor) will take you past hallways lined with the portraits of past and present military leaders, scale models of U.S. Air Force planes and U.S. Navy ships, and the Hall of Heroes, where the names of all the Congressional Medal of Honor winners are inscribed. Occasionally you'll catch a glimpse through an interior window of the Pentagon's 5-acre interior courtyard. In the center—at ground zero—is a hot dog stand. A photo ID is required for admission; children under 16 must be accompanied by an adult. ⊠ *Off I–395, Arlington, VA,* ☎ *703/695–1776.* 🖼 *Free.* 🕙 *Tour weekdays every ½ hr 9–3.*

Section 27. Some 3,800 former slaves are buried in this part of Arlington National Cemetery, all former residents of Freedman's Village, established within Arlington in 1863 to provide housing, education, and employment training for ex-slaves who had traveled to the capital. In the cemetery, the headstones are marked with their names and the word "Civilian" or "Citizen." Buried at Grave 19 in the first row of Section 27 is William Christman, a Union private who died of peritonitis in Washington on May 13, 1864. He was the first soldier interred at Arlington National Cemetery during the Civil War. ⊠ *Ord and Weitzel Dr. near Curtis Walk.*

Tomb of the Unknowns. Many countries established a memorial to their war dead after World War I. In the United States, the first burial at the Tomb of the Unknowns took place at Arlington National Cemetery on November 11, 1921, when the Unknown Soldier from the "Great War" was interred under the large white-marble sarcophagus. Unknown servicemen killed in World War II and Korea were buried in 1958. The unknown serviceman killed in Vietnam was laid to rest on the plaza on Memorial Day 1984. Soldiers from the Army's U.S. 3rd Infantry ("The Old Guard," portrayed in the movie *Gardens of Stone*) keep watch over the tomb 24 hours a day, regardless of weather conditions. Each sentinel marches exactly 21 steps, then faces the tomb for 21 seconds, symbolizing the 21-gun salute, America's highest military honor. The guard is changed with a precise ceremony during the day—every half hour from April 1 to September 30 and every hour the rest of the year. At night the guard is changed every two hours.

The Memorial Amphitheater west of the tomb is the scene of special ceremonies on Veterans Day, Memorial Day, and Easter. Decorations awarded to the unknowns by foreign governments and U.S. and foreign organizations are displayed in an indoor trophy room. Across from the amphitheater are memorials to the astronauts killed in the *Challenger* shuttle explosion and to the servicemen killed in 1980 while trying to rescue American hostages in Iran. Rising beyond that is the main mast from the USS *Maine,* the American ship that was sunk in Havana Harbor in 1898, killing 299 men and sparking the Spanish-American War. ⊠ *End of Crook Walk.*

United States Marine Corps War Memorial. Better known simply as the Iwo Jima, this memorial, despite its familiarity, has lost none of its power to stir the emotions. Honoring marines who have given their lives since the corps was formed in 1775, the statue, by Felix W. de Weldon, is based on Joe Rosenthal's Pulitzer Prize–winning photograph of five marines and a navy corpsman raising a flag atop Mt. Suribachi on the Japanese island of Iwo Jima on February 19, 1945. By executive order, a real flag flies 24 hours a day from the 78-ft-high memorial. On Tuesday evenings at 7 from late May to late August there is a Marine Corps sunset parade on the grounds of the memorial. On parade nights a free shuttle bus runs from the Arlington Cemetery visitors' parking lot. A few words of caution: it is dangerous to visit the memorial after dark.

Women in Military Service for America Memorial. What is now this memorial (opened in 1997) was once the Hemicycle, a huge carved retaining wall faced with granite at the entrance to Arlington National Cemetery. Built in 1932, the wall was restored, with added stairways leading to a rooftop terrace. Inside you'll find 16 exhibit alcoves, which show the contributions that women have made to the military—from the Revolutionary War to the present—as well as the history of the memorial itself. A 196-seat theater shows films and is used for lectures and conferences. A computer database has pictures, military histories, and stories of some 130,000 women veterans. A fountain and reflecting pool front the classical-style Hemicycle and entry gates.

Alexandria

Alexandria Black History Resource Center. The history of African-Americans in Alexandria and Virginia from 1749 to the present is recounted here. Alexandria's history is hardly limited to the families of George Washington and Robert E. Lee. The federal census of 1790 recorded 52 free blacks living in the city, and the port town was one of the largest slave exportation points in the South, with at least two bustling slave markets. ⊠ *638 N. Alfred St.,* ☎ *703/838-4356.* ⊠ *Free.* ☉ *Tues.–Sat. 10–4, Sun. 1–5.*

Boyhood Home of Robert E. Lee. The childhood home in Alexandria of the commander in chief of the Confederate forces during the Civil War is a fine example of a 19th-century town house with Federal architecture and antique furnishings and paintings. ⊠ *607 Oronoco St.,* ☎ *703/548-8454.* ⊠ *$4.* ☉ *Mon.–Sat. 10–4, Sun. 1–4; closed Dec. 15–Feb. 1 except on Sun. closest to Jan. 19 for Lee's birthday celebration; occasionally closed weekends for private events.*

Captain's Row. Many of Alexandria's sea captains once lived on this block. The cobblestones in the street were allegedly laid by Hessian mercenaries who had fought for the British during the Revolution and were held in Alexandria as prisoners of war. ⊠ *Prince St. between Lee and Union Sts.*

Carlyle House. The grandest of Alexandria's older houses, Carlyle House was patterned after a Scottish country manor house. The structure was completed in 1753 by Scottish merchant John Carlyle. This was General Braddock's headquarters and the place where he met with five royal governors in 1755 to plan the strategy and funding of the early campaigns of the French and Indian War. ⊠ *121 N. Fairfax St.,* ☎ *703/549-2997.* ⊠ *$4.* ☉ *Tues.–Sat. 10–4:30, Sun. noon–4:30; tour every ½ hr.*

Christ Church. Both Washington and Lee were pewholders in this Alexandria, Virginia, Episcopal church. (Washington paid £36 and 10 shillings—a lot of money in those days—

for Pew 60.) Built in 1773, Christ Church is a good example of an English Georgian country-style church. It has a fine Palladian window, an interior balcony, and a wrought-brass-and-crystal chandelier brought from England at Washington's expense. ⊠ *118 N. Washington St.,* ☎ *703/549–1450.* ⌨ *Free.* ☉ *Mon.–Sat. 9–4, Sun. 2–4:30; occasionally closed weekends for private events.*

Gadsby's Tavern Museum. This museum is housed in the old City Tavern and Hotel, which was a center of political and social life in the late 18th century. George Washington attended birthday celebrations in the ballroom here. A tour takes you through the taproom, dining room, assembly room, ballroom, and communal bedrooms. ⊠ *134 N. Royal St.,* ☎ *703/838–4242.* ⌨ *$4.* ☉ *Oct.–Mar., Tues.–Sat. 11–4, Sun. 1–4 (last tour at 3:15); Apr.–Sept., Tues.–Sat. 10–5, Sun. 1–5 (last tour at 4:15); tours 15 mins before and 15 mins after the hr.*

Lloyd House. A fine example of Georgian architecture, Lloyd House, built in 1797, is now operated as part of the Alexandria Library and houses a collection of rare books and documents relating to city and state history. ⊠ *220 N. Washington St.,* ☎ *703/838–4577.* ⌨ *Free.* ☉ *Mon.–Sat. 9–5.*

Lyceum. Built in 1839, the Lyceum served as a library, a Civil War hospital, a residence, and an office building. It was restored in the 1970s and now houses two galleries with exhibits on the history of Alexandria, a third gallery with changing exhibits, and a gift shop. Some travel information for the entire state is also available here. ⊠ *201 S. Washington St.,* ☎ *703/838–4994.* ⌨ *Free.* ☉ *Mon.–Sat. 10–5, Sun. 1–5.*

Old Presbyterian Meetinghouse. Built in 1774, the Old Presbyterian Meetinghouse was, as its name suggests, more than a church. It was a gathering place in Alexandria vital to Scottish patriots during the Revolution. Eulogies for George Washington were delivered here on December 29, 1799. In a corner of the churchyard you'll find the Tomb of the Unknown Soldier of the American Revolution. ⊠ *321 S. Fairfax St.,* ☎ *703/549–6670.* ⌨ *Free.* ☉ *Sanctuary weekdays 9–4 (if it's locked, obtain key from church office at 316 S. Royal St.).*

Ramsay House. The best place to start a tour of Alexandria's Old Town is at the **Alexandria Convention & Visitors Association,** in Ramsay House, the home of the town's first postmaster and lord mayor, William Ramsay. The structure is believed to be the oldest house in Alexandria. Ramsay was a Scot, as a swatch of his tartan on the door proclaims. Travel counselors here provide brochures and maps for self-guided walking tours. You're given a 24-hour permit that allows you to park free at any two-hour metered spot. ⊠ *221 King St.,* ☎ *703/838–4200 or 800/ 388–9119; 703/838–6494 TDD.* ⊙ *Daily 9–5.*

Stabler-Leadbeater Apothecary. Once patronized by George Washington and the Lee family, Alexandria's Stabler-Leadbeater Apothecary is the second-oldest apothecary in the country (the oldest is reputedly in Bethlehem, PA). It was here, on October 17, 1859, that Lt. Col. Robert E. Lee received orders to move to Harper's Ferry to suppress John Brown's insurrection. The shop now houses a small museum of 18th- and 19th-century apothecary memorabilia, including one of the finest collections of apothecary bottles in the country (some 800 bottles in all). ⊠ *105–107 S. Fairfax St.,* ☎ *703/836–3713.* ☞ *$2.50.* ⊙ *Mon.–Sat. 10– 4, Sun. 1–5.*

3 Dining

By
Deborah
Papier

Updated
by Thomas
Head

AS THE NATION'S CAPITAL, Washington hosts an international array of visitors and new residents. This infusion of cultures means that D.C. restaurants are getting better and better. (And sometimes, cheaper and cheaper: more of the top dining rooms now offer reasonably priced fare and fixed-price specials.) Despite the dearth of ethnic neighborhoods and the kinds of restaurant districts found in many other cities, you *can* find almost any type of food here, from Burmese to Ethiopian. Even the French-trained chefs who have traditionally set the standard in fine dining are turning to health-conscious new American cuisine, spicy southwestern recipes, or appetizer-size Spanish tapas for inspiration.

In the city's one officially recognized ethnic enclave, Chinatown (centered on G and H streets NW between 6th and 8th), Burmese, Thai, and other Asian cuisines add variety to the many traditional Chinese restaurants. The latter entice you with huge, brightly lit signs and offer such staples as beef with broccoli or *kung pao* chicken in a spicy sauce with roasted peanuts. But discriminating diners will find far better food at the smaller, less obvious restaurants. Look for recent reviews in the *Washingtonian* magazine, the *Washington Post,* and the *Washington Times;* proud restaurant owners display good reviews on doors or in windows.

Chinatown has received a shot in the arm since the opening of the MCI Arena. The fans who throng the arena for professional hockey and basketball have to eat somewhere, and Chinatown is handy and cheap. This has made Chinatown and the area around the Gallery Place Metro station the city's hottest area for new restaurant development.

For fine dining, don't overlook restaurants in the city's luxury hotels (☞ Chapter 4). The formal dining room at the Willard Inter-Continental, Seasons at the Four Seasons, Lespinasse at the Carlton, Citronelle at the Latham, and the dining room at the Morrison-Clark Inn are noteworthy. The cuisine is often artful and fresh. Of course, such attention to detail comes at a price. One less-expensive way to experience these nationally recognized restaurants is a weekday lunch.

Note that although most restaurants are accessible by Metro, some are not. Details on Metro stops are provided when this form of public transportation is realistic. For details on price categories, *see* Dining *in* Smart Travel Tips.

Adams-Morgan/Cleveland Park

Eighteenth Street NW extending south from Columbia Road is wall-to-wall restaurants. Small ethnic restaurants open and close frequently, and it's worth taking a walk down the street to see what looks new and interesting. Although the area has retained some of its Latin American identity, the new eating establishments tend to be Asian, new American, Italian, and Ethiopian. Parking can be impossible on weekends. The nearest Metro stop—Woodley Park/Zoo—is a 10- to 15-minute walk; although it's a safe stroll at night, it may be more convenient to take a cab. Woodley Park has culinary temptations of its own, with a lineup of popular ethnic restaurants right by the Metro.

Asian

$$ ✕ **Saigon Gourmet.** Service is brisk and friendly at this popular, French-influenced Vietnamese restaurant. The upscale neighborhood patrons return for the ultracrisp *cha-gio* (spring rolls), the savory *pho* (beef broth), seafood soups, and the delicately seasoned and richly sauced entrées. Shrimp Saigon mixes prawns and pork in a peppery marinade, and another Saigon dish—grilled pork with rice crepes—is a Vietnamese variation on Chinese moo shu. ✉ *2635 Connecticut Ave. NW,* ☎ *202/265–1360. AE, D, DC, MC, V. Metro: Woodley Park/Zoo.*

Contemporary

$$$–$$$$ ✕ **Cashion's Eat Place.** The casual atmosphere of Ann Cashion's very personal restaurant, which is hung with family photos, shouldn't lead you to underestimate the cooking. The restaurant is usually jammed with regulars who come to feast on the up-to-date home-style cooking. Roast chicken, a steak entrée, and several seafood dishes are frequent choices. Meat and fish are often local and sea-

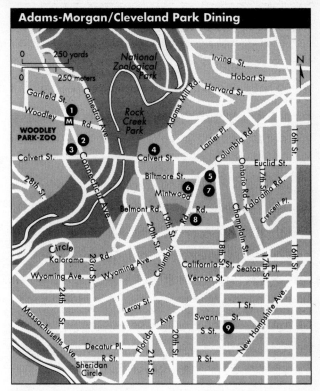

Adams-Morgan/Cleveland Park Dining

Cashion's Eat Place, **6**

Felix, **7**

Grill from Ipanema, **8**

I Matti, **5**

Lauriol Plaza, **9**

Lebanese Taverna, **2**

Mama Ayesha's Restaurant, **4**

New Heights, **3**

Saigon Gourmet, **1**

sonal and always skillfully cooked. Side dishes such as garlicky mashed potatoes or buttery potatoes Anna sometimes upstage the main course. Desserts, made by pastry chef Beth Christianson, range from homey to sophisticated. If it's offered, don't miss the chocolate cake, one of the best anywhere. ☒ *1819 Columbia Rd. NW,* ☎ *202/797–1819. MC, V. Closed Mon. No lunch Tues.–Sat. Metro: Woodley Park/Zoo.*

$$$–$$$$ ✕ **Felix.** The neon on the exterior and the stylized cityscape in the dining room may cause you to have momentary doubts about whether this is a restaurant or nightclub, but tasting chef David Scribner's new American cooking should allay any fears. Start with spring rolls made from duck confit and leeks; then go on to pork chops or seared loin of tuna served with wasabi cream. If you come on a Friday, you'll find an unlikely treat—challah, matzo-ball soup, and brisket, just like Scribner's mother used to make. ☒ *2406 18th St. NW,* ☎ *202/483–3549. AE, MC, V. No lunch Mon.–Sat. Metro: Woodley Park/Zoo.*

$$$–$$$$ ✕ **New Heights.** This inviting restaurant has 11 large windows that overlook nearby Rock Creek Park. Chef John Wabeck's sophisticated new American cooking blends the bold flavors of Asia and the Southwest into the traditional dishes of the American repertoire. Oysters may be traditionally fried in buttermilk batter and then served with sage aioli. Quail might be grilled and served with roasted beets and ginger-lime vinaigrette. Sunday brunch is a particular treat in this lovely room. ☒ *2317 Calvert St. NW,* ☎ *202/234–4110. AE, D, DC, MC, V. No lunch Mon.–Sat. Metro: Woodley Park/Zoo.*

Italian

$$$ ✕ **I Matti.** A less formal trattoria from Roberta Donna, local Italian restaurant entrepreneur and owner of the much more expensive Galileo (☞ Downtown, *below*), I Matti serves a varied menu of sophisticated dishes to a largely neighborhood clientele. If you stop for lunch or a light snack, try one of the thin, crisp-crust pizzas or a pasta dish. Meat and fish dishes—which might include rabbit, veal, or *bollito misto* (meat and capon cooked in a flavorful broth)—are pricier but well worth it. Service is often perfunctory, particularly on busy weekend evenings. ☒ *2436 18th St.*

NW, ☎ 202/462–8844. AE, DC, MC, V. No lunch Sun. Metro: Woodley Park/Zoo.

Latin American

$$–$$$ ✕ **Grill from Ipanema.** The Grill focuses on Brazilian cuisine, from spicy seafood stews to grilled steak and other hearty meat dishes. Appetizers include fried yuca with spicy sausages and—for adventurous eaters—fried alligator. Second Lady Tipper Gore adores the *mexilhão á carioca*, garlicky mussels cooked in a clay pot. Traditional feijoada is served every day. ✉ 1858 Columbia Rd. NW, ☎ 202/986–0757. AE, D, DC, MC, V. No lunch weekdays. Metro: Woodley Park/Zoo.

$–$$$ ✕ **Lauriol Plaza.** A charming corner enclave on the border of Adams-Morgan and Dupont Circle, Lauriol Plaza serves Latin American and Spanish dishes—seviche, paella, and so on—in winning combinations. Rustic entrées such as Cuban-style pork and *lomo saltado* (Peruvian-style strip steak with onions, tomatoes, and fiery jalapeño peppers) are specialties. The simply decorated dining room, with white tablecloths and white walls enlivened by gilt-framed paintings, can get noisy; the alfresco terrace is preferable in good weather. ✉ 1801 18th St. NW, ☎ 202/387–0035. AE, D, DC, MC, V. Metro: Dupont Circle.

Middle Eastern

$$ ✕ **Lebanese Taverna.** Arched ceilings, cedar panels etched with intricate leaf patterns, woven rugs, and brass lighting fixtures give the Taverna a feeling of warm elegance. Be sure to start your meal with an order of Arabic bread, which is baked in a wood-burning oven. Small, fried pies filled with spinach, cheese, or meat are buttery and surprisingly light. Lamb, beef, chicken, and seafood are either grilled on kabobs, slow-roasted, or smothered with a garlicky yogurt sauce. Pomegranate seeds are sprinkled atop many dishes for a colorful accent. A group can make a meal of the *mezza* platters—a mix of appetizers and shawarma meats. A glass of *arak*, a strong, anise-flavored liquor, makes an excellent digestif. ✉ 2641 Connecticut Ave. NW, ☎ 202/265–8681. AE, D, DC, MC, V. Metro: Woodley Park/Zoo. ✉ 5900 Washington Blvd., Arlington, VA, ☎ 703/241–8681. AE, D, DC, MC, V.

$$ ✕ **Mama Ayesha's Restaurant.** Journalists and politicians frequent Ayesha's for the reasonably priced fare. At this family-run eatery, staples such as chicken and lamb kabobs can be had for less than $10, baskets of complimentary pita bread are served hot, and the crisp falafel is some of the best in town. Weekends bring Arabic bands and belly dancing. ⊠ *1967 Calvert St. NW,* ☎ *202/232–5431. AE, DC, MC, V. Metro: Woodley Park/Zoo.*

Capitol Hill

The Hill has a number of bar-eateries that cater to Congressional types in need of fortification after a day spent running the country. Dining options are augmented by Union Station, which contains some decent—if pricey—restaurants. It also has a large food court offering quick bites that range from barbecue to sushi.

American

$$–$$$$ ✕ **Monocle.** This, the nearest restaurant to the Senate side of the Capitol, is a great place to spot members of Congress at lunch and dinner. The regional American cuisine is rarely adventurous but is thoroughly reliable. The crab cakes, as either a platter or a sandwich, are a specialty, and depending on the day of the week, you might encounter pot roast or a first-rate fish dish as a special. Still, the draw is the old-style Capitol Hill atmosphere. ⊠ *107 D St. NE,* ☎ *202/546–4488. AE, DC, MC, V. Closed weekends. Metro: Union Station.*

French

$$$–$$$$ ✕ **Bistro Bis.** A zinc bar, spacious brown leather booths, and a glass-fronted display kitchen create delicious expectations at Bistro Bis, the second restaurant from chef Jeffrey Buben, owner of the much-acclaimed Vidalia (☞ Downtown, *below*) downtown. Buben describes his restaurant as a modern bistro serving French food with an American sensibility. His menu seamlessly merges the standards of the modern American repertory with French bistro classics. For a first course, don't miss the ragout of snails with artichokes and potatoes. Main-course hits include goujonettes of sole; seared sea scallops Provençale served in a sauce of garlic, tomato, and olives and accompanied by a custardy timbale of roasted eggplant; roast chicken; or veal stew. ✉ *In the Hotel George, 15 E St. NW,* ☎ *202/661–2700. AE, D, DC, MC, V. Metro: Union Station.*

$$-$$$$ ✕ **La Colline.** Chef Robert Gréault has worked to make La
★ Colline one of the city's best French restaurants. The seasonal menu emphasizes fresh vegetables and seafood, with offerings that range from simple grilled preparations to fricassees and gratins with imaginative sauces. Other choices include duck with orange or cassis sauce and veal with chanterelle mushrooms. ✉ *400 N. Capitol St. NW,* ☎ *202/737–0400. AE, DC, MC, V. Closed Sun. No lunch Sat. Metro: Union Station.*

Indian

$$-$$$ ✕ **Aatish.** "Aatish" means volcano, an appropriate name for a restaurant specializing in tandoori cooking—meats, seafood, vegetables, and breads cooked in the intense heat of a clay oven. What distinguishes this restaurant is not so much the variety of its menu as the quality of its cooking. The appetizer samosa is a model version, with flaky pastry enclosing a delicious spiced mixture of potatoes and peas. The tandoori chicken is moist and delicious. Lamb dishes, especially the lamb *karahi*, sautéed in a wok with ginger, garlic, tomatoes, vegetables, and spices, are very well cooked. ✉ *609 Pennsylvania Ave. SE,* ☎ *202/544–0931. AE, MC, V. Metro: Eastern Market*

Southern

$$-$$$ ✕ **B. Smith's.** The D.C. location of southern-influenced B. Smith's bears the distinctive mark of chef James Oakley. For appetizers, try the grilled cheddar cheese grits, jambalaya, or seafood croquettes—but skip the overly breaded fried green tomatoes and the too-sweet sweet potatoes. Signature entrée Swamp Thing may not sound pretty, but this mix of mustard-seasoned shrimp and crawfish with collard greens is delicious. Seafood and anything with barbecue sauce are highly recommended. Desserts are comforting classics, slightly dressed up: bananas Foster, warm bread pudding, and sweet-potato pecan pie. ✉ *50 Massachusetts Ave. NE (in Union Station),* ☎ *202/289–6188. AE, D, DC, MC, V. Metro: Union Station.*

Washington Dining

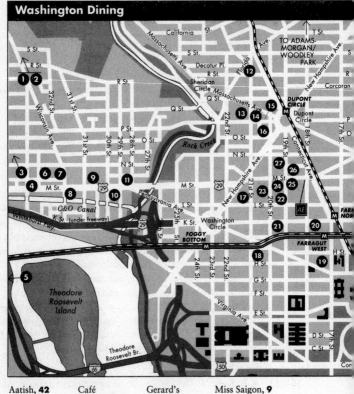

Aatish, **42**

Aditi, **4**

B. Smith's, **44**

Bistro Bis, **41**

Bistro Français, **8**

Bombay Club, **31**

Bread Line, **19**

Burma, **37**

Café Atlantico, **38**

Café Milano, **6**

Citronelle, **10**

Coppi's Restaurant, **28**

DC Coast, **35**

Gabriel, **13**

Galileo, **17**

Georgia Brown's, **30**

Gerard's Place, **34**

Hunan Chinatown, **36**

i Ricchi, **27**

Jaleo, **39**

Kinkead's, **18**

La Colline, **40**

Les Halles, **33**

Lespinasse, **29**

Miss Saigon, **9**

Monocle, **43**

Morton's of Chicago, **5, 7**

Nora, **12**

Obelisk, **14**

Old Ebbitt Grill, **32**

Oodles Noodles, **1, 22**

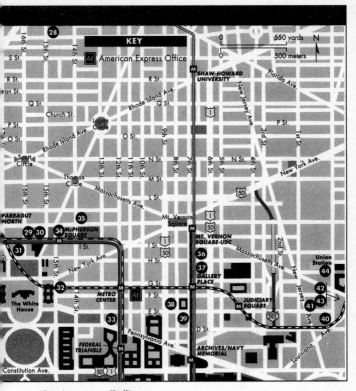

Osteria
Goldoni, **23**

Palm, **26**

Pizzeria
Paradiso, **15**

Sala Thai, **16**

Sam and
Harry's, **25**

1789, **3**

Sholl's
Colonial
Cafeteria, **21**

Sushi-Ko, **2**

Taberna del
Alabardero, **20**

Tahoga, **11**

Vidalia, **24**

Downtown

"Downtown" covers everything between Georgetown and Capitol Hill. The "new downtown," centered on Connecticut Avenue and K Street, has many of the city's blue-chip law firms and deluxe eateries—places that feed expense-account diners and provide the most elegant atmosphere, most attentive service, and often the best food. But the "old downtown," farther east, is where the action is these days. Nearby Chinatown is booming, and restaurants of all stripes (usually casual and moderately priced) have sprung up to serve the crowds that attend games at the MCI Arena. The entire downtown area, however, is in a state of flux gastronomically, with famed restaurants such as Le Lion d'Or closing their doors and new ones blossoming. Trendy microbrewery-restaurants and cigar lounges are part of the new wave.

American

\$\$\$–\$\$\$\$ ✕ **Sam and Harry's.** Cigar-friendly Sam and Harry's is understated, genteel, and packed at lunch and dinner. Although the miniature crab cakes are a good way to begin, the real draws are such prime meats as porterhouse and New York strip steaks served on the bone. For those who've sworn off beef, daily seafood specials include Maine lobster. End the meal with warm pecan pie laced with melted chocolate or a "turtle cake" full of caramel and chocolate that's big enough for two. ✉ *1200 19th St. NW,* ☎ *202/296–4333. AE, D, DC, MC, V. Closed Sun. No lunch Sat. Metro: Dupont Circle.*

\$\$–\$\$\$ ✕ **Old Ebbitt Grill.** People flock here to drink at the several bars, which seem to go on for miles, and to enjoy carefully prepared bar food that includes buffalo chicken wings, hamburgers, and Reuben sandwiches. The Old Ebbitt also has Washington's most popular oyster bar (called "raw bar" locally), which serves a rotating selection of farm-raised oysters from certified waters. But this is not just a place for casual nibbling; serious diners will appreciate the homemade pasta and the daily fresh fish or steak specials (served until 1 AM). Despite the crowds, the restaurant never feels cramped, thanks to its well-spaced, comfortable booths. Service can be slow at lunch; if you're in a hurry, try the quick, café-style Ebbitt Express next door. ✉ *675 15th St. NW,*

☎ *202/347–4800. AE, D, DC, MC, V. Metro: Metro Center.*

$ ✕ **Sholl's Colonial Cafeteria.** Here the slogan is "Where good foods are prepared right, served right, and priced right"— and truer words were never spoken. Suited federal workers line up next to pensioners and students to grab a bite at this D.C. institution, which is open for breakfast, lunch, and an early dinner. Favorites include chopped steak, roast beef, liver and onions, and baked chicken and fish for less than $5. Sholl's is famous for its fruit pies: all the desserts are scrumptious and cost around $1. ⊠ *1990 K St. NW,* ☎ *202/296–3065. No credit cards. No dinner Sun. Metro: Farragut West.*

Asian

$–$$$ ✕ **Burma.** The fact that Burma (now called Myanmar) the country is bordered by India, Thailand, and China gives an indication of the cuisine at Burma the Chinatown restaurant. Curry and tamarind share pride of place with lemon, cilantro, and soy seasonings. Batter-fried eggplant and squash are paired with complex, peppery sauces. Green Tea Leaf and other salads, despite their odd-sounding names and ingredients, leave the tongue with a pleasant tingle. Such entrées as mango pork, tamarind fish, and *kokang* chicken are equally satisfying. ⊠ *740 6th St. NW, 2nd floor,* ☎ *202/ 638–1280. AE, D, DC, MC, V. No lunch weekends. Metro: Gallery Place/Chinatown.*

$–$$$ ✕ **Hunan Chinatown.** One of Chinatown's most attractive and most attentive restaurants serves very good versions of familiar dishes. Try the fried dumplings, the tea-smoked duck, the Szechuan eggplant, and the crispy whole fish Hunan-style. ⊠ *624 H St. NW,* ☎ *202/783–5858. AE, D, DC, MC, V. Metro: Gallery Place/Chinatown.*

$–$$$ ✕ **Miss Saigon.** Shades of mauve and green, black Art Deco accents, and potted palms decorate this Vietnamese restaurant, where careful attention is paid to presentation as well as to seasoning. Begin with crisp egg rolls or chilled spring rolls, and then proceed to exquisite salads of shredded green papaya topped with shrimp or beef. The daily specials feature the freshest seafood prepared in exciting ways. "Caramel"-cooked meats are standouts, as are the grilled meats. Prices are moderate, especially for lunch,

but you may have to order several dishes to have your fill.
✉ *3057 M St. NW,* ☎ *202/333–5545. AE, DC, MC, V.
No lunch weekends. Metro: Foggy Bottom.*

$–$$ ✕ **Oodles Noodles.** Packed from the day they opened and
with long lines waiting for tables and takeout, these attractive
Pan-Asian noodle houses offer some terrific Asian cooking.
You'll find Chinese, Japanese, Thai, Indonesian, Malaysian,
and Vietnamese dishes. The quality of each is remarkably
high, and it's served in a dish appropriate to the country's
cuisine. Try the Thai drunken noodles, the Chinese clay-
pot noodles, or the Vietnamese rice noodles with grilled
chicken. ✉ *1120 19th St. NW,* ☎ *202/293–3138. AE,
DC, MC, V. Closed Sun. Metro: Farragut North.* ✉ *4907
Cordell Ave., Bethesda, MD,* ☎ *301/986–8833. AE, DC,
MC, V. No lunch Sun. Metro: Bethesda.*

Contemporary

$$$$ ✕ **DC Coast.** Washington is not on the coast, but chef Jeff
Tunks's menu at this sophisticated downtown spot brings
the foods of three coasts—Atlantic, Gulf, and Pacific—to
Washington. Try his version of the mid-Atlantic's best-
known seafood delicacy, crab cakes. They're among the best
in town. If you're homesick for New Orleans, the gumbo
is great, and for Pacific Rim cooking, you can't beat the
tea-smoked lobster. The bar scene here is one of the liveliest in the downtown area. ✉ *1401 K St. NW,* ☎ *202/216–
5988. Reservations essential. AE, D, DC, MC, V. Closed
Sun. No lunch Sat. Metro: McPherson Square.*

$$$–$$$$ ✕ **Vidalia.** Chef Jeffrey Buben's restaurant has the name
of an onion, and Vidalia onions, in season, are a specialty,
but there's a lot more to this distinguished restaurant. In-
spired by the cooking and the ingredients of the South and
the Chesapeake Bay region, Buben's version of new Amer-
ican cuisine revolves around the best seasonal fruits, veg-
etables, and seafood he can find. Don't miss the roasted
onion soup with spoon bread, the shrimp on yellow grits,
or the sensational lemon chess pie. ✉ *1990 M St. NW,* ☎
*202/659–1990. AE, D, DC, MC, V. No lunch weekends.
Metro: Dupont Circle.*

$ ✕ **Bread Line.** This crowded, quirky, sometimes chaotic
restaurant specializes in breads and bread-based foods and
not only makes the city's best baguette but is also home to

some of the best sandwiches in town. Owner Mark Furstenburg makes everything on the premises, from the breakfast bagels and muffins to the ciabatta loaves for the tuna salad sandwich with preserved lemons. Your french fries, if they are on the menu, will be served with homemade ketchup. It's best to arrive early or late to avoid the noontime office rush. ✉ *1751 Pennsylvania Ave. NW,* ☎ *202/822–8900. Reservations not accepted. MC, V. Closed weekends. No dinner. Metro: Farragut West.*

Eclectic

$$$–$$$$ ✗ **Kinkead's.** This multichambered restaurant includes a downstairs pub and raw bar and more formal dining rooms upstairs. The open kitchen upstairs allows you to watch Kinkead and company turn out an eclectic menu of mostly seafood dishes, inspired by chef Robert Kinkead's New England roots and by the cooking of Asia and Latin America. Main-course soups and seafood stews, such as Scandinavian salmon stew, are specialties. The menu also has a selection of simply grilled fish, without sauces. Save room for dessert—the chocolate *dacquoise* (layer cake) is a knockout. ✉ *2000 Pennsylvania Ave. NW,* ☎ *202/296–7700. AE, DC, MC, V. Metro: Foggy Bottom.*

$$$–$$$$ ✗ **Palm.** The walls are papered with caricatures of the famous who have dined here, and the restaurant is a favorite lunchtime hangout of power brokers. The main attractions are gargantuan steaks and Nova Scotia lobsters, several kinds of potatoes, and New York cheesecake. But one of Palm's best-kept secrets is that it's also a terrific, old-fashioned Italian restaurant. Try the veal marsala for lunch or, on Thursday, the terrific shrimp in marinara sauce. ✉ *1225 19th St. NW,* ☎ *202/293–9091. AE, DC, MC, V. No lunch weekends. Metro: Dupont Circle.*

French

$$$$ ✗ **Lespinasse.** The Washington Lespinasse, in the St. Regis hotel, may well be the most beautiful dining room in D.C., and although the prices are high, they're justified by the quality of the food and service. Chef Sandro Gamba's menu changes seasonally. Try risotto topped with a fricassee of wild mushrooms, or a royale of foie gras in chicken consommé for an appetizer. Main courses include breast of guinea hen with Napa cabbage and a "symphony" of lamb:

a single plate with a rack, a piece of the loin, and slices of the roast leg. The $36 fixed-price lunch menu is a good way to sample Gamba's cooking. ⊠ *923 16th St. NW,* ☎ *202/ 879–6900. AE, D, DC, MC, V. Closed Sun.–Mon. No lunch Sat. Metro: Farragut North.*

$$$–$$$$ ✕ **Gerard's Place.** Don't let the simplicity of the name
★   cause you to underestimate the quality of the cooking at this sophisticated spot owned by acclaimed French chef Gerard Pangaud. In the strikingly colored gray and burnt-umber dining room, you're served dishes that have intriguing combinations of ingredients. The menu, which changes daily, might include Gerard's signature poached lobster with a ginger, lime, and Sauternes sauce; venison served with dried fruits and pumpkin and beetroot purees; or seared tuna with black olives and roasted red peppers. Memorable desserts have included the Chocolate Tear, a teardrop-shape flourless chocolate cake veined with raspberry. ⊠ *915 15th St. NW,* ☎ *202/737–4445. AE, DC, MC, V. Closed Sun. No lunch Sat. Metro: McPherson Square.*

$$$–$$$$ ✕ **Les Halles.** Les Halles is about as close as you can come to a Parisian bistro without going to France. The cooking is plain and hearty, and the portions are large. The best first course is a sensational salad of *frisée* (a bitter salad green), bacon, and Roquefort cheese. Order steak for a main course, either the *onglet* (hanger steak) with the best pommes frîtes in town or, for two, the gargantuan grilled rib. If you're lucky enough to visit in February, don't miss the Choûcroute Festival, when four different versions of this hearty meat-and-sauerkraut treat are offered. ⊠ *1201 Pennsylvania Ave. NW,* ☎ *202/387–6888. AE, D, DC, MC, V. Metro: Metro Center.*

Indian

$$–$$$ ✕ **Bombay Club.** One block from the White House and a
★   favorite restaurant of the First Family, the beautiful Bombay Club tries to re-create the kind of solace the Beltway elite might have found in a private club had they been 19th-century British colonials in India rather than late-20th-century Washingtonians. The bar, which serves hot hors d'oeuvres at cocktail hour, is furnished with rattan chairs and paneled with dark wood. The dining room, with potted palms and a bright blue ceiling above white plaster moldings, is elegant and decorous. The menu includes unusual

seafood specialties and a large number of vegetarian dishes, but the real standouts are the breads and the seafood appetizers. ✉ *815 Connecticut Ave. NW,* ☎ *202/659–3727. AE, DC, MC, V. No lunch Sat. Metro: Farragut West.*

Italian

$$$$
★ ✕ **Galileo.** The flagship restaurant of Washington entrepreneur-chef Roberto Donna serves sophisticated Piedmontese-style cooking. The specials vary daily, but to get the full experience, order an antipasto, a pasta (perhaps split between two), and a main course of grilled fish, game, or veal. Preparations are generally simple: the veal chop might be served with mushroom-and-rosemary sauce, the beef with black-olive sauce and polenta. The $65 five-course fixed-price menu is a good value. In a move unusual for downtown restaurants, Galileo is open for breakfast on weekdays. ✉ *1110 21st St. NW,* ☎ *202/293–7191. AE, D, DC, MC, V. No lunch weekends. Metro: Foggy Bottom.*

$$$$ ✕ **Osteria Goldoni.** Chef Fabrizio Aielli, a veteran of Roberto Donna's kitchen at Galileo (☞ *above*), specializes in Venetian cooking. The new location of Osteria Goldoni, just a few blocks from the old one, has a lively downstairs café and a more sedate upstairs dining room, both with the same menu. Pastas, even familiar ones, achieve a new dimension of excellence under Aielli's skilled hand. Tiny veal ravioli are beautifully sauced with tomato, pesto, and mushrooms. Seafood is a specialty here. Try the whole fish baked in a parchment bag and garnished with artichokes and polenta. The house-made ice creams and sorbets are wonderful. ✉ *1120 20th St. NW,* ☎ *202/293–1511. AE, D, DC, MC, V. No lunch weekends. Metro: Farragut North.*

$$$–$$$$
★ ✕ **i Ricchi.** An airy dining room decorated with terra-cotta tiles, cream-color archways, and floral frescoes, i Ricchi is priced for expense accounts and remains a favorite of critics and upscale crowds for its earthy Tuscan cuisine, often prepared on its wood-burning grill or oven. The spring–summer menu includes such offerings as rolled pork roasted in wine and fresh herbs and skewered shrimp; the fall–winter bill of fare brings grilled lamb chops, thick soups, and sautéed beef fillet. ✉ *1220 19th St. NW,* ☎ *202/835–0459. AE, DC, MC, V. Closed Sun. No lunch Sat. Metro: Dupont Circle.*

Latin American

$$$ ✕ **Café Atlántico.** Offering the essence of *nuevo Latino* cooking, Café Atlántico always has exciting new dishes. Guacamole made tableside by your waiter is unmistakably fresh. The menu changes often, but if it's offered, try duck confit, baby chicken with mole sauce, Puerto Rican shrimp asopao, or *feijoada,* which also comes as a salad—minus the meat. Service is friendly and helpful, and the bar makes a mean pisco sour. ✉ *8th and E Sts. NW,* ☎ *202/393–0812. AE, DC, MC, V. No lunch Sun. Metro: Archives/Navy Memorial.*

Southern

$$-$$$ ✕ **Georgia Brown's.** The airy, curving dining room has white honeycomb windows and an unusual ceiling ornamentation of bronze ribbons. This elegant "new South" eatery, a favorite hangout of local politicians, serves shrimp Carolina-style (with the head on and steaming grits on the side); beef tenderloin medallions with a bourbon-pecan sauce; thick, rich crab soup; and such specials as grilled salmon and smoked-bacon green beans. Fried green tomatoes are given the gourmet treatment, as is the sweet-potato cheesecake. ✉ *950 15th St. NW,* ☎ *202/393–4499. AE, DC, MC, V. No lunch Sat. Metro: McPherson Square.*

Spanish

$$-$$$$ ✕ **Taberna del Alabardero.** The lovely formal dining room, skillful service, and sophisticated Spanish cooking make this restaurant one of Washington's best. Start with such tapas as *piquillo* peppers stuffed with *bacalao* (salted cod) or roasted leg of duck wrapped in a phyllo pastry pouch. Proceed to a hefty bowl of gazpacho or white garlic soup and venture on to authentic paella and elegant Spanish country dishes. Ask the sommelier to pick a good Spanish wine to accompany your meal. Pineapple tart is a light ending to rich fare. The plush old-world decor and handsome bar create a romantic atmosphere. The clientele is well heeled and cosmopolitan. ✉ *1776 I St. NW (entrance on 18th St.),* ☎ *202/429–2200. AE, D, DC, MC, V. Closed Sun. No lunch Sat. Metro: Farragut West.*

$$-$$$ ✕ **Jaleo.** This lively Spanish bistro encourages you to make ★ a meal out of its long list of tapas, although such entrées as grilled fish and paella—which comes in four versions—

are just as tasty. Tapas highlights are *gambas al ajillo* (sautéed garlic shrimp), fried potatoes with spicy tomato sauce, and *pinchitos* (a skewer of grilled chorizo) with garlic mashed potatoes. For dessert, don't miss the crisp apple Charlotte and the chocolate hazelnut tart. ⊠ *480 7th St. NW,* ☎ *202/628–7949. AE, D, DC, MC, V. Metro: Gallery Place/Chinatown.*

Dupont Circle

South from U Street and north from K Street is Dupont Circle, around which a number of restaurants are clustered. You'll also find a variety of cafés, most with outdoor seating. The District's better gay-friendly establishments are here as well, especially along 17th Street. Chains such as Starbuck's and Hannibal's have put fancy coffee on every corner, but long-established espresso bars, like the 24-hour Afterwords, are a better source for breakfast and light or late fare.

Asian

$$–$$$ ✕ **Sala Thai.** Who says Thai food has to be scalp-sweating hot? Sala Thai will make the food as spicy as you wish, but the chef is interested in flavor, not fire. Among the subtly seasoned offerings are *panang goong* (shrimp in curry-peanut sauce), chicken sautéed with ginger and pineapple, and flounder with a choice of four sauces. Mirrored walls and warm lights soften the ambience of this small downstairs dining room with friendly service and a largely neighborhood clientele. ⊠ *2016 P St. NW,* ☎ *202/872–1144. AE, DC, MC, V. Metro: Dupont Circle.*

Contemporary

$$$–$$$$ ✕ **Nora.** Although it bills itself as an "organic restaurant," Nora is no collective-run juice bar. The food, like the quilt-decorated dining room, is sophisticated and attractive. Peppered beef carpaccio with Manchego cheese is a good starter. Entrées—such as seared rockfish with artichoke broth, grilled lamb chops with white-bean ragù, and risotto with winter vegetables—exemplify the chef's emphasis on well-balanced, complex ingredients. Warm chocolate cake with cappuccino ice cream and pear-and-blueberry crisp with praline ice cream are among the sublime desserts. You may

also want to try chef Nora Pouillon's West End restaurant, **Asia Nora** (⊠ 2213 M St. NW, ☎ 202/797–4860), where you'll find a handsome Asian decor as well as organic ingredients put to good use in Pan-Asian dishes. ⊠ *2132 Florida Ave. NW, ☎ 202/462–5143. MC, V. Closed Sun. No lunch. Metro: Dupont Circle.*

Italian

$$$$ ✕ **Obelisk.** The attractions here are eclectic Italian cuisine and a five-course fixed-price menu ($42 Tuesday–Thursday, $45 Friday–Saturday) that changes every day and includes both traditional dishes and chef Peter Pastan's imaginative innovations. For the main course, you might try the lamb with garlic and sage or the braised grouper with artichoke and thyme. The minimally decorated dining room is tiny, with tables closely spaced. ⊠ *2029 P St. NW, ☎ 202/872–1180. DC, MC, V. Closed Sun.–Mon. No lunch. Metro: Dupont Circle.*

$–$$ ✕ **Pizzeria Paradiso.** A sister restaurant to the pricier Obelisk (☞ *above*) next door, the petite Pizzeria Paradiso sticks to crowd-pleasing basics: pizzas, *panini* (sandwiches such as Italian cured ham and sun-dried tomatoes and basil), salads, and desserts. Although the standard pizza is satisfying, you can enliven things by ordering it with fresh buffalo mozzarella or unusual toppings such as potatoes, capers, and mussels. The intensely flavored gelato is a house specialty. The trompe l'oeil ceiling adds space and light to a simple interior. ⊠ *2029 P St. NW, ☎ 202/223–1245. DC, MC, V. Metro: Dupont Circle.*

Latin American

$$–$$$$ ✕ **Gabriel.** Located in the Radisson Barceló Hotel, Gabriel takes a nouvelle approach to traditional Latin American and Spanish dishes. *Pupusas,* Salvadoran meat patties, are filled with chorizo. Appetizer sea scallops are grilled and served with lime, cilantro, and smoked garlic cream. Although you may prefer to order à la carte, the extensive lunch and happy-hour tapas buffets are sure winners. The brunch buffet is outstanding: in addition to traditional breakfast items, you can enjoy whole suckling pig and made-to-order quesadillas from the carving table, or Mediterranean specialties like paella, cassoulet, and salads. The dessert table offers tiny fruit tarts, bread pudding and rice pudding, mini crème brûlée, and cheesecake. ✉ *2121 P St. NW,* ☎ *202/956–6690. AE, D, DC, MC, V. No lunch Sat. Metro: Dupont Circle.*

Georgetown/West End/Glover Park

In Georgetown, whose central intersection is Wisconsin Avenue and M Street, you'll find white-tablecloth establishments next door to hole-in-the-wall joints. The closest Metro stop is Foggy Bottom, a 15- to 20-minute walk away; consult the Georgetown map before you set out, and consider taking a cab. Restaurants in the adjacent West End—bounded roughly by Rock Creek Park to the west, N Street to the north, 20th Street to the east, and K Street to the south—are worth checking out as well. Heading north from Georgetown on Wisconsin Avenue, you'll find a cluster of good restaurants in the Glover Park area, including the city's best sushi bar, Sushi-Ko.

American

$$$$ ✕ **Morton's of Chicago.** A national steak-house chain that claims to serve the country's best beef, Morton's is always jumping. In the classic steak-house tradition the emphasis is quantity as well as quality. The New York strip and porterhouse steaks are well over a pound each. If you have an even larger appetite (or you plan to share with someone else), there's a 48-ounce porterhouse. Morton's menu also includes prime rib, lamb, veal, chicken, lobster, and grilled fish. ✉ *3251 Prospect St.,* ☎ *202/342–6258. AE, DC, MC, V. No lunch.* ✉ *1050 Connecticut Ave.,* ☎ *202/955–5997. AE, DC, MC, V. No lunch weekends.* ✉ *8075 Leesburg Pike, Vienna, VA,* ☎ *703/883–0800. AE, DC, MC, V. No lunch weekends.*

Asian

$$–$$$ ✕ **Sushi-Ko.** At the city's best Japanese restaurant, daily spe-
★ cials are always innovative: sesame-oil-seasoned trout is layered with crisp wonton crackers, and a sushi special might be salmon topped with a touch of mango sauce and a tiny sprig of dill. And you won't find the whimsical desserts—green-tea ice cream or sake sorbet—at the local Baskin-Robbins. ✉ *2309 Wisconsin Ave. NW,* ☎ *202/333–4187. AE, MC, V. No lunch Sat.–Mon.*

Contemporary

$$$$ ✕ **Citronelle.** California-French chef Michel Richard's flag-
★ ship restaurant, in the Latham Hotel (☞ Chapter 4), has
his signature glass-front kitchen, which lets you see all the
action. Richard's witty appetizer specials might include an
impressive "tart" of thinly sliced grilled scallops or
"beignets" of foie gras coated with kataife and deep-fried.
Main-course loin of venison might come with chestnuts,
mushrooms, and wine sauce. Breast of squab is seasoned
with a hint of vanilla. Rabbit is served with a small rabbit
tort. Desserts are equally luscious: the crunchy napoleon—
layers of caramelized phyllo dough and creamy vanilla cus-
tard—is drizzled with butterscotch and dark chocolate. A
special chef's table in the kitchen gives lucky diners a ring-
side seat. ⊠ 3000 M St. NW, ☎ 202/625–2150. AE, DC,
MC, V.

$$$–$$$$ ✕ **1789.** The elegant dining room, with Early American
★ paintings and a fireplace, could easily be a room in the White
House. But although the decor is proper and genteel, the
food is down-to-earth and delicious. Soups, such as the rich
black bean soup with unsweetened chocolate and the
seafood stew, are flavorful. Rack of lamb and fillet of beef
are specialties, and seared tuna stands out among the ex-
cellent seafood dishes. Service is fluid and attentive. Hazel-
nut chocolate bars with espresso sauce will pep you up for
a night on the town, or opt for the homier nectarine cob-
bler. ⊠ 1226 36th St. NW, ☎ 202/965–1789. AE, D, DC,
MC, V. No lunch.

$$$ ✕ **Tahoga.** The stark white dining room of this popular spot
is a perfect setting for its beautifully prepared, elegantly pre-
sented new American cooking. Start your meal with duck
lasagna, savory confit of duck layered between crisp potato
slices and mashed potatoes. Main courses are modernized
versions of American and French classics and might include
roast chicken, braised lamb shank, bourbon-glazed pork
chops, and chicken-fried beef tenderloin. The pretty garden is a lovely place for lunch. Take advantage of the
lunchtime special: any wine on the wine list for half price.
⊠ 2815 M St. NW, ☎ 202/338–5380. AE, DC, MC, V.
No lunch weekends.

French

$$–$$$$ ✕ **Bistro Français.** Washington's chefs head here for the minute steak maître d'hôtel or the sirloin with black pepper or red wine sauce. For many, the big draw is the rotisserie chicken. Daily specials may include *suprême* of salmon with broccoli mousse and beurre blanc. The restaurant is divided into two parts—the café side and the more formal dining room; the café menu includes sandwiches and omelets in addition to entrées. There are also $11.95 fixed-price lunches and $17.95 early and late-night dinner specials. Bistro Français stays open until 3 AM Sunday–Thursday, 4 AM Friday–Saturday. ⊠ *3128 M St. NW,* ☎ *202/338–3830. AE, DC, MC, V.*

Indian

$–$$ ✕ **Aditi.** Aditi's two-story dining room—with its burgundy carpets and chairs and pastel-color walls with brass sconces—seems too elegant for a moderately priced Indian restaurant. The first floor is small, with a dramatic staircase leading to a larger room with windows that overlook the busy street. Tandoori and curry dishes are expertly prepared and not aggressively spiced; if you want your food spicy, request it. Rice *biryani* entrées are good for lighter appetites. ⊠ *3299 M St. NW,* ☎ *202/625–6825. AE, D, DC, MC, V.*

Italian

$$$–$$$$ ✕ **Cafe Milano.** Washington's beautiful people hang out at Cafe Milano. You're likely to rub shoulders with local socialites, sports figures, and visiting celebrities at the crowded bar. The authentic, sophisticated Italian cooking is very good, and specialties include pastas, like the elegant lobster with linguine, composed salads, and light-crusted pizzas. ⊠ *3251 Prospect St. NW,* ☎ *202/333–6183. AE, DC, MC, V.*

U Street

The U Street corridor begins just down the hill from 18th Street. In the 1930s and 1940s this was the place to enjoy a late-night drink and hear jazz greats such as Duke Ellington, Billie Holliday, and Charlie Parker. After decades of neglect and devastation from the '60s riots, the U Street area is being revitalized. With some of the hippest bars in the District, quirky vintage stores, small but lively nightclubs, and numerous cafés, the neighborhood draws a young crowd day and night. The area is still rough around the edges, however, so use caution. Restaurants stay open late on weekend nights and offer good food—everything from burgers to gourmet pizza to Ethiopian dishes—at low prices. The U Street vicinity is known for excellent fried-fish spots such as the **Big Fish Deli** (⊠ 1116 U St. NW, ☎ 202/328–9420) and **Webb's Southern Food** (⊠ 1361 U St. NW, ☎ 202/462–3474); unfortunately, they don't offer seating.

Italian

$–$$$ ✕ **Coppi's Restaurant.** An Italian bicycling motif permeates popular Coppi's, from the posters and gear that hang on the walls down to the monogrammed racing shirts worn by the staff. The wood-oven-baked pizzas are delicious and adventurous. When it appears as a special, the pizza *ai funghi di bosco* (with white oyster, shiitake, and cremini mushrooms) is a must. ⊠ 1414 U St. NW, ☎ 202/319–7773. AE, D, MC, V. No lunch. Metro: U Street/Cardoza.

4 Lodging

By Jan
Ziegler

Updated
by John A.
Kelly

WITH MORE THAN 340 LOCATIONS offering more than 63,000 guest rooms in the D.C. area, you can almost always find a place to stay—though it's prudent to make reservations. Hotels are often full of conventioneers, politicians in transit, or families and, in spring, school groups. Rates are especially high around the Cherry Blossom Festival in April; graduation and other big college weekends at Georgetown or George Washington University also strain the system. If you're interested in visiting Washington at a calm time—and if you can stand tropical weather—come in August, during the congressional recess. Rates drop in late December and January, except around an inauguration. Throughout the year, most hotels have weekend rates that are substantially lower than weekday rates; discounted group and weekend package rates that include some meals and parking are also available, though not at every hotel.

The properties below were chosen because of their beauty, historical significance, location, or value. All hotels in the $$$ and $$$$ categories have concierges; some in the $$ group do, too (for details on price categories, *see* Lodging *in* Smart Travel Tips). Because Washington is an international city with a diverse population and a variety of visitors, many hotel staffs are multilingual. Every hotel has no-smoking rooms, and many have no-smoking floors. Washington hotels equip their rooms to please their guests. Every place listed is air-conditioned, and many offer facilities and features—from state-of-the art exercise equipment to modest conference rooms—for business travelers. Oddly, in the most expensive hotels there is often an additional charge to use these facilities, which usually go almost unused by guests. Virtually every room in the $$ and $$$ categories has an iron and ironing board, telephone with an additional line for a computer modem connection, and hair dryer.

Some of the finer hotels have restaurants with superb food and prices to match (☞ Lespinasse *and* Michel Richard's Citronelle *in* Chapter 3).

The hotel reviews here are grouped within neighborhoods in descending order of price. Hotels' parking fees range from free (usually, but not always in the suburbs) to $24 (plus tax) per night. This sometimes involves valet parking, with its implied additional gratuities. Street parking is free on Sunday and usually after 6:30 PM. But there are often far more cars searching than there are spaces available, particularly downtown, in Georgetown, and in the upper Connecticut Avenue area. During weekday rush hours many streets are unavailable for parking; illegally parked cars are towed, and reclaiming a car is expensive and very inconvenient. *Read signs carefully;* some are very confusing, and the ticket writers are quick.

For a list of its member hotels, contact the **Washington, D.C., Convention and Visitors Association** (⊠ 1212 New York Ave. NW, 20005, ☎ 202/789–7000).

To find reasonably priced accommodations in small guest houses and private homes, try **Bed 'n' Breakfast Accommodations Ltd. of Washington, D.C.** (⊠ Box 12011, 20005, ☎ 202/328–3510), which is staffed weekdays 10–5. It handles about 85 different properties in the area.

Write to the **Bed and Breakfast League, Ltd.** (⊠ Box 9490, 20016-9490) for a list of its properties with accommodations priced to please.

Capitol Hill

$$$ 🏨 **Washington Court Hotel.** Terraced tiers of polished steps lead to the skylit atrium lobby of this luxury hotel. Within the lobby are an indoor waterfall and glass elevators. It's just off Massachusetts Avenue, near the Capitol, and close to Union Station. Rooms have modern, luxurious furnishings and a marble bathroom. Many have separate living rooms, and kitchens are available. ⊠ 525 New Jersey Ave. NW, 20001, ☎ 202/628–2100, 🖷 202/879–7918. 252 rooms, 11 suites. Restaurant, bar, in-room data ports, refrigerators, room service, health club, laundry service and dry cleaning, business services, parking (fee). AE, D, DC, MC, V. Metro: Union Station.

134

Washington Lodging

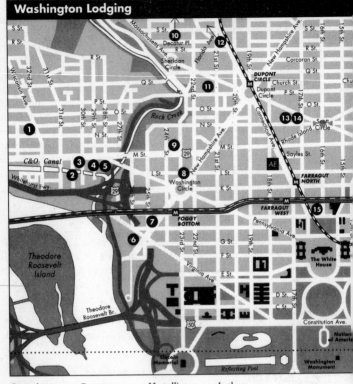

Canterbury
Hotel, **14**

Capitol
Hill Suites, **25**

Channel Inn, **23**

Doyle
Normandy, **12**

Four Seasons
Hotel, **5**

George
Washington
University
Inn, **7**

Georgetown
Dutch Inn, **2**

Georgetown
Inn, **1**

Georgetown
Suites, **4**

Hay-Adams
Hotel, **15**

Henley Park
Hotel, **18**

Holiday Inn
Capitol, **24**

Hostelling
International-
Washington
D.C., **17**

Hotel
George, **26**

Hotel Tabard
Inn, **13**

Hotel
Washington, **19**

J.W.
Marriott, **21**

Latham
Hotel, **3**

Loews L'Enfant
Plaza, **22**

Morrison-
Clark Inn, **16**

Omni
Shoreham
Hotel, **10**

One
Washington
Circle Hotel, **8**

Swissotel
Washington
Watergate, **6**

Washington
Court Hotel, **27**

Washington
Monarch, **9**

The Westin
Fairfax, **11**

Willard Inter-
Continental, **20**

$$-$$$ 🏨 **Hotel George.** The Hotel George is a spiffy new hotel at an old, old site near Union Station and the National Mall. Rooms are furnished with all the modern conveniences, including high-speed modem access and separate bath and shower in the marble bathrooms. All rooms and the lobby are ultramodern, and a Warhol-style portrait of George Washington is displayed throughout the hotel. ⊠ *15 E St. NW, 20001,* ☎ *202/347–4200 or 800/576–8331,* 𝔽𝔸𝕏 *202/ 347–4213. 139 rooms. Restaurant, bar, lobby lounge, in-room data ports, minibars, in-room VCRs, steam room, exercise room, meeting rooms, parking (fee). AE, D, DC, MC, V. Metro: Union Station.*

$$ 🏨 **Capitol Hill Suites.** On a quiet residential street behind the Library of Congress, this all-suite hotel's proximity to the House office buildings means that it's often filled with visiting lobbyists when Congress is in session. Guest rooms— which are actually renovated apartments—are large and cozy and have full-size kitchens; the sun-filled lobby has a fireplace. ⊠ *200 C St. SE, 20003,* ☎ *202/543–6000 or 800/ 424–9165,* 𝔽𝔸𝕏 *202/547–2608. 152 suites. Kitchenettes, parking (fee). AE, DC, MC, V. Metro: Capitol South.*

Downtown

$$$$ 🏨 **Hay-Adams Hotel.** This Italian Renaissance landmark
★   is near Lafayette Park and the White House. The Hay-Adams has an eclectic grandeur inside: European and Asian antiques; Doric, Ionic, and Corinthian touches; carved walnut wainscoting; and intricate ornamental ceilings. It sits on the site of houses owned by statesman and author John Hay and diplomat and historian Henry Adams. The Lafayette dining room serves contemporary American dishes. The hotel's afternoon tea is renowned. ⊠ *1 Lafayette Sq. NW, 20006,* ☎ *202/638–6600 or 800/424–5054,* 𝔽𝔸𝕏 *202/638–2716. 125 rooms, 18 suites. Restaurant, bar, room service, laundry service and dry cleaning, parking (fee). AE, DC, MC, V. Metro: McPherson Square or Farragut North.*

$$$$ 🏨 **Willard Inter-Continental.** Fronting Pennsylvania Avenue
★   and just two blocks from the White House, the Willard— whose present building dates from 1901—welcomed every American president from Franklin Pierce in 1853 to Dwight Eisenhower in the 1950s, before closing after years of decline. The new Willard, a faithful renovation, is an opulent Beaux

In case you want to see the world.

At American Express, we're here to make your journey a smooth one. So we have over 1,700 travel service locations in over 130 countries ready to help. What else would you expect from the world's largest travel agency?

do more

In case you want to be welcomed there.

We're here to see that you're always welcomed at establishments everywhere. That's why millions of people carry the American Express® Card – for peace of mind, confidence, and security, around the world or just around the corner.

do more

Cards

In case you're running low.

We're here to help with more than 190,000 Express Cash locations around the world. In order to enroll, just call American Express at 1 800 CASH·NOW before you start your vacation.

do more

Express Cash

And in case you'd rather be safe than sorry.

We're here with American Express® Travelers Cheques. They're the safe way to carry money on your vacation, because if they're ever lost or stolen you can get a refund, practically anywhere or anytime. To find the nearest place to buy Travelers Cheques, call 1 800 495-1153. Another way we help you do more.

do more **AMERICAN EXPRESS**

Travelers Cheques

Arts feast for the eye: the main lobby has spectacular proportions, great columns, huge chandeliers, mosaic floors, and elaborate ceilings. The hotel's formal dining room, the Willard Room, has won nationwide acclaim. ⊠ *1401 Pennsylvania Ave. NW, 20004,* ☎ *202/628–9100 or 800/327–0200,* ☒ *202/637–7326. 302 rooms, 38 suites. Restaurant, café, 2 bars, in-room safes, minibars, room service, health club, laundry service and dry cleaning, meeting rooms, parking (fee). AE, DC, MC, V. Metro: Metro Center.*

$$$ ▣ **Hotel Washington.** Since opening in 1918, the Hotel
★ Washington has been known for its view. Washingtonians bring visitors to the outdoor rooftop bar—open May to October—for cocktails and a panorama that includes the White House grounds and the Washington Monument. Now a National Landmark, the hotel sprang from the drawing boards of John Carrère and Thomas Hastings, who designed the New York Public Library. All rooms have mahogany furniture. ⊠ *515 15th St. NW, 20004,* ☎ *202/638–5900,* ☒ *202/638–1594. 344 rooms, 16 suites. 2 restaurants, bar, deli, lobby lounge, room service, exercise room, laundry service and dry cleaning, business services, parking (fee). AE, DC, MC, V. Metro: Metro Center.*

$$$ ▣ **J. W. Marriott.** This modern flagship hotel of the Marriott chain has a prime location near the White House and next to the National Theatre. The capacious, columned lobby includes a four-story atrium, marble and mahogany accents, and Asian rugs. You have indoor access to National Place, which has 80 shops and 18 restaurants and cafés. ⊠ *1331 Pennsylvania Ave. NW, 20004,* ☎ *202/393–2000 or 800/228–9290,* ☒ *202/626–6991. 772 rooms, 34 suites. 2 restaurants, 2 bars, room service, indoor pool, health club, laundry service and dry cleaning, parking (fee). AE, DC, MC, V. Metro: Metro Center.*

$$$ ▣ **Morrison-Clark Inn.** This inn is a merger of two 1864
★ Victorian town houses that were transformed into the Soldiers, Sailors, Marines and Airmen's Club in 1923. One house has a 1917 Chinese Chippendale porch; the antiques-filled public rooms have marble fireplaces, bay windows, 14-ft pier mirrors, and porch access. Rooms have neoclassic, French country, or Victorian furnishings. The inn's highly rated restaurant serves American cuisine with southern and other regional influences. ⊠ *Massachusetts*

Ave. and 11th St. NW, 20001, ☎ 202/898–1200 or 800/
332-7898, FAX 202/289–8576. 54 rooms. CP. Restaurant,
minibars, room service, exercise room, laundry service and
dry cleaning, parking (fee). AE, D, DC, MC, V. Metro: Metro
Center.

$$–$$$ 🏨 **Henley Park Hotel.** A Tudor-style building adorned with
★   119 gargoyles, this National Historic Trust hotel has the
cozy charm of an English country house. The Coeur de Lion
restaurant has a leafy atrium, stained-glass windows, and
an American menu. Amenities include hors d'oeuvres and
jazz nightly in Marley's Lounge and weekday morning
limousine service to any downtown destination. The hotel
is an eight-block walk to the Smithsonian museums and a
five-block walk to the MCI Sports Arena. ✉ 926 Massachusetts Ave. NW, 20001, ☎ 202/638–5200 or 800/222-
8474, FAX 202/638–6740. 79 rooms, 17 suites. Restaurant,
bar, minibars, room service, parking (fee). AE, DC, MC,
V. Metro: Metro Center or Gallery Place/Chinatown.

$ 🏨 **Hostelling International-Washington D.C.** This well-kept
hostel, formerly the Washington International AYH-Hos-
tel, has bunk beds and a kitchen, small grocery and souvenir shop, and living room. Rooms are generally dormitory
style, without private bathrooms, but families are given their
own room if the hostel is not full. Bring your own towel;
other linens are provided. The maximum stay is 29 days.
College-age travelers predominate, and July–September is
the busiest period. ✉ 1009 11th St. NW, 20001, ☎ 202/
737-2333, FAX 202/737–1508. 250 beds. Coin laundry.
MC, V. Metro: Metro Center.

Dupont Circle

$$–$$$ 🏨 **Canterbury Hotel.** On a quiet street near the embassies
of Massachusetts Avenue and Dupont Circle, the Canter-
bury was built in 1901 as an apartment building. Rooms
have 18th-century European reproduction furnishings and
interiors, with queen-, double queen-, or king-size beds
and separate dressing areas. Some rooms have stoves or
microwave ovens on request. The hotel offers free access
to the nearby YMCA and serves a Continental breakfast.
✉ 1733 N St. NW, 20036, ☎ 202/393–3000 or 800/424-
2950, FAX 202/785–9581. 99 rooms. CP. Restaurant, bar,

in-room safes, minibars, refrigerators, laundry service and dry cleaning, business services, meeting rooms, parking (fee). AE, D, DC, MC, V. Metro: Dupont Circle.

$$–$$$ ▥ **The Westin Fairfax.** Formerly a Ritz-Carlton, this intimate hotel was built as an apartment building. It was owned by the Gore family and was the childhood home of Al Gore. It has an English hunt-club theme and complimentary butler service. The Fairfax is close to Dupont Circle and not far from Georgetown or the Kennedy Center; rooms have views of Embassy Row or Georgetown and the National Cathedral. The renowned Jockey Club restaurant, with its half-timber ceilings, dark wood paneling, and red-checkered tablecloths, serves three meals daily in an intimate atmosphere. The Fairfax Bar is a cozy spot for a drink beside the fire (with piano entertainment some evenings). ✉ *2100 Massachusetts Ave. NW, 20008,* ☎ *202/293–2100 or 800/325–3589,* 𝔽𝔸𝕏 *202/293–0641. 154 rooms, 59 suites. Restaurant, bar, in-room data ports, in-room safes, minibars, room service, in-room VCRs, massage, sauna, exercise room, meeting room, parking (fee). AE, DC, MC, V. Metro: Dupont Circle.*

$–$$ ▥ **Hotel Tabard Inn.** Formed by a linkage of three Victorian town houses, the Tabard is one of the oldest continuously running hotels in D.C. It's furnished throughout with well-broken-in Victorian and American Empire pieces; the floors are creaky, but the hotel exudes a quaint charm. As in any private home, room size and facilities vary considerably (one guest room alternates as a private dining room, and many share bathrooms), and as a result there is a wide range of prices, so be sure to state your desires. Passes are provided to the nearby YMCA, which has extensive fitness facilities. The contemporary restaurant is popular with locals. ✉ *1739 N St. NW, 20036,* ☎ *202/785–1277,* 𝔽𝔸𝕏 *202/785–6173. 40 rooms, 25 with bath. CP. Restaurant, bar, lobby lounge. MC, V. Metro: Dupont Circle.*

Georgetown

$$$$ ▥ **Four Seasons Hotel.** The Four Seasons overlooks the
★   C&O Canal and Rock Creek at the White House edge of Georgetown, where Pennsylvania Avenue ends and the shops and restaurants begin. Rich mahogany paneling,

antiques, spectacular flower arrangements, and extensive greenery abound. Rooms are spacious and bright and have an incredible array of amenities; some bathrooms have sunken tubs. The Four Seasons is kid-friendly, too, with children's menus, games, and activities. Brunch is also a treat at this hotel. ⊠ *2800 Pennsylvania Ave. NW, 20007,* ☏ *202/342–0444 or 800/332–3442,* FAX *202/342–1673. 205 rooms, 55 suites. 2 restaurants, 2 bars, lobby lounge, room service, pool, health club, nightclub, concierge, parking (fee). AE, DC, MC, V. Metro: Foggy Bottom.*

$$ 🏨 **Georgetown Inn.** With an atmosphere reminiscent of a gentleman's sporting club, this quiet, Federal-era, redbrick hotel has an 18th-century flavor. Guest rooms are large and have a Colonial-style decor. The hotel is in the heart of historic Georgetown, near shopping, dining, galleries, and theaters. Free passes to a nearby fitness center are provided. ⊠ *1310 Wisconsin Ave. NW, 20007,* ☏ *202/333–8900 or 800/424–2979,* FAX *202/625–1744. 86 rooms, 10 suites. Restaurant, bar, in-room data ports, room service, parking (fee). AE, DC, MC, V. Metro: Foggy Bottom.*

$$ 🏨 **Georgetown Suites.** If you consider standard hotel rooms cramped and overpriced, the Georgetown Suites—in two buildings a block apart, in the heart of Georgetown—is a find. Suites vary in size but all have large kitchens and voice mail. Children under 12 stay free. ⊠ *1111 30th St. NW, 20007,* ☏ *202/298–7800 or 800/348–7203,* FAX *202/333–5792. 216 suites. CP. Kitchenettes, exercise room, laundry service and dry cleaning, parking (fee). AE, DC, MC, V. Metro: Foggy Bottom.*

$$ 🏨 **Latham Hotel.** This small European-style hotel on Georgetown's fashionable main avenue has immaculate, beautifully decorated rooms, many with treetop views of "George's town," the Potomac River, and the C&O Canal. The hotel is a favorite of Europeans, world leaders, and celebrities. The polished brass and glass lobby leads to Citronelle (☞ Chapter 3), one of the city's best restaurants; a La Madeleine coffee shop is also on site. ⊠ *3000 M St. NW, 20007,* ☏ *202/726–5000 or 800/368–5922,* FAX *202/337–4250. 122 rooms, 21 suites. Restaurant, bar, room service, pool, parking (fee). AE, DC, MC, V. Metro: Foggy Bottom.*

$–$$ 🏨 **Georgetown Dutch Inn.** A half block off M Street, Georgetown's main thoroughfare, this modest, Georgian-style all-suite hotel has large guest rooms and kitchens, and sofa beds and dinette sets in the living rooms. Breakfast is served in a small lobby decorated with 18th-century touches. ⊠ *1075 Thomas Jefferson St. NW, 20007,* ☎ *202/337–0900 or 800/388–2410,* ☎ *202/333–6526. 47 suites. CP. Kitchenettes, room service, laundry service and dry cleaning, meeting rooms, free parking. AE, DC, MC, V. Metro: Foggy Bottom.*

Southwest

$$$ 🏨 **Loews L'Enfant Plaza.** This hotel is just two blocks from the Smithsonian museums and atop a shopping mall–office complex and Metro stop. Guest rooms, which are on the top four floors, have spectacular river, Capitol, or monument views. The hotel's proximity to several government agencies (USDA, USPS, USIA, and DOT) makes it popular with business travelers. All rooms have coffeemakers, and both bathrooms and bedrooms have TVs and phones. "Club" guest rooms have fax machines. ⊠ *L'Enfant Plaza SW, 20024,* ☎ *202/484–1000 or 800/223–0888,* ☎ *202/646–4456. 348 rooms, 22 suites. Restaurant, 2 bars, minibars, room service, in-room VCRs, indoor pool, health club, parking (fee). AE, DC, MC, V. Metro: L'Enfant Plaza.*

$$–$$$ 🏨 **Holiday Inn Capitol.** One block from the National Air and Space Museum, this large hotel is family-friendly yet well equipped for business travelers. Guest rooms are attractively decorated in forest green and tan with mahogany furniture, paisley bedspreads, and richly textured upholstery. Children 19 and under stay free (and those under 12 eat free in the hotel's restaurant) when accompanied by a paying adult; cribs are also free. The downtown sightseeing trolley stops here, and you can buy discount tickets for NASM's IMAX movies at the front desk. Relax in the lounge and, with the purchase of a drink, enjoy an all-you-can-eat buffet from 4:30 to 6:30 for just a couple of dollars. ⊠ *550 C St. SW, 20024,* ☎ *202/479–4000,* ☎ *202/488–4627. 505 rooms, 24 suites. Restaurant, bar, food court, in-room data ports, no-smoking floors, room service, pool, exercise room, coin laundry, meeting rooms, parking (fee). AE, D, DC, MC, V. Metro: L'Enfant Plaza.*

$ 🏨 **Channel Inn.** The only hotel on Washington's waterfront, this property overlooks Washington Channel, the marina, and the Potomac River. Almost every room has a small balcony. Public areas and meetings rooms have a nautical motif with mahogany panels and marine artifacts. The terrace allows scenic cocktail-quaffing and dining in warm weather. The Mall, Smithsonian, Treasury, and several other government offices are close. Access to a nearby health club is free. ⊠ *650 Water St. SW, 20024,* ☎ *202/554–2400 or 800/368–5668,* FAX *202/863–1164. 100 rooms. Restaurant, bar, café, pool, meeting rooms, free parking. AE, D, DC, MC, V. Metro: Waterfront.*

Northwest/Upper Connecticut Avenue

$$$$ 🏨 **Omni Shoreham Hotel.** This immense facility, with seven ballrooms, has hosted the world's rich and famous since 1930, when its Art Deco– and Renaissance-style lobby opened its doors for business. Guest rooms have marble-floored baths with phones and hair dryers, traditional cherry furniture, and floral spreads with dust ruffles. The hotel is a moderate walk from Rock Creek Park, Adams-Morgan, and the National Zoo. ⊠ *2500 Calvert St. NW, 20008,* ☎ *202/234–0700 or 800/843–6664,* FAX *202/756–5145. 812 rooms, 24 suites. Restaurant, bar, deli, in-room data ports, minibars, room service, pool, exercise room, laundry and dry cleaning, parking (fee). AE, D, DC, MC, V. Metro: Woodley Park.*

$ 🏨 **Doyle Normandy.** A small, quaint European-style hotel
★   on a quiet street in the embassy area of Connecticut Avenue, the Doyle Normandy was formerly the Normandy Inn. Rooms are neat, cozy, and attractively decorated; all have refrigerators and coffeemakers. Each Tuesday evening a wine-and-cheese reception is held for guests. You can select a book from the small library and read by the fireplace in the lobby while enjoying the complimentary coffee and tea in the morning and afternoon. ⊠ *2118 Wyoming Ave. NW, 20008,* ☎ *202/483–1350 or 800/424–3729,* FAX *202/387–8241. 75 rooms. CP. In-room data ports, in-room safes, parking (fee). AE, D, MC, V. Metro: Dupont Circle.*

West End/Foggy Bottom

$$$$ 🏨 **Swissotel Washington Watergate.** The Watergate is
★   accustomed to serving the world's elite. The lobby sets a

genteel tone with its classic columns, Asian rugs on black-and-white checkerboard marble, subdued lighting, and soothing classical music. The hotel is on the Potomac River, across the street from the Kennedy Center, and a short walk from the State Department and Georgetown. Originally intended as apartments, the guest rooms are large, and all have walk-in closets, fax machines, kitchens or wet bars, and refrigerators. The riverside restaurant, Aquarelle, serves sophisticated Euro-American cuisine. There's complimentary limousine service weekdays 7 AM–10 AM. ✉ *2650 Virginia Ave. NW, 20037,* ☎ *202/965–2300 or 800/424–2736,* FAX *202/337–7915. 80 rooms, 144 suites. Restaurant, bar, in-room safes, refrigerators, room service, indoor pool, health club, parking (fee). AE, DC, MC, V. Metro: Foggy Bottom.*

$$$$ ★ 🏨 **Washington Monarch.** Formerly the ANA, this hotel is a stylish combination of the contemporary and the traditional located at the Georgetown end of downtown Washington. The glassed lobby and about a third of the bright, airy rooms have views of the central courtyard and gardens, which are popular for weddings. The hotel's informal restaurant, the Bistro, has the flavor of 19th-century Paris and contains an antique mahogany bar. ✉ *2401 M St. NW, 20037,* ☎ *202/429–2400 or 877/222–2266,* FAX *202/457–5010. 406 rooms, 9 suites. 2 restaurants, bar, café, lobby lounge, in-room data ports, in-room safes, minibars, room service, indoor lap pool, beauty salon, sauna, steam room, health club, parking (fee). AE, DC, MC, V. Metro: Foggy Bottom.*

$$ 🏨 **George Washington University Inn.** This hotel is a few blocks from the Kennedy Center and the State Department and two blocks from George Washington University, which allows free use of the its fitness center. The front entrance is through gray wrought-iron gates into a courtyard. Beveled glass doors open into a small lobby floored in gray marble. Rooms are varied in size and configuration and have Colonial-style furniture, refrigerators, microwaves, and coffeemakers. Zuki Moon, a Japanese noodle house and tea garden, is off the lobby. ✉ *824 New Hampshire Ave. NW, 20037,* ☎ *202/337–6620 or 800/426–4455,* FAX *202/ 298–7499. 48 rooms, 31 suites, 16 efficiencies. Restaurant, coin laundry, laundry service, meeting rooms, parking (fee). AE, D, DC, MC, V. Metro: Foggy Bottom.*

$$ ▣ **One Washington Circle Hotel.** For such an address, elegant rooms, and facilities, this hotel is a bargain. Rooms are like very well furnished apartments, with five different floor plans, all including separate bedrooms. Every room has a balcony, refrigerator, and at least a microwave; most have kitchenettes. Children under 16 stay free. The American-style West End Cafe has live music Tuesday–Saturday nights and during the Sunday brunch buffet. ✉ *1 Washington Circle NW, 20037,* ☎ *202/872–1680 or 800/424–9671,* FAX *202/223–3961. 151 suites. Restaurant, bar, minibars, refrigerators, room service, pool, exercise room, piano, coin laundry, laundry service and dry cleaning, meeting rooms, parking (fee). AE, D, DC, MC, V. Metro: Foggy Bottom.*

5 Nightlife and the Arts

THE ARTS

By John F.
Kelly

Updated
by Holly
Bass

For most of its history, the capital's main claim to fame has been its role as the nation's center of political power. But in the past 20 years, D.C. has gone from being a cultural desert to a thriving arts center—a place where national artists develop new works. The Kennedy Center is a world-class venue, home of the National Symphony Orchestra (NSO), now conducted by Leonard Slatkin, and host to Broadway shows, ballet, modern dance, opera, and more. Lines wrap around the block at the National Theatre for such big hit musicals as *The Wizard of Oz* and *Les Misérables*. Washington even has its own "off-Broadway": a half dozen or so plucky theaters scattered around the city offer new works and new twists on old works. Several art galleries present highly regarded chamber music series. The service bands from the area's numerous military bases ensure an endless supply of martial music of the John Philip Sousa variety as well as rousing renditions of more contemporary tunes.

Several publications have calendars of entertainment events. The *Washington Post* "Weekend" section comes out on Friday, and its "Guide to the Lively Arts" is printed daily. On Thursday, look for the *Washington Times* "Weekend" section and the free weekly *Washington CityPaper*. Also consult the "City Lights" section in the monthly *Washingtonian* magazine.

Tickets

ProTix (☎ 703/218–6500) takes reservations for events at Arena Stage, Center Stage, Ford's Theatre, the Holocaust Museum, the 9:30 Club, and Signature Theater. It also has outlets in selected Waxie Maxies.

Ticketmaster (☎ 202/432–7328 or 800/551–7328) takes phone charges for events at most venues around the city. You can purchase Ticketmaster tickets in person at all Hecht's department stores. No refunds or exchanges are allowed.

TicketPlace sells half-price, day-of-performance tickets for selected shows; a "menu board" lists available performances. Only cash is accepted, and there's a 10% service charge per order. TicketPlace is also a full-price Ticketmaster outlet. It's closed on Sunday and Monday, but tickets for performances on those days are sold on Saturday. ⊠ *Old Post Office Pavilion, 1100 Pennsylvania Ave. NW,* ☎ *202/ 842–5387. Metro: Federal Triangle.*

Concert Halls

Concert halls tend to focus on music, but many present performances of all types. It's not uncommon for a venue to present modern dance one week, a rock or classical music concert another week, and a theatrical performance the next.

Crampton Auditorium. This 1,500-seat auditorium on Howard University's campus regularly presents jazz, gospel, and R&B concerts. It is also the site of many special events. ⊠ *2455 6th St. NW,* ☎ *202/806–7198.*

DAR Constitution Hall. The 3,700-seat Constitution Hall hosts visiting musicians who perform everything from jazz to pop to rap. ⊠ *18th and C Sts. NW,* ☎ *202/628–4780.*

George Mason University. The GMU campus in suburban Virginia is home to the ambitious Center for the Arts, a glittering complex. Music, ballet, and drama performances regularly take place in the 1,900-seat concert hall, the 500-seat proscenium Harris Theater, and the intimate 150-seat Black Box Theater. Also on campus is the 9,500-seat Patriot Center, site of pop acts and sporting events. ⊠ *Rte. 123 and Braddock Rd., Fairfax, VA,* ☎ *703/993–8888, 703/993– 3000, or 202/432–7328.*

John F. Kennedy Center for the Performing Arts. Any search for cultured entertainment should start here, whether you want to see an international symphony orchestra, a troupe of dancers, a Broadway musical, or a comedic whodunit. The "KenCen" is actually five stages under one roof: the Concert Hall, home of the National Symphony Orchestra (NSO); the 2,200-seat Opera House, the setting for ballet, modern dance, opera, and large-scale musicals; the Eisenhower Theater, usually used for drama; the Terrace Theater, a Philip Johnson–designed space that showcases chamber groups and experimental works; and the Theater Lab, home to cabaret-style performances (since 1987 the audience-participation hit mystery *Shear Madness* has been playing here). You can also catch a free performance every evening at 6 PM on the Millennium Stage in the center's Grand Foyer. ⊠ *New Hampshire Ave. and Rock Creek Pkwy. NW,* ☎ *202/467–4600 or 800/444–1324.*

Lisner Auditorium. A 1,500-seat theater on the campus of George Washington University, Lisner Auditorium is the setting for pop, classical, and choral music shows as well as modern dance performances and musical theater. ⊠ *21st and H Sts. NW,* ☎ *202/994–6800.*

MCI Arena. In addition to being the home of the Washington Capitals hockey and Washington Wizards basketball teams, this brand-new 19,000-seat arena also hosts many concerts, ice-skating events, and the circus. Parking can be a problem, but the arena is conveniently situated near several Metro lines. ⊠ *601 F St. NW,* ☎ *202/628–3200.*

Merriweather Post Pavilion. In Columbia, Maryland, an hour's drive north of Washington, Merriweather Post is an outdoor pavilion with some covered seating. In warmer months it hosts big-name pop acts. ⊠ *Broken Land Pkwy., Exit 18B off Rte. 21 N,* ☎ *301/982–1800 concert information; 301/596–0660 off-season.*

National Gallery of Art. Free concerts by the National Gallery Orchestra, conducted by George Manos, and performances by visiting recitalists and ensembles are held in the venerable West Building's West Garden Court on Sunday evenings from October to June. Most performances highlight classical music, though April's American Music Festival often features jazz. Entry is first-come, first-served. ⊠ *6th St. and Constitution Ave. NW,* ☎ *202/842–6941 or 202/ 842–6698.*

Nissan Pavilion at Stone Ridge. Cellar Door Productions, the country's largest concert promoter, built its own 25,000-seat venue in 1995. In rural Virginia, about an hour from downtown Washington, the pavilion hosts all types of music. ⊠ *7800 Cellar Door Dr., Bristow, VA,* ☎ *703/ 754–6400 or 202/432–7328.*

Smithsonian Institution. The Smithsonian presents a rich assortment of music—both free and ticketed. Jazz, musical theater, and popular standards are performed in the National Museum of American History. In the third-floor Hall of Musical Instruments, musicians periodically play historic instruments from the museum's collection. In warm weather shows are held in the courtyard between the National Portrait Gallery and the National Museum of American Art. The Smithsonian Associates Program offers everything from a cappella groups to Cajun zydeco bands; many perform in the National Museum of Natural History's Baird Auditorium. *Smithsonian Castle:* ⊠ *1000 Jefferson Dr. SW; Baird Auditorium:* ⊠ *10th St. and Constitution Ave. NW;* ☎ *202/357–2700; 202/357–3030 Smithsonian Associates Program.*

USAirways Arena. The area's top venue for big-name pop, rock, and rap acts seats 20,000. ⊠ *1 Harry S. Truman Dr., Landover, MD,* ☎ *301/350–3400 or 202/432–7328.*

Wolf Trap Farm Park. Just off the Dulles Toll Road, about a half hour from downtown, Wolf Trap is the only national park dedicated to the performing arts. On its grounds is the Filene Center, an outdoor theater that is the scene of pop, jazz, opera, ballet, and dance performances each June through September. On performance nights, Metrorail operates a $3.50 round-trip shuttle bus between the West Falls Church Metro station and the Filene Center. The fare is exact change only, and the bus leaves 20 minutes after the show, or no later than 11 PM, whether the show is over or not. The rest of the year, the intimate, indoor Barns at Wolf Trap hosts folk, jazz, rock, chamber, opera, and other music. For tickets, call ProTix (☞ Tickets, *above*). ⊠ *1551 Trap Rd., Vienna, VA,* ☎ *703/255–1900; 703/938–2404 Barns at Wolf Trap.*

Dance

Dance Place. A studio theater that presented its first performance in 1980, Dance Place is the site of a wide assortment of modern and ethnic dance shows most weekends. It also conducts dance classes daily. ⊠ *3225 8th St. NE,* ☎ *202/269–1600.*

Joy of Motion. A dance studio by day, Joy of Motion is the home of several area troupes that perform in the studio's

Jack Guidone Theatre, including City Dance Ensemble (modern), New Release Dance Company (a student group), the Spanish Dance Ensemble (flamenco), and TAPestry (you guessed it—tap). A second studio in Dupont Circle offers classes only. ⊠ *5207 Wisconsin Ave. NW,* ☎ *202/387–3042;* ⊠ *1643 Connecticut Ave. NW,* ☎ *202/387–0911.*

Mount Vernon College. The In Series at this small, women's liberal arts college presents music, performance art, theater, classical music, and dance companies in the fall and spring. Past participants in the dance series have included the troupes of Robert Small, Nancy Meehan, and Gus Solomons Jr. ⊠ *2100 Foxhall Rd. NW,* ☎ *202/625–4655.*

Washington Ballet. Between September and May this company presents classical and contemporary ballets—including works by such choreographers as George Balanchine, Marius Petipa, and Choo-San Goh—at the Kennedy Center (☞ Concert Halls, *above*) and the Warner Theatre (☞ Theater and Performance Art, *below*). Each December the Washington Ballet performs *The Nutcracker.* ☎ *202/362–3606.*

Film

American Film Institute. More than 700 movies—including contemporary and classic foreign and American films—are shown each year at the American Film Institute's theater in the Kennedy Center. Filmmakers and actors are often present to discuss their work. ⊠ *Kennedy Center, New Hampshire Ave. and Rock Creek Pkwy. NW,* ☎ *202/785–4600.*

Arlington Cinema 'N' Drafthouse. A suburban Virginia alternative to movie theaters in the capital, Arlington Cinema 'N' Drafthouse serves various libations and hot dogs, pizza, and other snacks during its films. You must be 21 or over or have a parent with you to attend. ⊠ *2903 Columbia Pike, Arlington, VA,* ☎ *703/486–2345.*

Cineplex Odeon Uptown. You don't find many like this old beauty anymore: one huge, multiplex-dwarfing screen; Art Deco flourishes instead of a bland, boxy interior; a wonderful balcony; and—in one happy concession to modernity—crystalline Dolby sound. You'll find other Cineplex Odeon theaters near Dupont Circle, in Georgetown, and around upper Wisconsin Avenue. ⊠ *3426 Connecticut Ave. NW,* ☎ *202/966–5400.*

Filmfest DC. An annual citywide festival of international cinema, the DC International Film Festival, or Filmfest, as it is affectionately known, takes place in late April and early May. Films are shown at various venues throughout the city. You can purchase tickets in advance over the phone; otherwise, ticket sales and seating are on a first-come, first-served basis—and some films *do* sell out. ⊠ *Box 21396, 20009,* ☎ *202/724–5613.*

Hirshhorn Museum. If you love avant-garde and experimental film, check out the weekly movies—often first-run documentaries, features, and short films—that are shown here free. ⊠ *7th and Independence Ave. SW,* ☎ *202/357–2700.*

National Archives. Historical films are shown here daily. Check the calendar of events for listings. ⊠ *8th and Constitution Aves. NW,* ☎ *202/501–5000.*

National Gallery of Art East Building. Free classic and international films (they often complement exhibits) are shown in this museum's large auditorium. You can pick up a film calendar at the museum. ⊠ *4th and Constitution NW,* ☎ *202/737–4215.*

National Geographic Society. Free educational films with a scientific, geographic, or anthropological focus are shown here weekly. ⊠ *17th and M Sts. NW,* ☎ *202/857–7588.*

Music

Chamber Music

Corcoran Gallery of Art. Hungary's Takacs String Quartet and the Cleveland Quartet are among the chamber groups that appear in the Corcoran's Musical Evening Series, one Friday each month from October to May (there are also some summer offerings). Concerts are followed by a reception with the artists. ⊠ *17th St. and New York Ave. NW,* ☎ *202/639–1700.*

Folger Shakespeare Library. The library's internationally acclaimed resident chamber music ensemble, the Folger Consort, regularly presents a selection of instrumental and vocal pieces from the medieval, Renaissance, and Baroque periods. The season runs from October to May. ⊠ *201 E. Capitol St. SE,* ☎ *202/544–7077.*

National Academy of Sciences. Free performances are given October through May in the academy's 670-seat auditorium, which has almost perfect acoustics. Both the National Musical Arts Chamber Ensemble and the United States Marines Chamber Orchestra perform regularly. ⊠ *2100 C St. NW,* ☎ *202/334–2436.*

Phillips Collection. Duncan Phillips's mansion is more than an art museum. From September through May the long, paneled music room hosts Sunday-afternoon recitals. Chamber groups from around the world perform; May is devoted to artists from the Washington area. Concerts begin at 5 PM, but arrive early for decent seats. ⊠ *1600 21st St. NW,* ☎ *202/387–2151.*

Choral Music

Basilica of the National Shrine of the Immaculate Conception. Choral and church groups frequently perform in this impressive venue. ⊠ *Michigan Ave. and 4th St. NE,* ☎ *202/ 526–8300.*

Choral Arts Society of Washington. The 180-voice Choral Arts Society choir performs a varied selection of classical pieces at the Kennedy Center (☞ Concert Halls, *above*) from September to June. Three Christmas sing-alongs are scheduled each December. ☎ *202/244–3669.*

Washington National Cathedral. Choral and church groups frequently perform in this grand cathedral. Admission to these events is generally free. ⊠ *Wisconsin and Massachusetts Aves. NW,* ☎ *202/537–6200.*

Opera

Mount Vernon College. The college's intimate Hand Chapel is the setting for otherwise rarely produced chamber operas September–June. ⊠ *2100 Foxhall Rd. NW,* ☎ *202/ 625–4655.*

Opera Theater of Northern Virginia. During each of its three seasons (October, January through February, and May) this company stages an opera, sung in English, at an

Arlington, Virginia, community theater. Each December the company also presents a one-act opera especially for young audiences. ☎ 703/528–1433.

Summer Opera Theater Company. An independent professional troupe, the Summer Opera Theater Company stages one opera in June and one in July. ✉ *Hartke Theater, Catholic University, 620 Michigan Ave. NE,* ☎ *202/ 526–1669.*

Washington Opera. Eight operas—presented in their original languages with English supertitles—are performed each season (October–March) in the Kennedy Center's Opera House and Eisenhower Theater (☞ *Concert Halls, above*). Performances are often sold out to subscribers, but you can purchase returned tickets an hour before curtain time. Standing-room tickets go on sale at the Kennedy Center box office each Saturday at 10 AM for the following week's performances. ☎ *202/295–2400 or 800/876–7372.*

Orchestra
National Symphony Orchestra. The season at the Kennedy Center is from September to June. In summer the NSO performs at Wolf Trap (☞ *Concert Halls, above*) and gives free concerts at the Carter Barron Amphitheatre (☞ *Performance Series, below*) and, on Memorial Day and Labor Day weekends and July 4, on the West Lawn of the Capitol. The cheapest way to hear the NSO perform in the Kennedy Center Concert Hall is to get $13 second-tier side seats. ☎ *202/ 416–8100.*

Performance Series
Armed Forces Concert Series. From June to August, service bands from all four military branches perform on Monday, Tuesday, Thursday, and Friday evenings, on the East Terrace of the Capitol and several nights a week at the Sylvan Theater (☞ *below*) on the Washington Monument grounds. The traditional band concerts include marches, patriotic numbers, and some classical music. The air-force celebrity series features popular artists such as Earl Klugh and Keiko Matsui. The bands often perform free concerts at other locations throughout the year. ☎ *202/767–5658 air force; 703/696–3718 army; 202/433–4011 marines; 202/433– 2525 navy.*

Carter Barron Amphitheatre. On Saturday and Sunday nights from mid-June to August this lovely 4,250-seat outdoor theater in Rock Creek Park hosts pop, jazz, gospel, and rhythm-and-blues artists such as Chick Corea, Nancy Wilson, and Tito Puente. The National Symphony Orchestra also performs, and for two weeks in June the Shakespeare Theatre presents a free play by the Bard. ⊠ *16th St. and Colorado Ave. NW,* ☏ *202/426–6837.*

District Curators. This independent, nonprofit organization presents adventurous contemporary performers from around the world in spaces around the city, mostly in summer (June–August). Much of the group's season is encompassed by its Jazz Arts Festival. Past artists have included Laurie Anderson, Philip Glass, the World Saxophone Quartet, and Cassandra Wilson. ☏ *202/966–6310.*

Ft. Dupont Summer Theater. When it comes to music in Washington, even the National Park Service gets in on the act. The NPS presents national and international jazz artists at 8:30 on Friday and Saturday evenings from July to August at the outdoor Ft. Dupont Summer Theater. Wynton Marsalis, Betty Carter, and Ramsey Lewis are among the artists who have performed free concerts. ⊠ *Minnesota Ave. and Randall Circle SE,* ☏ *202/426–7723 or 202/619–7222.*

Sylvan Theater. Military bands from all four branches usually perform alfresco at the Sylvan Theater from June to August, Tuesday, Friday, and Sunday nights at 8 PM. The monument is undergoing renovation that is due to be completed in the year 2000, and schedules are subject to change. ⊠ *Washington Monument grounds,* ☏ *202/619–7222.*

Transparent Productions. Composed of a small group of dedicated jazz connoisseurs, this not-for-profit presenting organization regularly brings acclaimed avant-garde jazz musicians to intimate clubs and university stages. Past performers have included guitarist Joe Morris, bassist William Parker, and saxophonist Anthony Braxton. Tickets are usually in the $10 range, with 100% of the revenues going directly to the artists. ☏ *202/232–5061.*

Washington Performing Arts Society. This independent nonprofit organization books high-quality classical music, ballet, modern dance, and some drama and performance art into halls around the city. WPAS offers several series: Arte AmericA presents Latin American artists such as Tito Puente and Ballet Hispanico; the celebrity orchestra series presents stars like Itzhak Perlman and YoYo Ma; and the educational Family Friendly Series has everything from European circuses to Charlie Chaplin films. ☎ *202/833–9800.*

Theater and Performance Art

Commercial Theaters

Arena Stage. The city's most respected resident company (established in 1950) was also the first outside New York to win a Tony award. It presents a wide-ranging season in its three theaters: the Fichandler Stage, the proscenium Kreeger, and the cabaret-style Old Vat Room. ✉ *6th St. and Maine Ave. SW,* ☎ *202/488–3300.*

Ford's Theatre. Looking much as it did when President Lincoln was shot at a performance of *Our American Cousin,* Ford's hosts both dramas and musicals, many with family appeal. Dickens's *A Christmas Carol* is presented each holiday season. ✉ *511 10th St. NW,* ☎ *202/347–4833.*

Lincoln Theatre. From the 1920s to the 1940s, the Lincoln hosted the same performers as the Cotton Club and the Apollo Theatre in New York City: Cab Calloway, Lena Horne, Duke Ellington. The 1,250-seater shows films and welcomes such acts as the Count Basie Orchestra and the Harlem Boys and Girls Choir. ✉ *1215 U St. NW,* ☎ *202/ 328–6000.*

National Theatre. Destroyed by fire and rebuilt four times, the National Theatre has operated in the same location since 1835. It presents touring Broadway shows and offers free children's shows on Saturday. Winter and spring see a series of free Monday-night shows ranging from Asian dance to performance art to a cappella cabarets. ✉ *1321 Pennsylvania Ave. NW,* ☎ *202/628–6161.*

Shakespeare Theatre. Five plays—four by the Bard, another a classic from his era—are staged each year by the acclaimed Shakespeare Theatre troupe in a state-of-the-art 450-seat space. For two weeks each June the company has its own version of New York's Shakespeare in the Park: a free play under the stars at Carter Barron Amphitheatre (☞ Performance Series, *above*). ⊠ *450 7th St. NW,* ☎ *202/547–1122.*

Warner Theatre. One of Washington's grand theaters, this 1924 building hosts road shows, dance recitals, pop music, and the occasional comedy act. ⊠ *13th and E Sts. NW,* ☎ *202/783–4000.*

Small Theaters and Companies

Often performing in churches and other less-than-ideal settings, Washington's small theaters and companies offer some beautifully staged and acted plays and musicals that can be every bit as enthralling as—and often more daring than—their blockbuster counterparts. In the past few years there has been a veritable explosion of new companies, many of which tackle difficult, controversial, and specialized subjects. All compete fiercely for the Helen Hayes Award, Washington's version of the Tony. Several acclaimed alternative stages are on 14th Street NW and near Dupont Circle; take a cab after dark.

District of Columbia Arts Center. Known by area artists as DCAC, this cross-genre space shows changing exhibits in its gallery and presents avant-garde performance art and experimental plays in its small black-box theater. ⊠ *2438 18th St. NW,* ☎ *202/462–7833.*

Gala Hispanic Theatre. The company produces Spanish classics as well as contemporary and modern Latin American plays in both Spanish and English. ⊠ *1625 Park Rd. NW,* ☎ *202/234–7174.*

Olney Theatre. Musicals, comedies, and summer stock are presented in a converted barn, an hour from downtown in the Maryland countryside. ⊠ *2001 Olney–Sandy Spring Rd., Olney, MD,* ☎ *301/924–3400.*

Signature Theatre. This plucky group performs in a 126-seat black-box theater in a converted bumper-plating facility in suburban Virginia. Sondheim is a favorite with Signature, and Signature is said to be a favorite of Sondheim's. ⊠ *3806 S. Four Mile Run Dr., Arlington, VA,* ☎ *703/820–9771.*

Source Theatre. The 107-seat Source Theatre presents established plays with a sharp satirical edge and modern interpretations of classics. Each July and August, Source hosts the Washington Theater Festival, a series of new plays, many by local playwrights. ⊠ *1835 14th St. NW,* ☎ *202/ 462–1073.*

Studio Theatre. This small, independent company has an eclectic season of classic and offbeat plays. With two 200-seat theaters, the Mead and the Milton, as well as the 50-seat Secondstage (home to particularly experimental works), the Studio Theatre is one of the busiest groups in the city. ⊠ *1333 P St. NW,* ☎ *202/332–3300.*

Washington Stage Guild. Washington Stage Guild performs the classics as well as more contemporary works in historic Carroll Hall. Shaw is a specialty. ⊠ *924 G St. NW,* ☎ *202/ 529–2084.*

Woolly Mammoth. Unusual, imaginatively produced shows have earned Woolly Mammoth good reviews and favorable comparisons to Chicago's Steppenwolf. ⊠ *1401 Church St. NW,* ☎ *202/393–3939.*

NIGHTLIFE

Washington's nightlife includes watering holes, comedy clubs, discos, and intimate musical venues that cater to a variety of customers—from proper political appointees to blue-collar regulars in from the 'burbs. Many places are clustered in key areas, making a night of bar-hopping relatively easy. Georgetown has dozens of bars, nightclubs, and restaurants on M Street east and west of Wisconsin Avenue and on Wisconsin Avenue north of M Street. Along the 18th Street strip in Adams-Morgan, bordered by Columbia Road and Florida Avenue, you'll find several small live-music clubs, ethnic restaurants, and bars. West of Florida Avenue, the U Street corridor—which several publications have called one of the hippest neighborhoods in the country—appeals to young people looking for musical entertainment from hip-hop to alternative rock to reggae. On a stretch of Pennsylvania Avenue between 2nd and 4th streets, you'll find a half dozen Capitol Hill bars. For a happenin' happy hour, head to the intersection of 19th and M streets NW, which is near the lawyer- and lobbyist-filled downtown.

To check out the local scene, consult Friday's "Weekend" section in the *Washington Post* and the free weekly *Washington CityPaper*. The free *Metro Weekly* and *Women in the Life* magazines offer insights on gay and lesbian nightlife. It's also a good idea to call clubs ahead of time to find out what's on. Reservations are advised for comedy clubs; places where reservations are essential are noted below.

Most bars in D.C. have cover charges for live bands and DJs, generally on the weekends. Expect to pay anywhere from $5 to $15 at most dance clubs. Jazz and comedy clubs often have higher cover charges along with drink minimums. Last call in D.C. is 2 AM, and most bars and clubs close by 3 AM on weekends and between midnight and 2 AM during the week. The exceptions are after-hours dance clubs and bars with kitchens that stay open late.

Acoustic/Folk/Country Clubs

Washington has a very active folk scene. For information on different folk events—from *contra* (a form of folk) dancing to storytelling to open singing—call the recorded information line of the **Folklore Society of Greater Washington** (☎ 202/546–2228).

Birchmere. Birchmere is one of the best places this side of the Blue Ridge Mountains to hear acoustic folk and bluegrass acts. Audiences come to listen, and the management politely insists on no distracting chatter. ⊠ *3701 Mt. Vernon Ave., Alexandria, VA,* ☎ *703/549–7500.*

Soho Tea and Coffee. Quality singer-songwriters share the stage with poets and writers at Soho's open mike every Wednesday, in addition to appearing in featured performances throughout the month. Other pluses: the café serves as a gallery space with changing monthly exhibits, stays open very late, and serves breakfast all day along with its regular menu of light fare. ⊠ *2150 P St. NW,* ☎ *202/463–7646.*

Bars and Lounges

Bardo Rodeo. A Plymouth Fury crashing through the window of a converted car dealership sets the tone of this sub-

urban Virginia brew pub, which bills itself as the largest
such establishment on the East Coast. Sunday–Thursday
it's ladies' night at the pub's 18 pool tables, where women
can play free. It's a frenetic place—with loud music, mis-
matched furniture, and a sometimes lackadaisical approach
to service—but it brews a changing assortment of stouts,
ales, and bitters, and it has a wonderful approach to nam-
ing the food: "She Was So Fine I'd Eat the Corn Out of Her
Daddy's Garden" is a quesadilla. ✉ *2000 Wilson Blvd.,
Arlington, VA*, ☎ *703/527–9399.*

Brickskeller. This is *the* place to go when you want something more exotic than a Bud Lite. More than 800 brands
of beer are for sale—from Central American lagers to U.S.
microbrewed ales. Servers actually have to go to "beer
school" to land the job here. ✉ *1523 22nd St. NW*, ☎ *202/
293–1885.*

Capital City Brewing Company. At the New York Avenue
location of this microbrewery, a gleaming copper bar dom-
inates the airy room; metal steps lead up to where the
brews—from bitters to bocks—are made. Consult the brew-
master's chalkboard to see what's on tap. The fabulous Postal
Square site on Massachusetts Avenue has five 30-keg copper serving vessels in the center of the restaurant and a gorgeous vault door left over from the days when the building
was a post office. ✉ *1100 New York Ave. NW*, ☎ *202/
628–2222;* ✉ *2 Massachusetts Ave. NE*, ☎ *202/842–2337.*

Chi Cha Lounge. Groups of stylish young patrons relax on
sofas and armchairs—enjoying the bar's menu of Andean
appetizers, homemade sangria, and cocktails—while Latin
jazz plays in the background. It gets packed on weekends,
so come early to get a coveted sofa along the back wall,
where it's easier to see—and be seen. Sunday through Tuesday, for a small price, you can indulge in a Turkish water
pipe filled with imported honey-cured tobacco. ✉ *1624 U
St. NW*, ☎ *202/234–8400.*

Dubliner. Snug paneled rooms, thick Guinness, and nightly
live entertainment make Washington's premier Irish pub popular among Capitol Hill staffers. ✉ *520 N. Capitol St. NW*,
☎ *202/737–3773.*

Fishmarket. There's something different in just about every section of the Fishmarket—a multilevel, multiroom space in Old Town Alexandria—from piano-bar crooner to ragtime piano shouter to guitar strummer. The operative word here is *boisterous*. If you really like beer, order the largest size; it comes in a glass big enough to wash your face in. ⊠ *105 King St., Alexandria, VA,* ☏ *703/836–5676.*

Hawk 'n' Dove. Regulars at this friendly bar in a neighborhood dominated by the Capitol and the Library of Congress include politicos, lobbyists, and well-behaved marines from a nearby barracks. ⊠ *329 Pennsylvania Ave. SE,* ☏ *202/543–3300.*

Sign of the Whale. The best hamburger in town is available at the bar of this well-known post-preppie–neo-yuppie haven. ⊠ *1825 M St. NW,* ☏ *202/785–1110.*

Yacht Club. Enormously popular with well-dressed, older singles, this suburban Maryland lounge is the brainchild of irrepressible entrepreneur and matchmaker Tommy Curtis, who measures his success by the number of engagements and marriages spawned here. At last count it was approaching 103. The bar is closed Sunday–Tuesday. ⊠ *8111 Woodmont Ave., Bethesda, MD,* ☏ *301/654–2396.*

Comedy Clubs

The number of comedy groups in Washington that welcome, indeed rely on, the zany suggestions of audience members has mushroomed. These improvisation groups pop up at various venues, performing in the laughs-at-any-cost style of Chicago's Second City troupe, but many disappear as quickly as they appeared.

Capitol Steps. The musical political satire of the Capitol Steps, a group of current and former Hill staffers, is presented on Friday and Saturday at Chelsea's (☞ Dance Clubs, *below*), a Georgetown nightclub, and occasionally at other spots around town. ☏ *202/298–8222 Chelsea's; 703/683–8330 Capitol Steps.*

Comedy Connection. The Comedy Connection at the Arts Theater hosts comics every Friday and Saturday. Comedians such as Martin Lawrence, Tommy Davidson, and Jimmie Walker call the Connection home when in town. (Note: tennis shoes are not considered appropriate attire here, and the club has a two-drink minimum in addition to a cover charge.) ⊠ *312 Main St., Laurel, MD,* ☎ *301/490–1993.*

ComedySportz. Here, two teams of improv artists go to work to make you laugh on Friday and Saturday nights. ⊠ *Fun Factory, 3112 Mt. Vernon Ave., Alexandria, VA,* ☎ *703/ 684–5212.*

Gross National Product. After years of spoofing Republican administrations with such shows as *BushCapades* and *Man Without a Contra,* then aiming its barbs at the Democrats in *Clintoons,* the irreverent comedy troupe Gross National Product was most recently performing *All the President's Women.* ☎ *202/783–7212 GNP for location and reservations.*

Headliners. Intimate rooms in two suburban hotels host local and regional acts on weekdays and national talent on weekends. Reservations are essential. ⊠ *Holiday Inn, 2460 Eisenhower Ave., Alexandria, VA,* ☎ *703/379–4242;* ⊠ *Comfort Zone, Bethesda Naval Base, Bethesda, MD,* ☎ *301/942–4242.*

Improv. A heavyweight on the Washington comedy scene, the Improv is descended from the club that sparked the stand-up boomlet in New York City and across the country. Name headliners are common. ⊠ *1140 Connecticut Ave. NW,* ☎ *202/296–7008.*

Dance Clubs

Washington's dance clubs seem to be constantly re-creating themselves. Club owners rent their spaces to entrepreneurs who tailor the music and ambience to a certain type of crowd. Thus, a club might offer heavy "industrial" music on a Wednesday, host a largely gay clientele on a Thursday, and thump to the sounds of '70s disco on a Friday. Those who like to club-hop will find five club hubs: Georgetown; Adams-Morgan; U Street; the intersection of 18th and M streets, just south of Dupont Circle; and along 9th Street NW near Metro Center.

Chelsea's. At this elegant Georgetown club near the C&O Canal, the DJs trot the globe. Depending on the night, the club pulses to the rhythms of Arabic, Latin, or Iranian music. Call ahead to find out each night's theme. ⊠ *1055 Thomas Jefferson St. NW,* ☎ *202/298–8222.*

Dancers. In suburban Maryland, "dancers" is an apt description of the clientele as well as the club. This is no place for wallflowers; people come here to shake it. They're attracted by the 1,200-square-ft dance floor and the club's no-smoking, no-alcohol policy. The calendar of special events changes weekly but focuses on lessons followed by a dance party and everything from tango and waltz to salsa and swing. ⊠ *4609 Willow La., Bethesda, MD,* ☎ *301/654–7447.*

Habana Village. No matter what the temperature outside, it's always balmy inside Habana Village. The tiny dance floor is packed nightly with couples moving to the latest salsa and merengue tunes. When it's time to cool down, you can head to one of several lounges in this converted four-story town house and relax in a wicker chair surrounded by potted palms. Be sure to order a *mojito,* the house special made of white rum, sugar, and fresh crushed mint leaves. ⊠ *1834 Columbia Rd. NW,* ☎ *202/462–6310.*

Polly Esther's. Polly Esther's is the Hard Rock Cafe of dance clubs, with outlets in New York and Miami. Focusing on popular '70s and '80s tunes and catering to a crowd barely old enough to remember the tail end of the disco era, the club provides an unpretentious good time, especially for groups. You can sing out loud to your favorite Bee Gees song while striking a John Travolta pose, and no one will look twice (though you'll be noticed if you wear tennis shoes or a baseball cap, which aren't considered appropriate attire). ⊠ *605 12th St. NW,* ☎ *202/737–1970.*

Ritz. This downtown nightclub near the FBI building is popular with a professional crowd, though on Friday nights the club becomes "Decades" and caters to a mixed over-21 clientele. The Ritz has five separate rooms, with DJs spinning a different type of music—from Top 40 to reggae to house music—in each. It's best to dress up if you plan to come here. The club is open Wednesday and Friday–Sunday. ⊠ *919 E St. NW,* ☎ *202/638–2582.*

State of the Union. State draws a young, eclectic crowd dressed in the requisite wide-leg jeans of today's casually hip. Patrons here tend to be serious music fans who come to dance or hold down a spot at the bar while the city's best DJs spin a mix of house music, hip-hop, jungle, and classic R&B sounds. ✉ *1357 U St. NW,* ☎ *202/588–8926.*

Zei. Pronounced "zee," this New York–style dance club in a former electric power substation draws an international crowd that includes everything from dark-suited "hiplomats" to affluent exchange students. The relentless thump of Euro-pop complements a design that includes a wall of television sets peering down on the proceedings. (Tennis shoes aren't considered appropriate here.) ✉ *1415 Zei Alley NW (14th St. between H and I Sts. NW),* ☎ *202/842–2445.*

Gay and Lesbian Dance Clubs

Badlands. One of the best things about Badlands is that it's open on weeknights when other clubs are closed. It has a definite meat-market vibe, but with less attitude than you'll find at larger nightclubs. ✉ *1413 22nd St. NW,* ☎ *202/296–0505.*

Hung Jury. You can count on the women at Hung Jury to make the most of the dance floor, where you're just as likely to hear the innuendo-laden lyrics of rapper Lil' Kim as you are an upbeat Top 40 dance track. ✉ *1819 H St. NW,* ☎ *202/785–8181.*

Tracks 2000. A gay club with a large contingent of straight regulars, this warehouse-district disco has one of the largest dance floors in town and stays open well into the wee hours. In a scene where clubs disappear seasonally, Tracks stands out for its longevity. ✉ *1111 1st St. SE,* ☎ *202/488–3320.*

Ziegfeld's. This club tries to offer something for everyone and has a mixed clientele (mostly gay men and straight women). Half the club is dedicated to drag shows, male strippers, and go-go boys, while on the other side of the club patrons dance to the latest house tracks. *1345 Half St. SE,* ☎ *202/554–5141.*

Jazz and Blues Clubs

The **D.C. Blues Hotline** (☎ 202/828–3028) is a clearinghouse for information on upcoming shows, festivals, and jam sessions in the metropolitan area. In addition to the hot line, it has a monthly newsletter and a Web site.

Blues Alley. The restaurant turns out Creole cooking, while cooking onstage you'll find such nationally known performers as Nancy Wilson, Joshua Redman, and Stanley Turrentine. You can come for just the show, but those who come for a meal get better seats. ✉ *1073 Wisconsin Ave. NW (entrance in rear)*, ☎ *202/337–4141*.

City Blues Cafe. On weeknights you might encounter an acoustic duo or a feathery-voiced jazz chanteuse, but on weekends hard-driving blues bands rule (arrive early to get a good table). Situated in an enclave of excellent, moderately priced restaurants, City Blues Cafe serves lunch and dinner and has the same comfortable atmosphere as its neighbors. ✉ *2651 Connecticut Ave. NW,* ☎ *202/232–2300.*

Columbia Station. This place is a neighborhood favorite, with good food and great music. Amber lights illuminate the brass instrument–theme artwork that adorns the walls. The nightly live music usually consists of a quality local jazz band and sometimes blues. Either way, more often than not it will be an electric bass, rather than an upright, that will be used to help pound out tunes funky enough to dance to. ✉ *2325 18th St. NW,* ☎ *202/462–6040.*

One Step Down. Low-ceilinged, intimate, and home to the best jazz jukebox in town, One Step Down books talented local artists and the occasional national act. The venue of choice for many New York jazz masters, the place is frayed and smoky, as a jazz club should be. Live music is presented Thursday–Monday. ✉ *2517 Pennsylvania Ave. NW,* ☎ *202/ 955–7140.*

Takoma Station Tavern. In the shadow of the Metro stop that lends it its name, the Takoma Station Tavern hosts such local favorites as Marshall Keys and Keith Killgo, with the occasional nationally known artist stopping by to jam. The jazz happy hours starting at 6:30 Wednesday through Friday pack the joint. There's reggae on Saturday and comedy on Sunday. (Sneakers and athletic wear are not allowed, so put on some fancier duds before heading here.) ⊠ *6914 4th St. NW,* ☎ *202/829–1999.*

Twin's Lounge. Owned by twin sisters Kelly and Maze Tesfaye, the club hosts some of the city's strongest straight-ahead players as well as groups from New York City. Be sure to try the tasty Ethiopian appetizers. ⊠ *5516 Colorado Ave. NW,* ☎ *202/882–2523.*

219 Basin Street Lounge. Jazz combos perform Tuesday through Saturday in this attractive Victorian-style bar, across the Potomac in Old Town Alexandria and above the 219 Restaurant. Musicians from local service bands often stop by to sit in. ⊠ *219 King St., Alexandria, VA,* ☎ *703/549–1141.*

Vegas Lounge. This is the home of Dr. Blues, and he doesn't allow any soft-jazz-bluesy-fusion in his house, even during the weekly open-jam session. It's strictly no-nonsense wailing guitar rhythms by seasoned local players in this sweet dive bar. ⊠ *1415 P St. NW,* ☎ *202/483–3971.*

Rock and Pop Clubs

Black Cat. This is the place to see the latest local bands as well as a few up-and-coming indie stars from such labels as TeenBeat and Dischord Records. Occasionally, you'll hear MTV acts like alternative rockers Sleater Kinney, white-boy-funkster G. Love, or jazz-based rappers the Roots. The post-punk crowd whiles away the time in the Red Room, a side bar with pool tables, an eclectic jukebox, and no cover charge. ⊠ *1831 14th St. NW,* ☎ *202/667–7960.*

Metro Cafe. This club is a venue dedicated to good-quality emerging bands and books an eclectic range of artists, from alternative rock to jump blues to hip-hop and funk. ⊠ *1522 14th St. NW,* ☎ *202/518–7900.*

Nation. As one of the largest venues for alternative and rock music in Washington (it holds 1,000 people), Nation brings in such bands as David Bowie, the Fugees, and Jamiroquai. Depending on the act, tickets are available at Ticketmaster (☞ Tickets, *above*) or the door. On a separate side of the club, you can gyrate to a mix of dance music mostly in the alternative genre. On Friday night this warehouse space becomes "Buzz," a massive rave featuring the latest permutations of techno and drum-and-bass music. ⊠ *1015 Half St. SE,* ☎ *202/554–1500.*

9:30 Club. The 9:30 is a trendy club that books an eclectic mix of local, national, and international artists (most of them fall into the alternative-music category—from Sugar Ray and Fiona Apple to Ziggy Marley and Erykah Badu). The club has a balcony on three sides and a large dance floor in front of the stage, so you can see the show from almost anywhere. Vegetarian food catered from Planet X helps provide much-needed nourishment after you've been standing for several hours. Get tickets at the door or through ProTix (☞ Tickets, *above*). ⊠ *815 V St. NW,* ☎ *202/393–0930.*

6 Shopping

AFRICAN MASKS LIKE THOSE that inspired Picasso; kitchenware as objets d'art; bargains on apparel by Christian Dior, Hugo Boss, and Burberrys; paisley scarves from India; American and European antiques; books of every description; handicrafts from almost two dozen Native American tribes; music boxes by the thousands; textiles by the score; fine leather goods—all this and more can be found in the nation's capital.

By
Deborah
Papier

Updated by
Holly Bass

Discriminating shoppers can find satisfaction at Filene's Basement (the Boston-based fashion discounter) or at an upscale mall on the city's outskirts. Many of the smaller one-of-a-kind shops have survived urban renewal, the number of designer boutiques is on the rise, and interesting specialty shops and minimalls can be found all over town. Weekdays, downtown street vendors offer a funky mix of jewelry; brightly patterned ties; buyer-beware watches; sunglasses; and African-inspired clothing, accessories, and art. Of course, T-shirts and Capital City souvenirs are always in plentiful supply, especially on the streets ringing the Mall. Store hours vary greatly, so it's best to call ahead. We list the shops nearest Metro stations, but some shops might be a 15- to 20-minute walk from the Metro; we do not list Metro stops for the few stores that have no Metro within walking distance.

Adams-Morgan

Scattered among the dozens of Latin, Ethiopian, and Caribbean restaurants in this most bohemian of Washington neighborhoods are a score of eccentric shops. If quality is what you seek, **Adams-Morgan** is a minefield; tread cautiously. Still, for the bargain hunter it's great fun. A word of caution—call ahead to verify hours. Adams-Morganites are often not clock-watchers, but you can be sure a weekend afternoon stroll will find a good representation of the shops open and a few hours of great browsing. ⊠ *18th St. NW, between Columbia Rd. and California Ave. Metro: Woodley Park or Dupont Circle.*

Specialty Stores

ANTIQUES AND COLLECTIBLES

Chenonceau Antiques. The mostly American 19th- and 20th-century pieces on this shop's two floors were selected by a buyer with an exquisite eye. Merchandise includes beautiful 19th-century paisley scarves from India and from Scotland and 1920s glass lamps. It's closed weekdays. ☒ *2314 18th St. NW,* ☎ *202/667–1651. Metro: Woodley Park.*

Miss Pixie's. Two levels of well-chosen collectibles include gorgeous parasols and umbrellas, antique home furnishings, glass- and silverware, vintage clothes, and hardwood bedframes. Low prices keep shoppers' attention. ☒ *1810 Adams Mill Rd. NW,* ☎ *202/232–8171. Metro: Woodley Park.*

BOOKS

Yawa. Featuring a large collection of African and African-American fiction and nonfiction, magazines, and children's books, Yawa also sells ethnic jewelry, crafts, and greeting cards. ☒ *2206 18th St. NW,* ☎ *202/483–6805. Metro: Dupont Circle.*

CRAFTS AND GIFTS

Skynear and Company. The owners travel the world to find the unusual. Their journeys have been successful, and here you'll find an extravagant assortment of rich textiles, furniture, and home accessories—all for the art of living. ☒ *2122 18th St. NW,* ☎ *202/797–7160. Metro: Dupont Circle.*

MEN'S AND WOMEN'S CLOTHING

Kobos. A rainbow of clothing and accessories imported from West Africa is for sale at Kobos. ☒ *2444 18th St. NW,* ☎ *202/332–9580. Metro: Dupont Circle.*

MUSIC

DC CD. This upstart music store caters to the club crowd with its late hours and wide selection of indie releases, rock, hip-hop, alternative, and soul. The knowledgeable staff will often open packages, allowing customers to listen before they buy. ☒ *2423 18th St. NW,* ☎ *202/588–1810. Metro: Woodley Park*

SHOES

Shake Your Booty. Trend-conscious Washingtonians used to travel to Manhattan's West Village for modish leather boots and platform shoes. Now they come here. It's closed Tuesdays. ⊠ *2324 18th St. NW,* ☎ *202/518–8205. Metro: Woodley Park.*

WOMEN'S CLOTHING

Khismet Wearable Art Showroom. Traditional garments from West Africa and original fashions designed by Millée Spears, who lived in Ghana, fill colorful Khismet. Spears uses ethnic-print fabrics to create garments that are suitable for both work and an evening out and will custom-design if desired. Hours vary. ⊠ *1800 Belmont Rd. NW,* ☎ *202/234–7778. Metro: Dupont Circle.*

Capitol Hill/Eastern Market

As the Capitol Hill area has become gentrified, unique shops and boutiques have sprung up. Many are clustered around the redbrick structure known as **Eastern Market.** Inside are produce and meat counters, plus the Market Five art gallery; outside are a farmers' market (on Saturday) and a flea market (on weekends). Along 7th Street you'll find a number of quaint shops that sell everything from art books to handwoven rugs to antiques and knickknacks. ⊠ *7th and C Sts. SE. Metro: Eastern Market, Union Station, or Capitol South.*

Mall

Union Station. This delightful shopping enclave is resplendent with marble floors and gilded, vaulted ceilings. It's now both a working train station and a mall with three levels of stores—one with food stands and a cinema multiplex—and, appropriately, the Great Train Store, which sells train memorabilia and toy versions from the inexpensive to four-figure Swiss models. The east hall, reminiscent of London's Covent Garden, is filled with vendors of expensive and ethnic wares in open stalls. Christmas is an especially pleasant time to shop here. ⊠ *Massachusetts Ave. NE near N. Capitol St.,* ☎ *202/371–9441. Metro: Union Station.*

Specialty Stores

ANTIQUES AND COLLECTIBLES

Antiques on the Hill. This store has the feel of an old thrift shop where *nothing* is ever thrown away. From floor to roof, knickknacks of every kind fill the shelves. The center of the floor is filled with furniture, and light fixtures hang from every available spot on the ceiling. It's closed Mondays. ✉ *701 N. Carolina Ave. SE,* ☎ *202/543–1819. Metro: Eastern Market.*

BOOKS

Bird-in-Hand Bookstore & Gallery. This store specializes in books on art and design and also carries exhibition catalogs. It's closed Sunday–Tuesday. ✉ *323 7th St. SE,* ☎ *202/543–0744. Metro: Eastern Market.*

Trover Books. The latest political volumes and out-of-town newspapers are here. ✉ *221 Pennsylvania Ave. SE,* ☎ *202/547–2665. Metro: Capitol South.*

CRAFTS AND GIFTS

Appalachian Spring. Appalachian Spring's two Washington stores sell traditional and contemporary American-made crafts, including quilts, jewelry, weavings, pottery, and blown glass. ✉ *Union Station,* ☎ *202/682–0505. Metro: Union Station.*

Silk Road/Woven History. These connected stores sell handmade treasures from small villages around the world. Silk Road sells home furnishings, gifts, clothing, and accessories made in mountain communities in South America and Asia as well as such contemporary items as aromatherapy candles from the not-so-rural Village in New York. Woven History's rugs are made the old-fashioned way, with vegetable dyes and hand-spun wool. ✉ *311–315 7th St. SE,* ☎ *202/543–1705. Metro: Eastern Market.*

WOMEN'S CLOTHING

Forecast. If you favor a classic, contemporary look in clothing, Forecast should be in your future. It sells silk sweaters and wool blends in solid, muted tones that won't quickly fall out of fashion. It's closed Monday. ✉ *218 7th St. SE,* ☎ *202/547–7337. Metro: Eastern Market.*

Downtown

The domain of the city's many office workers, downtown tends to shut down at 5 PM sharp with the exception of the larger department stores. Old **downtown** is where you'll find Hecht's and sundry specialty stores, while established chains such as Ann Taylor and the Gap tend to be concentrated in the area near Farragut Square. Avoid the lunch-hour crowds to ensure more leisurely shopping. ⊠ *North of Pennsylvania Ave. between 7th and 18th Sts., up to Connecticut Ave. below L St. Metro: Archives/Navy Memorial, Farragut North and West, Foggy Bottom, Gallery Place, or Metro Center.*

Department Stores

Filene's Basement. At this mecca for bargain hunters, you'll find steep discounts on Christian Dior, Hugo Boss, Burberrys, and other designer men's and women's labels. Off-price shoes, perfume, and accessories are sold as well. The downtown Filene's is especially well appointed in wood and brass; a handsome elevator takes you to the upper level. ⊠ *1133 Connecticut Ave. NW, ☎ 202/872–8430. Metro: Farragut North.*

Hecht's. Bright and spacious, Hecht's has sensible groupings and attractive displays of merchandise that make shopping easy on the feet and the eyes. The clothes sold here are a mix of conservative and trendy lines, with the men's department assuming increasing importance. Cosmetics, lingerie, and housewares are also strong departments. As a clothing-department store it's roughly comparable to Macy's. ⊠ *12th and G Sts. NW, ☎ 202/628–6661. Metro: Metro Center.*

Malls

Old Post Office Pavilion. The city is justly proud of its Old Post Office Pavilion, a handsome shopping center in a historic 19th-century building. In addition to a dozen food vendors, there are 17 shops. The observation deck in the building's clock tower has an excellent view of the city. ⊠ *1100 Pennsylvania Ave., ☎ 202/289–4224. Metro: Federal Triangle.*

Shops at National Place. The Shops takes up three levels, one of which is devoted to food stands. Although the stores are mainly youth-oriented (this is a good place to drop off teenagers weary of the Smithsonian and more in the mood to buy T-shirts), Perfumania and clothing stores such as Oaktree and August Max have branches here, too. ⊠ *13th and F Sts. NW,* ☎ *202/662–1250. Metro: Metro Center.*

Specialty Stores

BOOKS

Borders. In addition to a large selection of all types of books, Borders also sells recorded music, has a coffee bar, and regularly presents free films and jazz performances. ⊠ *1801 K St. NW (entrance at 18th and L Sts. NW),* ☎ *202/ 466–4999. Metro: Farragut North.*

Chapters. A "literary bookstore," Chapters eschews cartoon collections and diet guides, filling its shelves instead with serious contemporary fiction, classics, and poetry. ⊠ *1512 K St. NW,* ☎ *202/347–5495. Metro: Farragut North.*

Olsson's Books & Records. You'll find a large and varied collection of books and a good selection of classical and folk records, tapes, and CDs at the Olsson's stores. Hours vary significantly from store to store. In addition to the downtown locations, there are branches in Dupont Circle (⊠ 1307 19th St. NW, ☎ 202/785–1133) and Georgetown (⊠ 1239 Wisconsin Ave. NW, ☎ 202/338–9544). ⊠ *1200 F St. NW,* ☎ *202/347–3686; Metro: Metro Center.* ⊠ *418 7th St. NW,* ☎ *202/638–7610; Metro: Archives/Navy Memorial.*

CRAFTS AND GIFTS

Discovery Channel Store. Shopping is just one of the activities at this half store, half museum. You can also play high-tech interactive games, walk through the fuselage of a B-25 bomber, or stand awestruck before a 42-ft cast of the world's largest T-rex. Items for sale include everything from telescopes and science kits to authentic amber jewelry. After browsing, consider slipping into the on-site theater to see the movie *Destination DC* before heading out on the store's 1½-hour "Discover Historic Downtown D.C." tour. ⊠ *601 F St. NW,* ☎ *202/639–0908.*

Fahrney's. It started out as a pen bar—a place to fill your fountain pen before embarking on the day's business. Today, Fahrney's sells pens in silver, gold, and lacquer by the world's leading manufacturers. ⊠ *1430 G St. NW,* ☎ *202/628–9525. Metro: McPherson Square.*

Indian Craft Shop. Handicrafts, such as jewelry, pottery, sand paintings, weavings, and baskets from almost two dozen Native American tribes—including Navajo, Pueblo, Zuni, Cherokee, Lakota, and Seminole—are for sale. Items range from inexpensive (as little as $6) jewelry on up to collector-quality antiques that cost more than $1,000. It's closed weekends. ⊠ *Dept. of Interior, 1849 C St. NW, Room 1023,* ☎ *202/208–4056. Metro: Farragut West.*

Music Box Center. An exquisite specialty store, the Music Box Center provides listening opportunities via more than 1,500 music boxes that play a total of 500 melodies. ⊠ *918 F St. NW,* ☎ *202/783–9399. Metro: Gallery Place/Chinatown.*

JEWELRY

Pampillonia Jewelers. Traditional designs in 18-karat gold and platinum are found here, including many pieces for men. ⊠ *1213 Connecticut Ave. NW,* ☎ *202/628–6305. Metro: Farragut North.*

Tiny Jewel Box. Here you'll find well-chosen estate jewelry, contemporary jewelry, and unique gifts. ⊠ *1147 Connecticut Ave. NW,* ☎ *202/393–2747. Metro: Farragut North.*

MEN'S AND WOMEN'S CLOTHING

Britches of Georgetown. The larger of the two Washington branches, this store has a wide selection of traditional but trend-conscious men's clothing. In addition to the store's private label, you'll find menswear by St. Andrews and Hickey Freeman. ⊠ *1776 K St. NW,* ☎ *202/347–8994. Metro: Farragut North.*

Brooks Brothers. This venerable institution moved its flagship store in 1999 to a newer, more visible location at the corner of Connecticut and Rhode Island avenues. While the attention to detail and the high-quality classic style haven't changed, the women's department is given more attention and the new store has a more open, airy quality, making browsing more pleasant. ⊠ *1201 Connecticut Ave. NW,* ☎ *202/659–4650. Metro: Farragut North.*

Burberrys. Burberrys made its reputation with the trench coat, but this British company also manufactures other traditional men's and women's apparel. ⊠ *1155 Connecticut Ave. NW,* ☎ *202/463–3000. Metro: Farragut North.*

J. Press. J. Press was founded in 1902 as a custom shop for Yale University. It is a resolutely traditional clothier: Shetland and Irish wool sport coats are a specialty. ⊠ *1801 L St. NW,* ☎ *202/857–0120. Metro: Farragut North.*

REJUVENATION

Andre Chreky Salon. Housed in an elegantly renovated, four-story Victorian town house, this salon offers complete services—hair, nails, facials, waxing, massage, and makeup. Adjacent whirlpool pedicure chairs make it possible for two friends to get simultaneous pampering. While you splurge on a treatment, enjoy complimentary espresso and pastries (mornings) or wine and live piano music (evenings). ⊠ *1604 K St. NW,* ☎ *202/293–9393. Metro: Farragut North.*

The Healthy Back Store. To get the knots out quickly, stop here for a seated 15-, 20-, or 30-minute shoulder rub by a certified masseuse. The shop also sells such products as hand-held back-rub aids to get to those hard-to-reach spots and ergonomic chairs designed to release back stress and relieve aches and pains. It's closed weekends. ⊠ *1341 G St. NW,* ☎ *202/393–2225. Metro: Metro Center.*

Victoria's Day Spa. What it lacks in fancy amenities it more than makes up for with its homespun appeal and comparatively low prices. This spa's special services include paraffin manicures, pedicures, seaweed masks, and body wraps. ⊠ *1926 I St. NW,* ☎ *202/254–0442. Metro: Farragut West.*

SHOES

Church's. Church's is an English company whose handmade men's shoes are noted for their comfort and durability. ⊠ *1820 L St. NW,* ☎ *202/296–3366. Metro: Farragut North.*

Parade of Shoes. This store's house-label women's shoes feature designer knockoffs and classically styled Italian imports. During seasonal clearances, shoes are often marked down as low as $15 and $20 a pair. ⊠ *1020 Connecticut Ave. NW,* ☎ *202/872–8581. Metro: Farragut North.*

WOMEN'S CLOTHING

Ann Taylor. This store sells sophisticated, trend-conscious fashions for women and has an excellent shoe department. In addition to its downtown store, other locations include Mazza Gallerie (☎ 202/244–1940), Georgetown (⊠ 3222 M St. NW, ☎ 202/338–5290), and Union Station (☎ 202/371–8010). ⊠ *1720 K St. NW, ☎ 202/466–3544. Metro: Farragut West.*

Betsy Fisher. Stylish is the word that best describes Betsy Fisher's clothing—a contemporary look for women of all ages. ⊠ *1224 Connecticut Ave. NW, ☎ 202/785–1975. Metro: Farragut North.*

Chanel Boutique. The Willard Hotel annex is where to find goodies from this legendary house of fashion. ⊠ *1455 Pennsylvania Ave. NW, ☎ 202/638–5055. Metro: Metro Center.*

Earl Allen. Earl Allen offers conservative but distinctive dresses and sportswear, wearable art, and one-of-a-kind items—much of it made exclusively for this small chain. ⊠ *1825 I St. NW, ☎ 202/466–3437. Metro: Farragut West.*

Rizik Bros. Rizik Bros. combines designer clothing and accessories with expert service. The sales staff is trained to find just the right style from the large inventory, and prices are right. Take the elevator up from the northwest corner of Connecticut Avenue and L Street. ⊠ *1100 Connecticut Ave. NW, ☎ 202/223–4050. Metro: Farragut North.*

Dupont Circle

You might call **Dupont Circle** a younger, hipper version of Georgetown—almost as pricey, and not quite as well kept, with more apartment buildings than houses. The neighborhood has had its ups and downs, but today Dupont Circle is fashionable, and its many restaurants, offbeat shops, and specialty book and record stores lend it a distinctive, cosmopolitan air. The street scene here is more urban than Georgetown's, with bike messengers and chess aficionados filling up the park while shoppers frequent the many coffee shops and stores. ⊠ *Connecticut Ave. between M and S Sts. Metro: Dupont Circle.*

Specialty Stores

ANTIQUES AND COLLECTIBLES

Marston Luce. Focusing on French country furniture and folk art, Marston Luce also carries home and garden accessories such as weather vanes, stone carvings from building facades, and decorative cast-iron work. ⊠ *1314 21st St. NW,* ☏ *202/775–9460. Metro: Dupont Circle.*

BOOKS

Kramerbooks. Open 24 hours on weekends, Kramerbooks shares space with a café that has late-night dining and weekend entertainment. The stock is small but well selected. ⊠ *1517 Connecticut Ave. NW,* ☏ *202/387–1400. Metro: Dupont Circle.*

Lambda Rising. Dupont Circle's gay bookstore is a major player in the area. ⊠ *1625 Connecticut Ave. NW,* ☏ *202/ 462–6969. Metro: Dupont Circle.*

Lammas Books. A selection of music by women as well as women's and lesbian literature is for sale here. Customers can connect with like minds via the store's public Internet-ready computer. ⊠ *1607 17th St. NW,* ☏ *202/775–8218. Metro: Dupont Circle.*

Mystery Books. Mystery Books has Washington's largest collection of detective, crime, suspense, and spy fiction. It delivers gift baskets anywhere in the United States. ⊠ *1715 Connecticut Ave. NW,* ☏ *202/483–1600; 800/955–2279 gift and book orders. Metro: Dupont Circle.*

Second Story Books. A mecca for bibliophiles that encourages hours of browsing, this used-books and -records emporium stays open late. ⊠ *2000 P St. NW,* ☏ *202/659– 8884. Metro: Dupont Circle.*

Vertigo Books. Just south of Dupont Circle, Vertigo Books emphasizes international politics, world literature, and African-American studies and presents an impressive series of regular author readings. ⊠ *1337 Connecticut Ave. NW,* ☏ *202/429–9272. Metro: Dupont Circle.*

CRAFTS AND GIFTS

Beadazzled. Head to Beadazzled for a dazzling array of ready-to-string beads and jewelry and books on crafts history and techniques. ⊠ *1507 Connecticut Ave. NW,* ☎ *202/265–2323. Metro: Dupont Circle.*

KITCHENWARE

Coffee & the Works. This shop offers every amenity a coffee or tea lover could desire, from flavored brews to colorful ceramic pots. ⊠ *1627 Connecticut Ave. NW,* ☎ *202/483–8050. Metro: Dupont Circle.*

MEN'S AND WOMEN'S CLOTHING

Secondi. This is the city's finest consignment shop, with a wide selection of women's clothing, accessories, and shoes as well as a small but distinctive men's section. ⊠ *1702 Connecticut Ave. NW,* ☎ *202/667–1122. Metro: Dupont Circle.*

SHOES

Shoe Scene. The fashionable, moderately priced shoes for women found here are imported from Europe. ⊠ *1330 Connecticut Ave. NW,* ☎ *202/659–2194. Metro: Dupont Circle.*

Georgetown

Georgetown remains Washington's favorite shopping area. This is the capital's center for famous citizens (*Washington Post* matriarch Katharine Graham and celebrity biographer Kitty Kelley are among the luminaries who call Georgetown home), as well as for restaurants, bars, nightclubs, and trendy shops. Although Georgetown is not on a subway line (the nearest Metro is a 10- to 15-minute walk from the shops) and parking is impossible, people still flock here. The attraction (aside from the lively street scene) is the profusion of specialty shops in a charming, historic neighborhood. In addition to housing tony antiques, elegant crafts, and high-style shoe and clothing boutiques, the area offers wares that attract local college students and young people: books, music, and fashions from such popular chain stores as Banana Republic and Urban Outfitters. ⊠ *Intersection of Wisconsin Ave. and M St.; most stores lie to the east and west on M St. and to the north on Wisconsin. Metro: Foggy Bottom.*

Mall

Shops at Georgetown Park. Near the hub of the Georgetown shopping district, at the intersection of Wisconsin Avenue and M Street, is this trilevel mall, which looks like a

Victorian ice cream parlor inside. The pricey clothing and accessory boutiques and the ubiquitous chain stores (such as Victoria's Secret) in the posh place draw international visitors in droves. Next door is a branch of Dean & Deluca, New York's premier gourmet food store. ⊠ *3222 M St. NW,* ☎ *202/298–5577. Metro: Foggy Bottom.*

Specialty Stores

ANTIQUES AND COLLECTIBLES

Georgetown Antiques Center. The center, in a Victorian town house, has two dealers who share space: Cherub Gallery specializes in Art Nouveau and Art Deco, and Michael Getz Antiques sells fireplace equipment and silverware. ⊠ *2918 M St. NW,* ☎ *202/337–2224 Cherub Gallery; 202/ 338–3811 Michael Getz Antiques. Metro: Foggy Bottom.*

Miller & Arney Antiques. English, American, and European furniture and accessories from the 17th, 18th, and early 19th centuries give Miller & Arney Antiques a museum-gallery air. Asian porcelain adds splashes of color. ⊠ *1737 Wisconsin Ave. NW,* ☎ *202/338–2369. Metro: Foggy Bottom.*

Old Print Gallery. The capital's largest collection of old prints and maps (including Washingtoniana) is housed in this gallery. ⊠ *1220 31st St. NW,* ☎ *202/965–1818. Metro: Foggy Bottom.*

Opportunity Shop of the Christ Child Society. A Georgetown thrift store, Opportunity Shop sells secondhand clothing and good-quality household goods. Consigned fine antiques, crystal, and silver at moderate prices are available on the second floor. ⊠ *1427 Wisconsin Ave. NW,* ☎ *202/333–6635. Metro: Foggy Bottom.*

Susquehanna. With three rooms upstairs, four rooms downstairs, and a garden full of cast-iron birdbaths, Susquehanna is the largest antiques shop in Georgetown. Paintings cover every inch of wall space, though the shop specializes in American and English furniture. ⊠ *3216 O St. NW,* ☎ *202/333– 1511. Metro: Foggy Bottom.*

BOOKS

Barnes & Noble. This new three-story store in a former warehouse has a coffee bar. ⊠ *3040 M St. NW,* ☎ *202/965– 9880. Metro: Foggy Bottom.*

CRAFTS AND GIFTS

American Hand. This is a wonderful place for one-of-a-kind functional and nonfunctional pieces—teakettles, corkscrews, glassware, and jewelry—by international designers. ⊠ *2906 M St. NW,* ☎ *202/965–3273. Metro: Foggy Bottom.*

Appalachian Spring. The largest of this chain's four outlets (there are two suburban shops and another one on the Hill), Appalachian Spring has a wide selection of traditional and contemporary American-made crafts: quilts, jewelry, weavings, pottery, and blown glass. ⊠ *1415 Wisconsin Ave. NW,* ☎ *202/337–5780.*

Martin's. Martin's is a long-established Georgetown purveyor of china, crystal, and silver. ⊠ *1304 Wisconsin Ave. NW,* ☎ *202/338–6144.*

Phoenix. Phoenix sells contemporary clothing in natural fibers by designers such as Aileen Fisher and Flax, as well as jewelry and art pieces (fine and folk) from Mexico. ⊠ *1514 Wisconsin Ave. NW,* ☎ *202/338–4404.*

KITCHENWARE

Little Caledonia. Little Caledonia has nine rooms crammed with thousands of unusual and imported items for the home. Candles, cards, fabrics, and lamps round out the stock of decorative kitchenware. ⊠ *1419 Wisconsin Ave. NW,* ☎ *202/333–4700.*

LEATHER GOODS

Coach Store. For fine leather, Coach carries a complete (and expensive) line of well-made handbags, briefcases, belts, and wallets. ⊠ *1214 Wisconsin Ave. NW,* ☎ *202/ 342–1772. Metro: Foggy Bottom.*

MEN'S AND WOMEN'S CLOTHING

Britches Great Outdoors. The casual version of Britches of Georgetown, Britches Great Outdoors has filled many Washington closets with rugby shirts and other sportswear. ⊠ *1225 Wisconsin Ave. NW,* ☎ *202/333–3666. Metro: Foggy Bottom.*

Britches of Georgetown. Britches carries an extensive selection of traditional but trend-conscious designs in natural fibers for men. ⊠ *1247 Wisconsin Ave. NW,* ☎ *202/ 338–3330. Metro: Foggy Bottom.*

Commander Salamander. This funky outpost sells trendy clothes for the alternative set—punk kids and ravers. Sifting through the assortment of leather, chains, toys, and candy-color makeup is as much entertainment as it is shopping. The store is open till 10 PM on weekends. ✉ *1420 Wisconsin Ave. NW,* ☎ *202/337–2265. Metro: Foggy Bottom.*

REJUVENATION

Better Botanicals. Handmade herbal soaps in delicious scents, a potpourri of herbs to steam the face, gentle herb-infused shampoos, and essential oils for massage and aromatherapy—all the products sold here are guaranteed free of alcohol, mineral oil, and synthetic and animal-derived ingredients. They're perfect for do-it-yourself treatments. ✉ *3066 M St. NW,* ☎ *202/625–2440 or 888/884–3727. Metro: Foggy Bottom.*

efx SPA. The store up front sells soaps, lotions, cosmetics, and nail polishes in trendy colors. Behind the glass door, the spa offers an array of services in its "skin gym." In addition to facials, waxing, and massage, you can get the "B Side" treatment for the back and oxygen treatments. ✉ *3059 M St. NW,* ☎ *202/965–1300 spa; 202/462–1300 store. Metro: Foggy Bottom.*

Roche Salon. On the Georgetown waterfront, this salon specializes in hair. Owner Dennis Roche has been featured in *Vogue, Bazaar,* and *Glamour* magazines and is the city's best source for the latest hair-coloring techniques. ✉ *3050 K St. NW,* ☎ *202/775–0003.*

SHOES

Bootlegger. Chunky platforms, Birkenstock sandals, black boots by NaNa, and Doc Marten's in all colors are staples at this retailer. ✉ *1420 Wisconsin Ave. NW,* ☎ *202/333–0373. Metro: Foggy Bottom.*

WOMEN'S CLOTHING

Betsey Johnson. This shop sells fanciful frocks for the young and restless. ✉ *1319 Wisconsin Ave. NW,* ☎ *202/338–4090. Metro: Foggy Bottom.*

Earl Allen. Earl Allen offers conservative but distinctive dresses and sportswear, wearable art, and one-of-a-kind items, much of it made exclusively for this small chain. ✉ *3109 M St. NW,* ☎ *202/338–1678. Metro: Foggy Bottom.*

TATA Boutique. Owned by Theresa Atkins, a former Howard University beauty queen who still turns heads, this boutique offers stylish attention-getting eveningwear, suits, and separates for women who like to wear silky rayon crepes and form-fitting velvets and knits. Also on display are bold and distinctive accessories. It's closed Sunday and Monday. ✉ *2603 P St. NW,* ☎ *202/342–8282. Metro: Dupont Circle.*

U Street

In the '30s and '40s, **U Street** was known for its classy theaters and jazz clubs. After decades of decline following the 1968 riots, the neighborhood has been revitalized. Although the area is far from gentrified, U Street's mainstay is its devoted, local community, a mix of multiethnic young adults and older, working-class African-Americans. In 1997, the *Utne Reader* declared U Street one of the hippest neighborhoods in the country. At night the neighborhood's club scene comes alive. During the day, the street scene is more laid-back, with more locals than tourists occupying the few lunch spots and distinctive array of shops. ✉ *U St. between 12th and 17th Sts. Metro: U Street/Cardozo.*

ANTIQUES AND COLLECTIBLES

Good Wood. This shop sells new and refurbished fine wood furniture. ✉ *1428 U St. NW,* ☎ *202/986–3640. Metro: U Street/Cardozo.*

Millennium. This store calls its unique blend of housewares, clothing, records, books, and furniture "20th-century antiques." Depending on the week, you might find Bakelite silverware or an eight-track tape player. ✉ *1528 U St. NW,* ☎ *202/483–1218. Metro: U Street/Cardozo.*

BOOKS

Sisterspace and Books. Sisterspace specializes in books written by and appealing to African-American women. In addition to selling titles by authors such as Iyanla Vanzant, Maya Angelou, and Toni Morrison, the store offers seminars on everything from money and health to spirituality and creative fulfillment. ⊠ *1515 U St. NW,* ☎ *202/332–3433. Metro: U Street/Cardozo.*

MEN'S AND WOMEN'S CLOTHING

Mood Indigo. This vintage-clothing store once had a 1940s theme, but now it has expanded to include suits, dresses, and hats and accessories from the '50s through the '70s. ⊠ *1214 U St. NW,* ☎ *202/256–6366. Metro: U Street/Cardozo.*

Trade Secrets. The textured wool, velvet, and silk designs in African-inspired patterns sold here seem almost too pretty to wear. Almost. ⊠ *1515 U St. NW, lower level,* ☎ *202/256–6366. Metro: U Street/Cardozo.*

Wisconsin Avenue

A major shopping district, upper **Wisconsin Avenue** straddles the Maryland border. Between the malls, department stores, and chic small boutiques, this area has everything you could want to buy. ⊠ *Wisconsin Ave. between Jennifer St. NW and Western Ave. Metro: Friendship Heights.*

Department Stores

Filene's Basement. To really appreciate the bargains here, do some window-shopping in Mazza Gallerie (☞ *below*) before entering this store from the mall. In addition to big savings on men's and women's clothing by well-regarded designers such as Hugo Boss and Christian Dior, Filene's has discounts on shoes, perfume, and accessories. ⊠ *5300 Wisconsin Ave. NW,* ☎ *202/966–0208. Metro: Friendship Heights.*

Lord & Taylor. Lord & Taylor lets the competition be all things to all people while it focuses on classic men's, women's, and children's clothing by such designers as Anne Klein and Ralph Lauren. ⊠ *5255 Western Ave. NW,* ☎ *202/362–9600. Metro: Friendship Heights.*

Neiman Marcus. If price is an object, this is definitely not the place to shop, although it's still a fun place to browse. Headquartered in Dallas, Neiman Marcus caters to customers who value quality above all. The carefully selected merchandise includes couture clothes, furs, precious jewelry, crystal, and silver. ✉ *Mazza Gallerie, 5300 Wisconsin Ave. NW,* ☎ *202/966–9700. Metro: Friendship Heights.*

Saks Fifth Avenue. Though not technically a Washington department store because it is just over the Maryland line, Saks is nonetheless a Washington institution. It has a wide selection of European and American couture clothes; other attractions are the shoe, jewelry, fur, and lingerie departments. ✉ *5555 Wisconsin Ave.,* ☎ *301/657–9000. Metro: Friendship Heights.*

Malls

Chevy Chase Pavilion. Across from Mazza Gallerie (☞ *below*) is the newer, similarly upscale Chevy Chase Pavilion. Its exclusive women's clothing stores include Joan & David and Steilmann European Selection (which carries Karl Lagerfeld's sportier KL line). Other specialty shops of note here are Pottery Barn and Country Road Australia. ✉ *5335 Wisconsin Ave. NW,* ☎ *202/686–5335. Metro: Friendship Heights.*

Mazza Gallerie. The four-level Mazza Gallerie is anchored by the ritzy Neiman Marcus department store and the discount department store Filene's Basement. Other stores include Williams-Sonoma's kitchenware and Laura Ashley Home as well as branches of Ann Taylor, Pampillonia Jewelers, and Skynea. ✉ *5300 Wisconsin Ave. NW,* ☎ *202/966–6114. Metro: Friendship Heights.*

Specialty Stores

BOOKS

Politics and Prose. With a wide selection of topical novels and literary nonfiction as well as provocative author readings almost every night, this bookstore-coffeehouse lives up to its name. The nearest Metro is 15 minutes away. ✉ *5015 Connecticut Ave. NW,* ☎ *202/364–1919. Metro: Friendship Heights.*

Travel Books & Language. One of the largest specialty bookshops of its kind in the country, Travel Books & Language has an enormous stock of travel guides, cookbooks, travel narratives, maps, and language-study workbooks and audiotapes. ✉ *4437 Wisconsin Ave. NW,* ☎ *202/237–1322. Metro: Tenleytown/American University.*

JEWELRY

Charles Schwartz & Son. A full-service jeweler, Charles Schwartz specializes in precious stones in traditional and modern settings. Fine watches are also offered. ⊠ *Mazza Gallerie, 5300 Wisconsin Ave. NW,* ☎ *202/363–5432. Metro: Friendship Heights.*

MEN'S AND WOMEN'S CLOTHING

Brooks Brothers. The oldest men's store in America, Brooks Brothers has sold traditional formal and casual clothing since 1818. It is the largest men's specialty store in the area and has a small women's department as well. ⊠ *5504 Wisconsin Ave.,* ☎ *301/654–8202. Metro: Friendship Heights.*

REJUVENATION

Georgette Klinger Skin Care Salon. The doyenne of spas, Georgette Klinger specializes in skin care but can also pamper you with a full range of services. Treatments here are pricey, but regular patrons say they're well worth it. ⊠ *5345 Wisconsin Ave. NW,* ☎ *202/686–8880. Metro: Friendship Heights.*

INDEX

A

Aatish ✕, *115*
Acoustic music, *158*
Adams, John, *44, 45*
Adams Building, *53*
Adams-Morgan/Cleveland Park, *94–95, 97–99*
restaurants, *110, 112–114*
shopping, *168–170*
Aditi ✕, *129*
Airports and transfers, *x–xi*
Air travel, *x*
Alexandria, VA, *105–107*
Alexandria Black History Resource Center, *105*
Alexandria Convention & Visitors Association, *107*
American Film Institute, *150*
American Hand (shop), *180*
American Pharmaceutical Association, *91*
Anderson House, *81, 83*
Andre Chreky Salon (shop), *175*
Ann Taylor (shop), *176*
Antiques and collectibles, *169, 171, 177, 179, 182*
Antiques on the Hill (shop), *171*
Appalachian Spring (shop), *171, 180*
Arena Stage (theater), *155*
Arlington, *100–105*
Arlington Cinema 'N' Drafthouse, *150*
Arlington House, *100–101*
Arlington National Cemetery, *101*
Armed Forces Concert Series, *153*
Arthur M. Sackler Gallery, *14*
Art Museum of the Americas, *34*
Arts, *146–157*
concert halls, *147–149*
dance, *149–150*
film, *150–151*
music, *151–155*
theater and performance art, *155–157*
tickets, *146–147*
Arts and Industries Building, *14–15*
ATMs, *xvii–xviii*
Australian Embassy, *83–84*

B

B. Smith's ✕, *115*
Bacon, Henry, *28*
Badlands (dance club), *163*
Ballet, *150*
Bardo Rodeo (bar), *158–159*
Barnes & Noble (shop), *179*
Bartholdi, Frédéric-Auguste, *48*
Bartholdi Fountain, *48*
Basilica of the National Shrine of the Immaculate Conception, *152*
Beadazzled (shop), *177–178*
Bethune, Mary McLeod, *85*
Betsey Johnson (shop), *181*
Betsy Fisher (shop), *176*
Better Botanicals (shop), *181*
Bicycle tours, *xix*
Big Fish Deli ✕, *130*
Birchmere (music club), *158*
Bird-in-Hand Bookstore & Gallery, *171*
Bison Bridge, *84*
Bistro Bis ✕, *114–115*
Bistro Français ✕, *129*
Black cat (music club), *165*
Blair House, *36*
Blue Room, White House, *45*
Blues Alley (music club), *164*
Blues clubs, *164–165*
B'nai B'rith Klutznick Museum, *84*
Boat tours, *xix*
Bombay Club ✕, *122–123*
Bookstores, *169, 171, 173, 177, 179, 182–183, 184*
Booth, John Wilkes, *62–63*
Bootlegger (shop), *181*
Borders (shop), *173*
Boy Scouts Memorial, *36*
Bread Line ✕, *120–121*
Brickskeller (bar), *159*
Britches Great Outdoors (shop), *180*
Britches of Georgetown (shop), *174, 180*
Brooks Brothers (shop), *174, 185*
Brown, John, *107*
Brumidi, Constantino, *49–50*

Burberrys (shop), *175*
Bureau of Engraving and Printing, *15*
Burma ✕, *119*
Burnham, Daniel, *54*
Bus tours, *xix–xx*
Bus travel, *xi–xii*
Bush, George, *44*

C

Café Atlántico ✕, *124*
Cafe Milano ✕, *129*
Cameroon Embassy, *84*
Canadian Embassy, *59*
C & O Canal, *74, 76*
Canterbury Hotel 🏨, *138–139*
The Capitol, *7, 48–51*
Capitol City Brewing Company (bar),
159
Capitol Hill, *46, 48–58*
 hotels, 133, 136
 restaurants, 114–115
 shopping, 170–171
Capitol Hill Suites 🏨, *136*
Capitol Steps (cabaret), *160*
Captain's Row, *105*
Car rental, *xii–xiii*
Car travel, *xiii*
Carlyle House, *105*
Carroll, John, *78*
Carter Barron Amphitheater, *154*
Cashion's Eat Place ✕, *110, 112*
Chamber music, *151–152*
Chanel Boutique, *176*
Channel Inn 🏨, *141–142*
Chapters (shop), *173*
Charles Schwartz & Son (jewelry
 store), *185*
Charles Sumner School, *84–85*
Chelsea's (dance club), *162*
Chenonceau Antiques (shop), *169*
Cherry Blossom Festival, *30*
Chesapeake & Ohio Canal, *74, 76*
Chevy Chase Pavilion (mall), *184*
Chi Cha Lounge (bar), *159*
Children, activities for, *6, 15, 19, 21–
 23, 27, 29–30, 32–34, 37, 43–46,
 48–51, 54, 58, 62–63, 64–65, 66–
 67, 70–71, 74, 76, 87, 97–99*
Chinatown, *59*
Choral Arts Society of Washington,
152
Choral music, *152*

Christ Church, *105–106*
Churches
 *Basilica of the National Shrine of the
  Immaculate Conception, 152*
 Christ Church, 105–106
 *Metropolitan African Methodist
  Episcopal Church, 87*
 Old Presbyterian Meetinghouse, 106
 St. John's Church, 79
 St. John's Episcopal Church, 42–43
 St. Matthew's Cathedral, 89
 Washington National Cathedral, 152
Church's (shop), *175*
Cineplex Odeon Uptown, *150–151*
Citronelle ✕, *128*
City Blues Cafe (music club), *164*
Clinton, Bill, *44, 87*
Clothes, shopping for, *169, 170, 171,
 174–175, 176, 178, 180–181, 182,
 183, 185*
Coach Store, *180*
Cockburn, George, *48–49*
Coffee & the Works (shop), *178*
Columbia Station (music club), *164*
Columbus Memorial Fountain, *58*
Comedy clubs, *160–161*
Comedy Connection (club), *160–161*
ComedySportz (club), *161*
Commander Salamander (shop), *181*
Concert halls, *147–149*
Congressional Cemetery, *51*
Constitution Gardens, *27*
Consumer protection, *xiii*
Coppi's Restaurant, *130*
Corcoran, William Wilson, *42, 78*
Corcoran Gallery of Art, *36–37, 151*
Council House, *85*
Country music, *158*
Cox, John, *76*
Cox's Row, *76*
Crafts and gifts, *169, 171, 173–174,
 177–178, 180*
Crampton Auditorium, *147*
Credit cards, *xviii*
Cret, Paul Philippe, *51–52, 92*
Customs, *xiii–xv*

D

Dance, *149–150*
Dance clubs, *161–163*
Dance Place (studio theater), *149*
Dancers (club), *162*

DAR Constitution Hall, 147
DAR Museum, 37
DC CD (shop), 169
DC Coast ✕, 120
Decatur, Stephen, 37–38
Decatur House, 37–38
Department of Agriculture, 15
Department of State, 91–92
Department of the Interior, 38–39
Department of the Interior Museum, 38
Department stores, 172, 183–184
Disabilities and accessibility, xv
Discovery Channel Store (shop), 173
Discovery Room, 23
District Curators, 154
District of Columbia Arts Center, 95, 156
Douglass, Frederick, 87
Downtown
hotels, 136–138
restaurants, 118–125
shopping, 172–176
Doyle Normandy 🏨, 142
Dubliner (bar), 159
Dumbarton House, 76
Dumbarton Oaks, 76–77
Dupont Circle, 81, 83–90
hotels, 138–139
restaurants, 125–127
shopping, 176–178
Duties, xiii–xv

E

Earl Allen (shop), 176, 181–182
East Potomac Park, 27
East Room, White House, 44–45
Eastern Market, 170
efx SPA (shop), 181
Ellipse, 39
Emergencies, xv–xvi

F

Fahrney's (shop), 173–174
FBI building, 63–64
Federal Reserve Building, 92
Federal Triangle, 59, 62
Felix ✕, 112
Filene's Basement (department stores), 172, 183
Film, 150–151

Filmfest D.C., 151
Fishmarket (bar), 160
Flagg, Ernest, 36
Foggy Bottom, 90–94
hotels, 142–144
Folger Shakespeare Library, 51–52, 151–152
Folk music, 158
Folklore Society of Greater Washington, 158
Fondo Del Sol Visual Arts Center, 86
Ford's Theatre, 62–63, 155
Forecast (shop), 171
Ft. Dupont Summer Theater, 154
Four Seasons Hotel 🏨, 139–140
Francis Dodge Warehouses, 77
Franklin Delano Roosevelt Memorial, 27–28
Freedom Plaza, 63
Freer Gallery of Art, 18
French, Daniel Chester, 28–29
Friendship Arch, 63

G

Gabriel ✕, 126–127
Gadsby's Tavern Museum, 106
Gala Hispanic Theatre, 156
Galileo ✕, 123
Garfield, James, 44, 52
Gay and lesbian dance clubs, 163
George Mason University, 147
George Washington University, 92–93
George Washington University Inn 🏨, 143
Georgetown, 6, 72–74, 76–81
hotels, 139–141
restaurants, 127–129
shopping, 178–182
Georgetown Antiques Center, 179
Georgetown Dutch Inn 🏨, 140–141
Georgetown Inn 🏨, 140
Georgetown Suites 🏨, 140
Georgetown University, 78
Georgette Klinger Skin Care Salon (shop), 185
Georgia Brown's ✕, 124
Gerard's Place ✕, 122
Gilbert, Cass, 56
Glenwood Cemetery, 52
Glover Park, restaurants in, 127–129
Good Wood (shop), 182

Grant, Ulysses S., *52*
Grant Memorial, *52*
Green Room, White House, *45*
Grill from Ipanema ✕, *113*
Gross National Product (cabaret), *161*

H

Habana Village (dance club), *162*
Hamilton, Alexander, *43*
Hawk 'n' Dove (bar), *160*
Hay-Adams Hotel ☒, *136*
Headliners (club), *161*
Healthy Back Store (shop), *175*
Hecht's (department store), *172*
Henley Park Hotel ☒, *138*
Heurich House Museum, *86–87*
Hillwood Museum and Gardens, *95*
Hirshhorn Museum and Sculpture Garden, *18–19, 151*
Hoban, James, *43–44*
Holiday Inn on the Hill ☒, *141*
Hostelling International-Washington D.C. ☒, *138*
Hotel George ☒, *136*
Hotel Tabard Inn ☒, *139*
Hotel Washington ☒, *137*
Hotels, *132–133, 136–144*
  Capitol Hill, *133, 136*
  Downtown, *136–138*
  Dupont Circle, *138–139*
  Georgetown, *139–141*
  Northwest/Upper Connecticut Avenue, *142*
  price chart, *xvi*
  Southwest, *141–142*
  West End/Foggy Bottom, *142–144*
House of Representatives, *51*
Houses, on the Hill, *51*
Hunan Chinatown ✕, *119*
Hung Jury (dance club), *163*
Hunt, E. Howard, Jr., *94*

I

I Matti, *112–113*
I Ricchi ✕, *123*
Improv (comedy club), *161*
Indian Craft Shop, *174*
Insurance, *xvi*
Islamic Mosque and Cultural Center, *87*

J

J. Edgar Hoover Federal Bureau of Investigation Building, *63–64*
J. Press (shop), *175*
J. W. Marriott ☒, *137*
Jackson, Andrew, *40, 44*
Jacqueline Kennedy Rose Garden, *44*
Jaleo ✕, *124–125*
James Garfield Memorial, *52*
James Madison Building, *53*
Janet Annenberg Hooker Hall of Geology, Gems and Minerals, *23*
Jazz clubs, *164–165*
Jefferson, Thomas, *53*
Jefferson Memorial, *7, 28*
Jewelry, *174, 185*
John F. Kennedy Center for the Performing Arts, *93–94, 147–148*
Johnson, Andrew, *43*
Joy of Motion, *149–150*

K

Kennedy, John F., *76, 89*
  grave of, 101, 102
Kennedy-Warren, *95, 97*
Key, Francis Scott, *79*
Khismet Wearable Art Showroom (shop), *170*
King, Martin Luther, *63*
Kinkead's ✕, *121*
Kitchenware, *178, 180*
Kobos (shop), *169*
Kramerbooks (shop), *177*

L

La Colline ✕, *115*
Lafayette Square, *39–40*
Lambda Rising (shop), *177*
Lammas Books (shop), *177*
Lannuier, Charles-Honoré, *45*
Latham Hotel ☒, *140*
Latrobe, Benjamin, *42–43, 49*
Lauriol Plaza ✕, *113*
Layman, Christopher, *79*
Leather goods, *180*
Lebanese Taverna ✕, *113*
Lee, Robert E., *105*
L'Enfant, Pierre, *32, 39–40, 58, 63*
Les Halles ✕, *122*
Lespinasse ✕, *121–122*
Library of Congress, *53–54*

Liddy, G. Gordon, *94*
Lin, Maya Ying, *31*
Lincoln, Abraham, *49, 62–63, 68, 71*
Ford's Theatre and, 62–63
portrait of, 45
Lincoln Memorial, *7, 28–29*
Lincoln Theater, *155*
Lisner Auditorium, *148*
Little Caledonia (shop), *180*
Lloyd House, *106*
Lockkeeper's House, *29*
Lodging. ☞ Hotels
Loews L'Enfant Plaza ⊞, *141*
Lord & Taylor (department store), *183*
Lyceum, *106*

M

Madison, Dolley, *44*
The Mall, *6–7, 13–15, 18–25*
Mama Ayesha's Restaurant ✕, *114*
Marston Luce (shop), *177*
Martin's (shop), *180*
Masonic Lodge, *78*
Mazza Gallerie (mall), *184*
MCI Arena, *148*
Mellon, Andrew, *20*
Meridian Hill Park, *99*
Meridian House, *97*
Merriweather Post Pavilion, *148*
Metro (subway) travel, *xvii*
Metro Cafe (music club), *165*
Metropolitan African Methodist Episcopal Church, *87*
Mexican Cultural Institute, *97*
Millenium (shop), *182*
Miller & Arney Antiques (shop), *179*
Miss Pixie's (shop), *169*
Miss Saigon ✕, *119–120*
Money, *xvii–xviii*
Monocle ✕, *114*
Monroe, James, *45*
Monuments, *xviii, 6–7, 25, 27–34*
Mood Indigo (shop), *183*
Morrison-Clark Inn ⊞, *137–138*
Morton's of Chicago ✕, *127*
Mount Vernon College, *150, 152*
Mullett, Alfred B., *41*
Museums
Arthur M. Sackler Gallery, 14
Art Museum of the Americas, 34
Arts and Industries Building, 14–15
B'nai B'rith Klutznick Museum, 84
Corcoran Gallery of Art, 36–37
Council House, 85
DAR Museum, 37
Department of the Interior Museum, 38
District of Columbia Arts Center, 95
Fondo Del Sol Visual Arts Center, 86
Freer Gallery of Art, 18
Gadsby's Tavern Museum, 106
Heurich House Museum, 86–87
Hillwood Museum and Gardens, 95
Hirshhorn Museum and Sculpture Garden, 18–19, 151
National Air and Space Museum, 7, 19
National Building Museum, 66–67
National Gallery of Art, 7, 20–21, 151
National Geographic Society, 87, 151
National Museum of African Art, 21
National Museum of American Art, 67–68
National Museum of American History, 6, 21–22
National Museum of American Jewish Military History, 87–88
National Museum of Natural History, 6, 22–23
National Museum of Women in the Arts, 68
National Portrait Gallery, 68–69
National Postal Museum, 54
Phillips Collection, 88, 152
Renwick Gallery, 42
Smithsonian museums, 7, 23–24
Stabler-Leadbeater Apothecary, 107
Textile Museum, 89–90
United States Holocaust Memorial Museum, 7, 24–25
Music, *151–155*
stores, 169
Music Box Center (shop), *174*
Mystery Books (shop), *177*

N

Nation (music club), *165–166*
National Academy of Sciences, *94, 152*
National Air and Space Museum, *7, 19*
National Aquarium, *64–65*
National Archives, *65–66, 151*
National Building Museum, *66–67*

National Gallery of Art, 7, 20–21, 148, 151

National Garden, 58

National Geographic Society, 87, 151

National Law Enforcement Officers Memorial, 67

National Museum of African Art, 21

National Museum of American Art, 67–68

National Museum of American History, 6, 21–22

National Museum of American Jewish Military History, 87–88

National Museum of Natural History, 6, 22–23

National Museum of Women in the Arts, 68

National Portrait Gallery, 68–69

National Postal Museum, 54

National Symphony Orchestra, 153

National Theatre, 155

National Zoological Park, 97–98

Navy Memorial, 69

Neiman Marcus (department store), 183–184

Netherlands Carillon, 102

New Executive Office Building, 40

New Heights ✕, 112

Nightlife, 157–166
acoustic, folk, and country clubs, 158
bars and lounges, 158–160
comedy clubs, 160–161
dance clubs, 161–163
gay and lesbian dance clubs, 163
jazz and blues clubs, 164–165
rock and pop clubs, 165–166
9:30 Club (music club), 166

Nissan Pavilion at Stone Ridge, 148

Nixon, Richard M., 94

Nora ✕, 125–126

Northwest, hotels in, 142

O

Oak Hill Cemetery, 78

Obelsik ✕, 126

Octagon, 40

Old Adas Israel Synagogue, 69

Old Downtown and Federal Triangle, 58–59, 62–72

Old Ebbitt Grill ✕, 118–119

Old Executive Office Building, 40–41

Old Patent Office Building, 69–70

Old Post Office Building, 70–71

Old Post Office Pavilion (mall), 172

Old Presbyterian Meetinghouse, 106

Old Print Gallery (shop), 179

Old Stone House, 79

Olmsted, Frederick Law, Sr., 48, 97

Olney Theatre, 156

Olsson's Books & Records (shop), 173

Omni Shoreham Hotel 🏨, 142

One Step Down (music club), 164

One Washington Circle Hotel 🏨, 144

Oodles Noodles ✕, 120

O. Orkin Insect Zoo, 23

Opera, 152–153

Opera Theater of Northern Virginia, 152–153

Opportunity Shop of the Christ Child Society (shop), 179

Orchestral music, 153

Organization of American States, 41

Osteria Goldoni ✕, 123

Oval Office, White House, 45

P

Palm ✕, 121

Pampillonia Jewelers (shop), 174

Paper currency, printing of, 15

Parade of Shoes (shop), 175

Passports, xviii–xix

Peace Monument, 54

Peary, Robert E., 101

Pennsylvania Avenue, 71

Pentagon, 102–103

Performance art, 155–157

Performance Series, 153–155

Pershing, General John "Blackjack," 41–42, 101

Pershing Park, 41–42

Personal care (spas), 175, 181, 185

Personal guides, xx

Petersen House, 71

Phillips Collection, 88, 152

Phoenix (shop), 180

Pierce Mill, 98

Pizzera Paradiso ✕, 126

Politics and Prose (shop), 184

Polly Esther's (dance club), 162

Pop clubs, 165–166

Pope, John Russell, 65–66, 91, 97

Pulaski, General Casimir, 63

R

Ramsay, William, *107*
Ramsay House, *107*
Reagan, Ronald, *71*
Red Room, White House, *45*
Renwick, James, *42, 78*
Renwick Gallery, *42*
Restaurants, *109–110, 112–115, 118–130*
American, 114, 118–119, 127
Asian, 110, 119–120, 125–126, 127
Contemporary, 110, 112, 120–121, 128
Eclectic, 121
French, 114–115, 121–122, 129
Indian, 115, 122–123, 129
Italian, 112–113, 123, 126, 129, 130
Latin American, 113, 124, 126–127
Middle Eastern, 113–114
price chart, xv
Southern, 115, 124
Spanish, 124–125
Ritz (dance club), *162*
Rizik Bros. (shop), *176*
Roche Salon (shop), *181*
Rock clubs, *165–166*
Rock Creek Cemetery, *55*
Rock Creek Park, *98–99*
Ronald Reagan Building and International Trade Center, *71*
Roosevelt, Franklin Delano, *27–28*
Roosevelt, Theodore, *45*
Russian Embassy, *89*

S

Saigon Gourmet ✕, *110*
St. John's Church, *79*
St. John's Episcopal Church, *42–43*
St. Matthew's Cathedral, *89*
Saks Fifth Avenue (department store), *184*
Sala Thai ✕, *125*
Sam and Harry's ✕, *118*
Scruggs, Jan, *31*
Sculpture Garden, *20–21*
Second Story Books (shop), *177*
Secondi (shop), *178*
Section 27, *103*
Senate chambers, *51*
1789 ✕, *128*
Sewall-Belmont House, *55*

Shake Your Booty (shop), *170*
Shakespeare Theatre, *155–156*
Shoe Scene (shop), *178*
Shoe stores, *170, 175, 178, 181*
Sholl's Colonial Cafeteria ✕, *119*
Shopping, *168–185*
antiques and collectibles, 169, 171, 177, 179, 182
books, 169, 171, 173, 177, 179, 182–183, 184
clothing, 169, 170, 171, 174–175, 176, 178, 180–181, 182, 183, 185
crafts and gifts, 169, 171, 173–174, 177–178, 180
department stores, 172, 183–184
jewelry, 174, 185
kitchenware, 178, 180
leather goods, 180
malls, 170, 172–173, 178–179, 184
music, 169
personal care, 175, 181, 185
shoes, 170, 175, 178, 181
Shops at Georgetown Park (mall), *178–179*
Shops at National Place (mall), *172–173*
Sightseeing tours, *xix–xxi*
Sign of the Whale (bar), *160*
Signature Theatre, *156*
Silk Road/Woven History (shop), *171*
Sisterspace and Books (shop), *182–183*
Skynear and Company (shop), *169*
Smithson, James, *24*
Smithsonian Information Center, *24*
Smithsonian Institution, *148–149*
Smithsonian Institution Building, *23–24*
Smithsonian museums, *7, 23–24*
Soho Tea and Coffee (dance club), *158*
Source Theatre, *156–157*
Southwest, hotels in the, *141–142*
Special-interest tours, *xx*
Stabler-Leadbeater Apothecary, *107*
State Dining Room, White House, *45*
State of the Union (dance club), *163*
Statuary Hall, *50*
Studio Theatre, *157*
Summer Opera Theater Company, *153*
Supreme Court Building, *56*
Sushi-Ko ✕, *127*

Susquehanna (shop), *179*
Swissotel Washington Watergate 🖼,
   142–143
Sylvan Theater, *154*

T

Taberna del Alabardero ✕, *124*
Taft, Lorado, *58*
Taft, William Howard, *55, 56, 101*
Tahoga ✕, *128*
Takoma Station Tavern (music club),
   164–165
TATA Boutique (shop), *182*
Taxis, *xxi*
Telephones, *xxi*
Textile Museum, *89–90*
Theater and performance art, *155–
   157*
Theme trips, *xx–xxi*
Thomas Jefferson Building, *53*
Thornton, William, *40, 48, 79*
Tickets, *146–147*
Tidal Basin, *7, 29–30*
Timing the trip, *xxiii*
Tiny Jewel Box (shop), *174*
Tomb of the Unknowns, *103–104*
Tracks 2000 (dance club), *163*
Trade Secrets (shop), *183*
Train travel, *xxi–xxii*
Transparent Productions, *154*
Transportation
bus, xi–xii
car, xii–xiii
plane, x
subway, xvii
taxi, xxi
train, xxi–xxii
Travel Books & Language (shop), *184*
Treasury Building, *43*
Trover Books (shop), *171*
Truman, Harry, *36, 44*
Tudor Place, *79–80*
Twin's Lounge (music club), *165*
219 Basin Street Lounge (music club),
   165

U

U Street
restaurants, 129–130
shopping, 182–183
Union Station, *56–58, 170*

United States Botanic Garden, *58*
United States Holocaust Memorial
   Museum, *7, 24–25*
United States Marine Corps War
   Memorial, *104*
Upper Connecticut Avenue, hotels on,
   142
USAirways Arena, *149*

V

Vaux, Calvert, *48*
Vegas Lounge (music club), *165*
Vertigo Books (shop), *177*
Victoria's Day Spa (shop), *175*
Vidalia ✕, *120*
Vietnam Veterans Memorial, *7, 31*
Vietnam Women's Memorial, *31*
Visas, *xviii–xix*
Visitor information, *xxii*

W

Walking tours, *xxi*
Warner Theatre, *156*
Washington, George, *44, 48, 74, 79*
Washington Ballet, *150*
Washington Court Hotel 🖼, *133*
Washington Harbour, *80*
Washington Monarch 🖼, *143*
Washington Monument, *6, 32–34*
Washington National Cathedral, *80–
   81, 152*
Washington Opera, *153*
Washington Performing Arts Society,
   154–155
Washington Stage Guild, *157*
Watergate Hotel 🖼, *94, 142–143*
Web sites, *xxii–xxiii*
Webb's Southern Food ✕, *130*
West End
hotels in, 142–144
restaurants, 127–129
West Potomac Park, *34*
Westin Fairfax 🖼, *139*
White House, *7, 34, 43–46*
Blue Room, 45
East Room, 44–45
Green Room, 45
Oval Office, 45
Red Room, 45
State Dining Room, 45
tickets, 45–46
visitor center, 44, 45–46

White-Meyer House, *97*
Willard Inter-Continental ⛟, *71–72,
   136–137*
William Tecumseh Sherman
   Monument, *46*
Wisconsin Avenue, shopping on,
   183–185
Wolf Trap Farm Park, *149*
Women in Military Service for
   America Memorial, *104–105*
Wood, Waddy, *68, 89–90*
Woodley Park, *99*
Woodrow Wilson House, *90*
Woolly Mammoth (theater company),
   157

Y

Yacht Club (bar), *160*
Yawa (shop), *169*

Z

Zei (dance club), *163*
Ziegfeld's (dance club), *163*
Zoos
   National Zoological Park, 97–98
   O. Orkin Insect Zoo, 23

NOTES

NOTES

NOTES

NOTES

NOTES

Looking for a different kind of vacation?

Fodor's makes it easy with a full line of specialty guidebooks to suit a variety of interests—from adventure to romance to language help.

Fodor's. For the world of ways you travel.